Scott Foresman - Addison Wesley

MATH

Another Look

Reteaching Masters

Grade 3

Scott Foresman - Addison Wesley

Editorial Offices: Menlo Park, California • Glenview, Illinois
Sales Offices: Reading, Massachusetts • Atlanta, Georgia • Glenview, Illinois
Carrollton, Texas • Menlo Park, California

http://www.sf.aw.com

Overview

Another Look (Reteaching Masters) provide additional teaching options for teachers to use with students who have not yet mastered key skills and concepts covered in the student edition. A pictorial model is provided when appropriate, followed by worked-out examples and a few partially worked-out exercises. These exercises match or are similar to the simpler exercises in the student edition.

For Learn lessons and Explore lessons, the masters provide an alternative approach to the lesson development. This approach simplifies or clarifies the concept presented on the student edition page.

For Problem Solving and Decision Making lessons, the masters provide additional problems with problem solving hints or problems that focus on the skills needed for the student edition lesson.

ISBN 0-201-31253-0

Printed in the United States of America

3 4 5 6 7 8 9 10 – BW – 02 01 00 99 98

Contents

Chapter 1: Data, Graphs, and Facts Review

Chapter 2: Place Value and Time

Chapter 3: Adding Whole Numbers and Money

Chapter 4: Subtracting Whole Numbers and Money

Chapter 5: Multiplication Concepts and Facts

Chapter 6: More Multiplication Facts

Chapter 7: Division Concepts and Facts

Name ______________________________

Another Look
1-1

Reading Pictographs

The pictograph shows that ☺ = 5 people.

There are 3 faces next to face painting.

Face Painting	☺☺☺

How many people were at the face painting? 15

How do you know? There are 3 symbols, so count 5, 10, 15.

People at Carnival Events

Face Painting	☺☺☺
Relay Races	☺☺☺☺☺
Pie Eating	☺☺☺☺
Ball Toss	☺

☺ = 5 people

1.

Relay Races	☺☺☺☺☺

How many people were at the Relay Races? ______

How do you know? ______

2.

Pie Eating	☺☺☺☺

How many people were at the Pie Eating? ______

How do you know? ______

3.

Ball Toss	☺

How many people were at the Ball Toss? ______

How do you know? ______

Name ______________________________

Another Look
1-2

Reading Bar Graphs

Use the bar graph to answer each question.

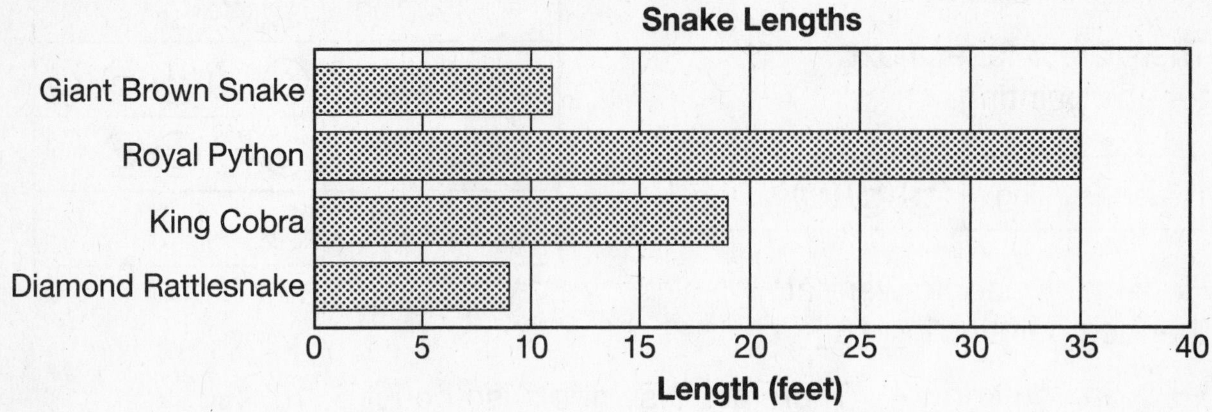

About how long is a Giant Brown Snake? 11 feet

How do you know? The bar goes a little past the 10 mark.

1. 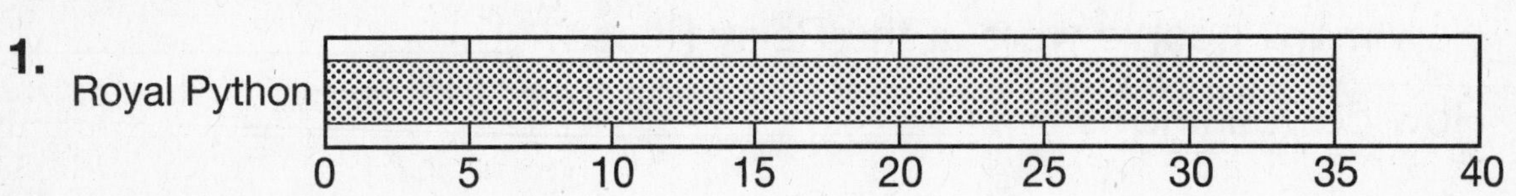

How long is a Royal Python? ______________________________

How do you know? ______________________________

2. 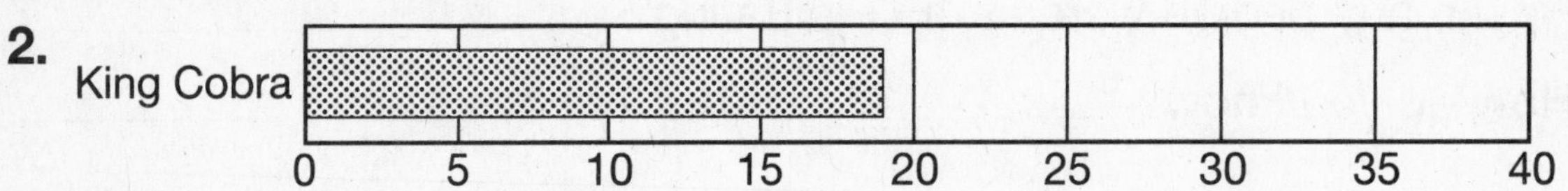

About how long is a King Cobra? ______________________________

How do you know? ______________________________

3. 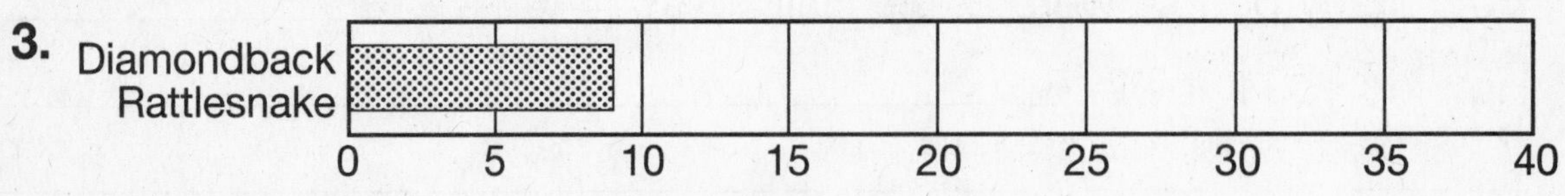

About how long is a Diamond Rattlesnake?

____

How do you know? ______________________________

Name ______________________

Reading Line Graphs

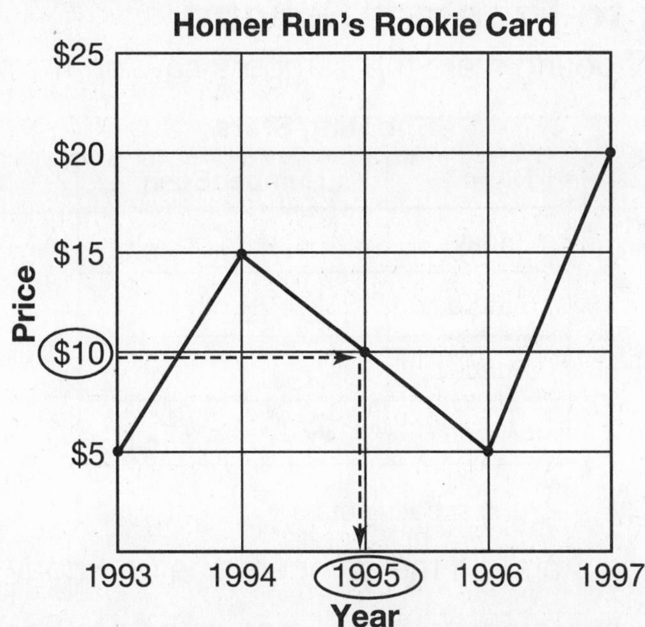

In what year was Homer Run's card worth $10.00?

Circle $10 on the graph. Draw a straight line from $10 across the graph until you reach a point. Draw a line straight from the point until you reach a year. Circle the year.

Homer Run's card was worth $10 in 1995.

Use the line graph to answer each question.

1. How much was Homer Run's card worth in 1996?

a. Circle 1996 on the graph.

b. Draw a straight line up from 1996 until you reach a point.

c. Draw a line to the left of the point until you reach a money amount.

d. Circle the money amount.

e. Homer Run's card was worth __________ in 1996.

2. In what year was Homer Run's card worth $15? __________

3. How much was Homer Run's card worth in 1997? __________

Name ______________________________

Another Look
1-4

Analyze Word Problems: Introduction to Problem Solving

Look how many shooting stars the campers saw on their trip!

Shooting Stars

Night	Number Seen
Friday	☆ ☆
Saturday	☆ ☆ ☆
Sunday	☆
Monday	☆ ☆ ☆ ☆

☆ = 5 shooting stars

How many shooting stars did the campers see on Friday and Saturday?

You want to know the total number of stars seen on 2 days.

Friday ☆ ☆ Saturday ☆ ☆ ☆

2 + 3 = 5

5 stars in the pictograph show 25 shooting stars. So, they saw 25 shooting stars on Friday and Saturday.

Use the pictograph to answer each question.

1. How many more shooting stars did they see on Monday than on Sunday?

a. I need to compare, so I will ______________.

b. Write the operation and the answer.

☆ ☆ ☆ ☆ ☆

4 ☐ 1 = ______________

c. ______________ stars on the pictograph show

______________ shooting stars.

2. How many shooting stars did they see on Saturday and Sunday? ______________

3. How many more stars did they see on Monday than on Saturday? ______________

Name ____________________

Another Look
1-5

Analyze Word Problems: Choose an Operation

Add or subtract? Juan's family owns 7 cows and 6 sheep. How many animals do they own?

The question asks for the total number of animals. I will add.

Solve: $7 + 6 = 13$. Juan's family owns 13 animals.

1. The first grade has 10 boys and 9 girls. How many students are in the first grade?

   a. Will you add or subtract? ____________

   b. Solve: ____________________

2. Jacob has 6 videotapes. He gives 3 of them to his school library. How many does he have left?

   a. Will you add or subtract? ____________

   b. Solve: ____________________

3. Beth reads 5 books in March and 6 books in April. How many books does she read in March and April?

   a. Will you add or subtract? ____________

   b. Solve: ____________________

4. Amir has 6 drawers to clean out. He cleans out 4. How many more drawers does he have to clean?

   a. Will you add or subtract? ____________

   b. Solve: ____________________

Name ______________________________

Exploring Algebra: What's the Rule?

In your book you explored algebra using tables. Here is another way to complete tables and find the rule.

You can use counters to help you find rules in a table.

In	1	2	4	7	8	10
Out	4	5	7			

The first In number is 1. Place 1 counter on your desk.

The first Out number is 4. Place more counters so that you have 4 in all.

Write the step you took to change 1 counter into 4 counters. Added 3

The next In number is 2. Place 2 counters on your desk.

The next Out number is 5. Place more counters so that you have 5 in all.

Write the step you took to change 2 counters into 5 counters. Added 3

Check your rule on the third pair of numbers in the table.

In	**Rule**	**Out**
4	+ 3	= 7

If your rule works, it is correct. Use the rule to complete the table.

____

Complete each table. Write the rule for each. Use counters to help.

1.

In	1	3	4	6	10	12
Out	6	8	9			

Rule: ______________________________

2.

In	2	3	5	8	9	12
Out	1	2	4			

Rule: ______________________________

Name ______________________________

Exploring Organizing Data

In your book you used tally tables to organize data. Here is another way to organize data.

Favorite Vegetables

Squash	Peas	Carrots
Jenny Michael Taylor Sara Maggie	Sue Maria	Jordan Mark Milo

Sue took a survey to find her friends' favorite vegetables. She has decided to organize the data in a bar graph.

Sue colored in one square for each of her friends who like squash. Color in squares to show how many of Sue's friends like peas and carrots.

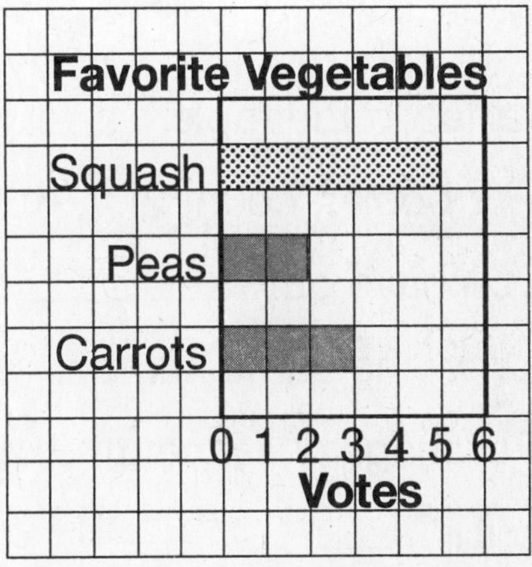

Favorite Fruit

Apples	Oranges	Grapes
Margo Thomas	Elaine Agatha Kelly Max	Matt Mary Ann Martin Vi

Matt took a survey of his friends' favorite fruits. Complete the bar graph shown to organize the data.

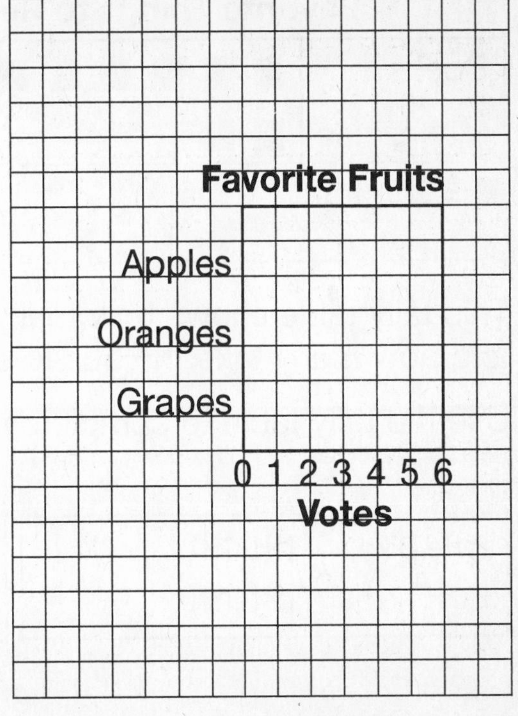

Name ______________________________

Exploring Making Pictographs

In your book you made pictographs. Here is another way to make pictographs. You can use counters to help you make a pictograph.

This tally table shows students' favorite things to read.

Books	卌 卌 II
Magazines	IIII

Each symbol in your pictograph will equal 2 students' votes.

Use counters to figure out how many symbols to draw.

Use counters to count by 2s until you reach the number of tallies in the table.

For books, count 2, 4, 6, 8, 10, 12. How many counters do you have out? ________

Draw the same number of symbols in the pictograph.

For magazines, count 2, 4. How many counters do you have out? ________

Complete the pictograph.

Favorite Things to Read

Books	■ ■ ■ ■ ■ ■
Magazines	■ ■

■ = 2 votes

This tally table shows how many students ride their bikes and how many take the bus to school.

Use the tally table to complete the pictograph.

Ride Bike	卌 卌
Bus	卌 卌 II

Ways to Get to School

Ride Bike	
Bus	

= 2 votes

Name ______________________________

Exploring Making Bar Graphs

In your book you made bar graphs using data from a tally table. Here is another way to make bar graphs.

You can make a bar graph of the data in the table. This table shows students' favorite seasons.

Favorite Seasons	
Season	**Number**
Winter	4
Spring	12
Summer	10
Fall	8

Use a scale of 1. Start with 0 at the bottom of the scale in the graph. Number each mark by 1s.

Draw bars on the graph by coloring 1 square for each vote. Four squares have been colored in for winter since there are 4 votes for winter.

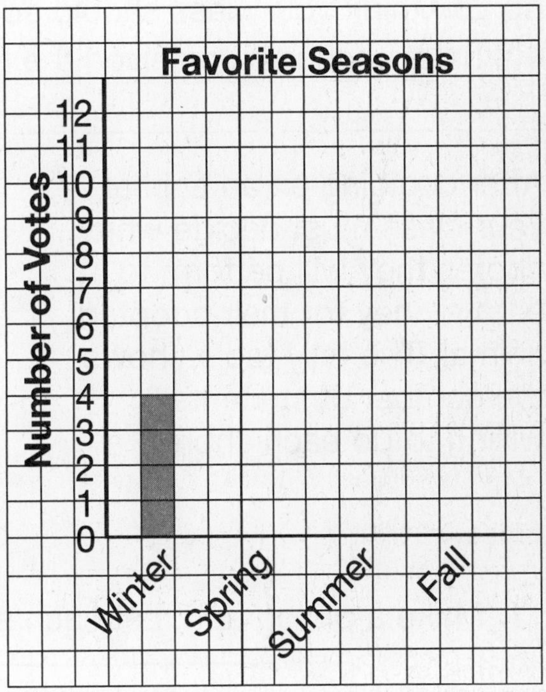

Favorite Seasons

Number of Votes: 0 1 2 3 4 5 6 7 8 9 10 11 12

Winter Spring Summer Fall

1. Complete the bar graph. Draw bars for spring, summer, and fall.
2. Which number on the scale matches the height of the bar for Summer? __________
3. Which number on the scale matches the height of the bar for Fall? __________
4. Suppose the next 3 people surveyed said that winter is their favorite season. Add this data to the bar graph.

Name ______________________________

Another Look
1-10

Decision Making

Your class has decided to adopt a wild animal through an environmental charity. To the right is a tally table showing the votes for which animal to adopt.

Whale	~~IIII~~ ~~IIII~~
Dolphin	IIII
Elephant	~~IIII~~ III

Complete the pictograph to organize the data.

Have each symbol = 2 votes.

Whale	♥ ♥ ♥ ♥ ♥
Dolphin	♥ ♥
Elephant	♥ ♥ ♥ ♥

Based on the graph, which animal do you think your class should adopt? Explain.

Whale; because it received the most votes

After deciding on an animal, your class must decide which chores they will perform to earn money for their adopted animal. The tally table shows the number of students willing to do each chore.

Chores	Tally
Garden Work	~~IIII~~ ~~IIII~~ IIII
Baby Sit	~~IIII~~ I
School Fundraising Fair	~~IIII~~ ~~IIII~~ II
Deliver Papers	~~IIII~~ III

1. Make a pictograph. Let each symbol show 2 votes.

Students' Chores	
Garden Work	
Baby Sit	
School Fundraising Fair	
Deliver Papers	

2. Which chore are most students willing to do? ______________

3. How many students are willing to deliver papers? ______________

Name ________________________________

Another Look 1-11

Analyze Strategies: Look for a Pattern

What are the next three numbers?

3, 6, 9, 12, ▒, ▒, ▒

Start comparing between numbers in the pattern.

3 + [3] = 6

6 + [3] = 9

9 + [3] = 12

What is the pattern? __Add 3__

Add 3 to get the next three numbers.

12 + 3 = __15__

[15] + 3 = __18__

[18] + 3 = __21__

---

1. 37, 31, 25, 19

a. What is the difference of each pair of numbers? ________

b. What is the pattern? ________________

c. What are the next three numbers? ________, ________, ________

2. a. What are the next three numbers?

4, 8, 12, 16, ________, ________, ________

b. What is the pattern?

____

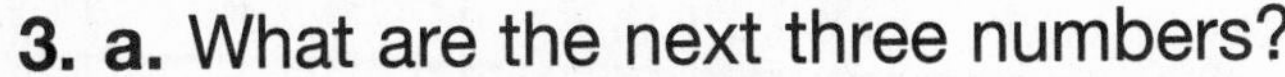

3. a. What are the next three numbers?

35, 30, 25, 20, ________, ________, ________

b. What is the pattern?

____

Name ____________________

Another Look 2-1

Place Value Through Hundreds

The place-value chart shows how many.

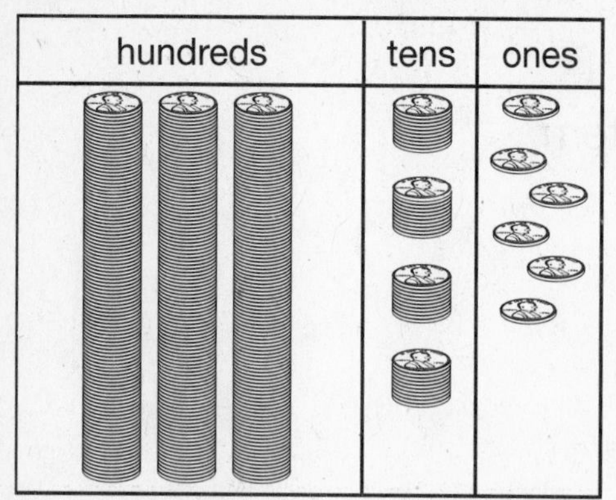

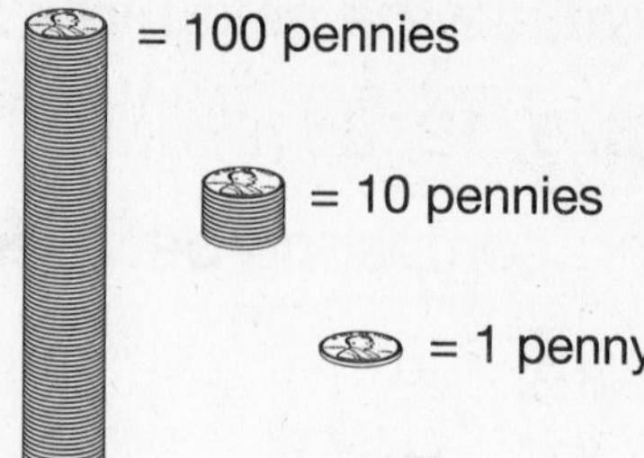

300 + 40 + 6 = 346

Write how many in standard form. Then write the word name.

1.

hundreds	tens	ones

____ ____________________

2.

hundreds	tens	ones

____ ____________________

3.

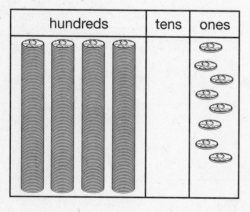

hundreds	tens	ones

____ ____________________

4.

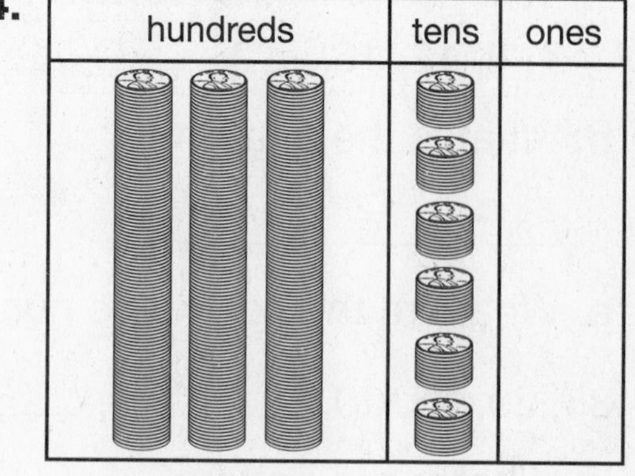

____ ____________________

 Use with pages 52–53.

Name ___________________________________

Another Look 2-2

Exploring Place-Value Relationships

In your book, you played a game using place-value blocks. Here is another way to use place-value blocks to explore number patterns.

10 tens = 1 hundred

Use place value blocks. Write how many.

1. _______ ones = _______ ten

2. _______ hundreds = _______ thousand

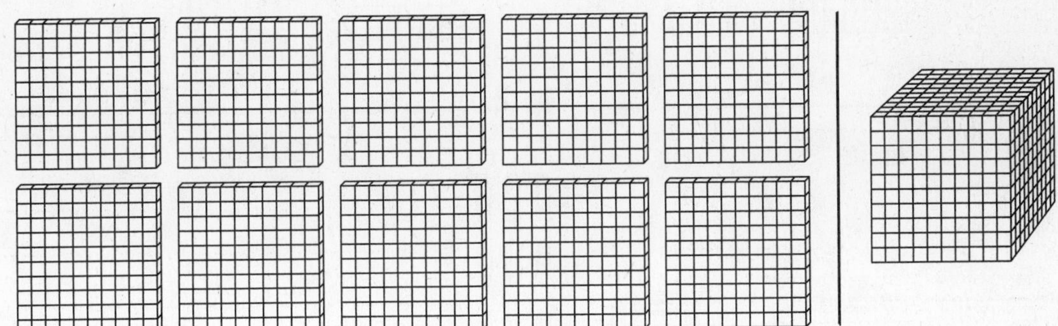

3. _______ ones = _______ tens

Name ______________________________

Another Look 2-3

Place Value Through Thousands

The place-value chart shows how many. The number can be written in standard form.

thousands	hundreds	tens	ones
2	3	0	7

two thousand , three hundred seven

Write how many.

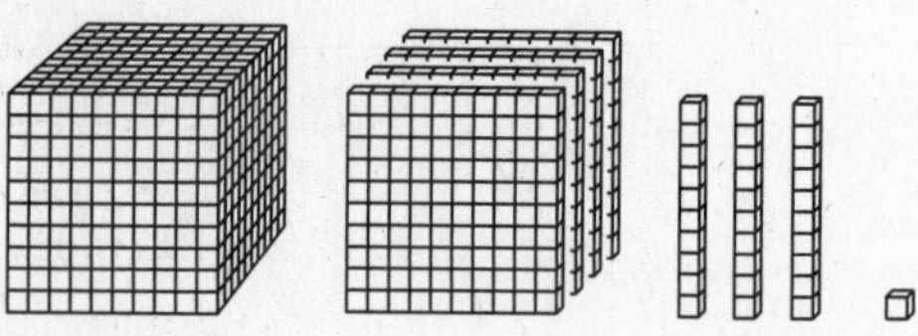

1. ____, ____ ____ ____

2. ____, ____ ____ ____

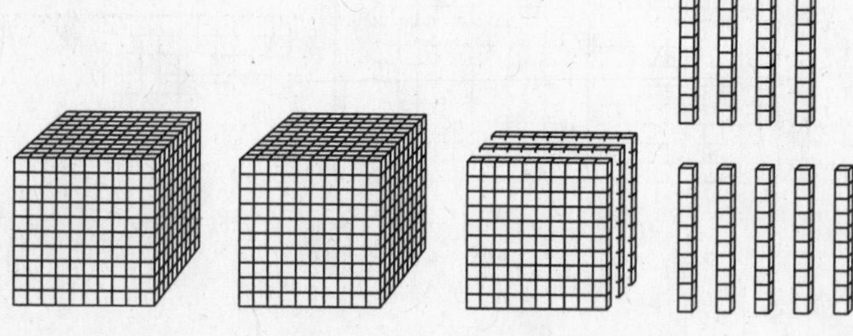

3. ____, ____ ____ ____

4. six thousand, four hundred fifty

____, ____ ____ ____

5. eight thousand, five hundred five

____, ____ ____ ____

Name ______________________

Another Look 2-4

Place Value Through Hundred Thousands

The place-value chart shows the value of each digit.

Thousands			Ones		
hundred thousands	ten thousands	thousands	hundreds	tens	ones
4	2	7	8	9	1

Read: 427 thousand, 891

1. Complete the table.

hundred thousands	ten thousands	thousands	hundreds	tens	ones	read
1	6	2	3	7	5	162 thousand, 375
3	0	9	2	6	0	
8	4	9	7	5	5	
5	7	0		9	1	570 thousand, 291
1			5			122 thousand, 567
						694 thousand, 321

Write each number in standard form.

2. five hundred thousand ______

3. forty-five thousand ______

4. six hundred sixty-four thousand, five hundred seventy-three ______

5. 30,000 + 4,000 + 500 + 60 + 1 ______

6. 10,000 + 3,000 + 600 + 80 + 9 ______

7. 600,000 + 40,000 + 7,000 + 300 + 2 ______

8. 200,000 + 60,000 + 5,000 + 200 + 10 + 8 ______

Name ______________________________

Another Look
2-5

Analyze Strategies: Make an Organized List

Make a list or use any strategy to help solve each problem. You can use place-value blocks to help.

Suppose Marilee packed 35 Venus's-flytraps in boxes that hold 10 plants or 1 plant. How many ways could she pack the boxes?

How many plants can she pack in 3 tens boxes? 30

List all possible ways Marilee could pack the plants.

tens boxes	3	2	1	0
ones boxes	5	15	25	35

How many ways are there? 4 ways

---

1. Suppose you are choosing pots for Marilee. You can pick 2 pots. There are 2 yellow pots, 2 red pots, and 2 blue pots. How many different combinations could you choose?

a. List all the possible combinations. Use Y to stand for yellow. Use R to stand for red. Use B to stand for blue.

____

b. How many combinations are there? ____________

2. Suppose Peter wants to order 52 pounds of soil. He can buy the soil in ten-pound bags or 1-pound bags. How many ways could he order the soil?

a. List all possible ways Peter could order the soil.

ten-pound bags						
one-pound bags						

b. How many ways are there? ________ ways

Name ____________________

Comparing Numbers

Place-value blocks can help you compare numbers.

Compare 1,440 and 1,550. Circle the greater number.

thousands	hundreds	tens	ones
1	4	4	0

thousands	hundreds	tens	ones
1	5	5	0

Circle 1,550 because there are more hundreds in 1,550 than 1,440.

---

1. Compare 146 and 126. Circle the greater number.

thousands	hundreds	tens	ones
0	1	4	6

thousands	hundreds	tens	ones
0	1	2	6

2. Compare 1,101 and 1,111. Circle the greater number.

thousands	hundreds	tens	ones
1	1	0	1

thousands	hundreds	tens	ones
1	1	1	1

Name ______________________

Another Look 2-7

Ordering Numbers

You can use a number line to help you order numbers.

Order 100, 200 and 150. First, show each number on a number line.

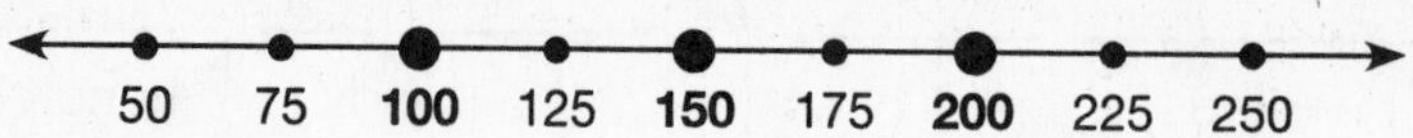

Look at the number line.

Which of the three numbers is farthest to the right? 200

Which number is greatest? 200

Which of the three numbers is farthest to the left? 100

Which number is least? 100

Order the numbers from greatest to least. 200, 150, 100

Show each number on the number line. Then list them in order.

1. Order 50, 70, and 30 from greatest to least.

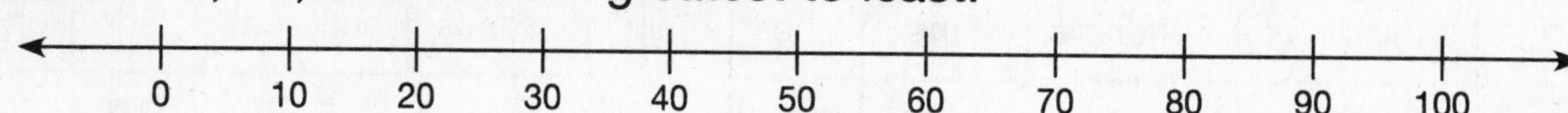

____

2. Order 3,000, 1,500, and 4,500 from least to greatest.

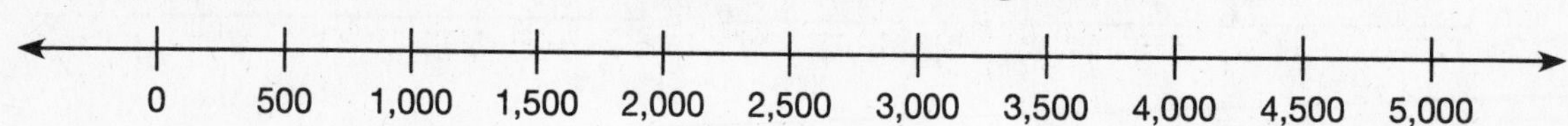

____

3. Order 45, 90, and 60 from least to greatest.

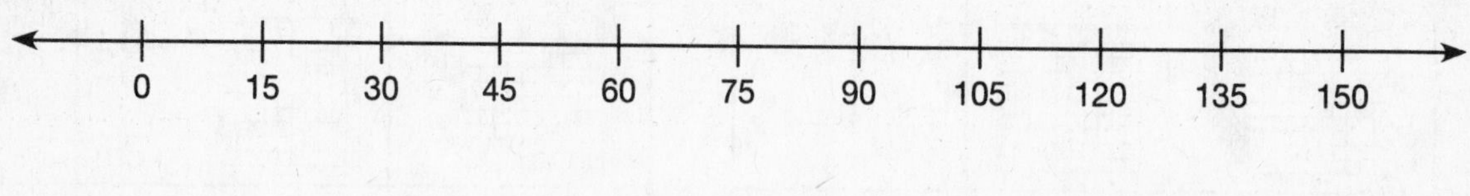

____

Name ____________________

Another Look
2-8

Rounding to Tens

You can use place value to round to the nearest ten.

If the digit in the ones place is 5, 6, 7, 8, or 9, then round to the next greater ten. If the digit is less than 5, do not change the digit in the tens place.

Round 17 to the nearest ten: 20

Explain. 7 is in the ones place. Round to the next greater ten.

Round 53 to the nearest ten: 50

Explain. Because 3 is in the ones place and 3 is less than 5, the digit in the tens place doesn't change.

Round 75 to the nearest ten: 80

Explain. Because the 5 in the ones place is 5 or greater, round to the next greater ten.

1. Round 12 to the nearest ten: ________

   Explain. ____________________

2. Round 236 to the nearest ten: ________

   Explain. ____________________

Look carefully at the following numbers. You are going to round to the nearest ten.

127	22	351	918	892
84	75	9	41	103

3. In which numbers should you *not* change the digits in the tens place?

   ____

   Explain. ____________________

4. Which numbers should you round to the next greater ten?

   ____

   Explain. ____________________

Name ______________________

Another Look
2-9

Rounding to Hundreds

You can use place value to round to the nearest hundred.

If the digit in the tens place is 5, 6, 7, 8, or 9, round to the next greater hundred. If the digit in the tens place is less than 5, do not change the digit in the hundreds place.

Round 117 to the nearest hundred: 100

Explain. Because the digit in the tens place is 1, do not change the digit in the hundreds place.

Round 152 to the nearest hundred: 200

Explain.
Since the digit in the tens place is 5, round to the next greater hundred.

1. Round 186 to the nearest hundred: ________

   Explain. ______________________

2. Round 236 to the nearest hundred: ________

   Explain. ______________________

3. Round 9,124 to the nearest hundred: ________

   Explain. ______________________

1,207 220 351 918 892

840 175 199 410 103

4. When rounding to the nearest hundred, in which of the numbers given above will you *not* change the digit in the hundreds place?

   ____

5. When rounded to the nearest hundred, which numbers will round to greater hundreds?

   ____

Name ______________________________

Another Look
2-10

Time to the Nearest Five Minutes

Circle the last number that the hour hand has passed. Circle the number that the minute hand points to on the clock.

Hour hand last passed the 2. → 2 : 25

Minute hand points to the 5.
5, 10, 15, 20, 25

It is 25 minutes after 2.

Circle the last number that the hour hand has passed. Circle the number that the minute hand points to on the clock. Write the time two ways.

1.

_____ : _____ _____

____

2.

_____ : _____ _____

____

3.

_____ : _____ _____

____

4.

_____ : _____ _____

____

5. Continue the pattern. 5, 10, 15, 20, _____, _____, _____, _____

6. How many minutes are in one hour? _____

7. What is another way to write 20 minutes before 8? _____

Name ______________________

Another Look
2-11

Exploring Time to the Nearest Minute

Circle the last number the hour hand has passed. Then count the minutes.

9:22 p.m.

Hour hand last passed the 9.

Minute hand is at 2 marks after the 4.

5, 10, 15, 20, 21, 22

9 : 22

The time is 22 minutes after 9.

Circle the last number the hour hand has passed. Then count the minutes. Write the time two ways.

1. 

_____ : _____

____

2. 

_____ : _____

____

3. 

_____ : _____

____

4. 

_____ : _____

____

5. 

_____ : _____

____

 Use with pages 76–77.

Name ______________________

Time to the Half Hour and Quarter Hour

In the book, you looked at clocks and read the times. Here is another way to tell time using quarter to, quarter past and half past the hour. You can shade $\frac{1}{4}$ or $\frac{1}{2}$ of the circle.

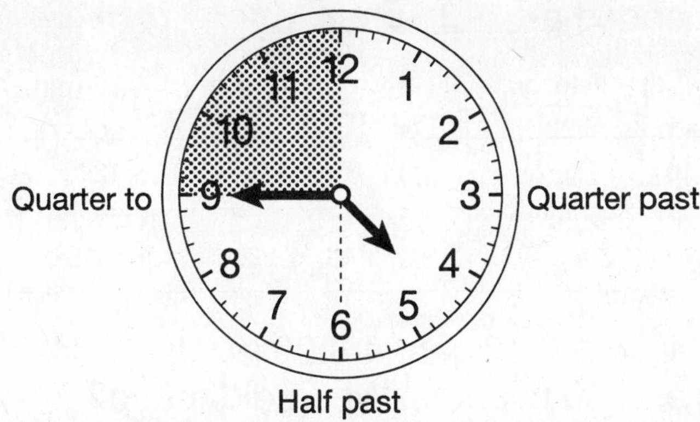

Write the time in words: Quarter to five.

Write each time in words.

1. 

____

2. 

____

3. 

____

4. 

____

Name ______________________

Another Look 2-13

Elapsed Time

You can use a time line to help you calculate elapsed time.

A baseball game began at 9:00 A.M. and lasted for 3 hours and 15 minutes. It ended at 12:15 P.M.

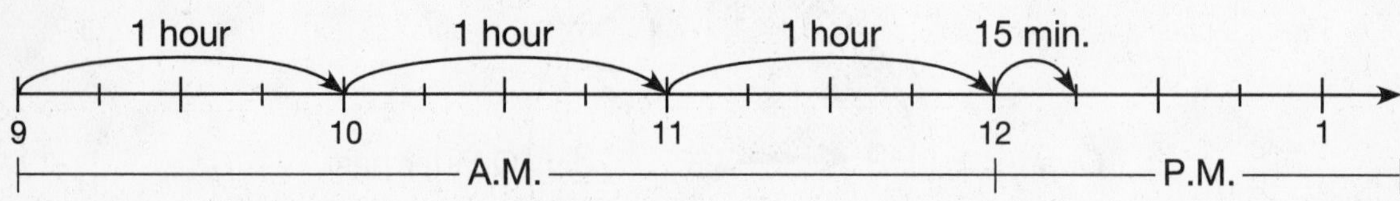

---

1. The annual spelling bee began at 3:00 P.M. It lasted 4 hours and 30 minutes! When did it end? ______

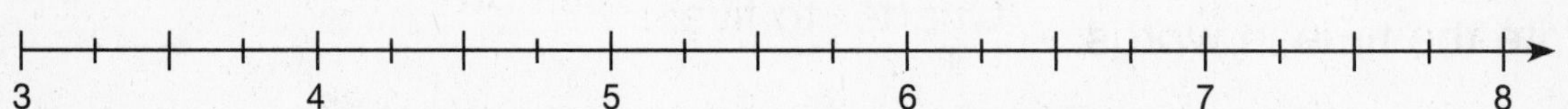

2. A snake begins shedding its skin at 6:00 P.M. It takes 1 hour and 45 minutes. When is it done? ______

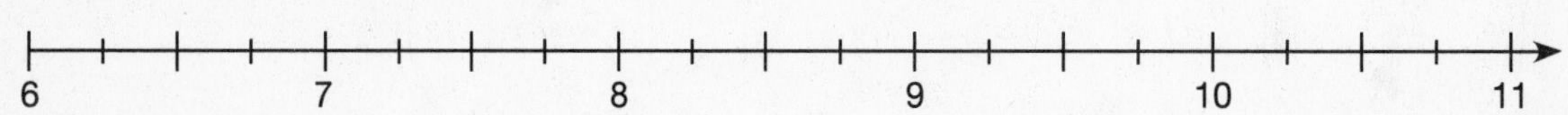

3. The parade begins at 10:00 A.M. It is expected to last for 1 hour and 30 minutes. When will it end? ______

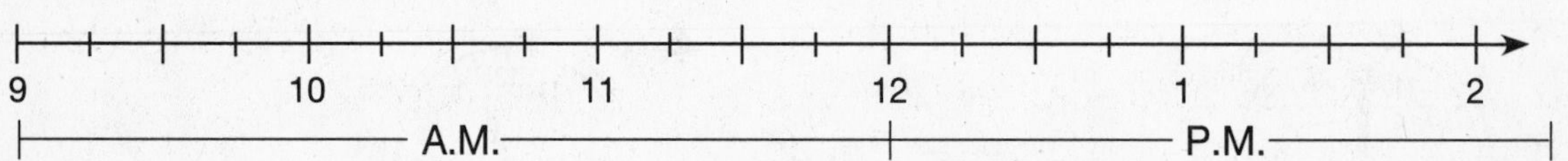

4. Fido's nap begins at 1:00 P.M. and lasts for 4 hours and 15 minutes. What time does he wake up? ______

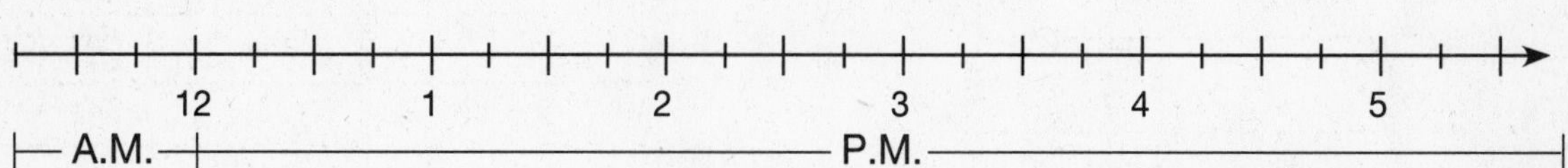

 Use with pages 80–81.

Name ______________________________

Another Look
2-14

Ordinal Numbers and the Calendar

In your book you used ordinal numbers to name dates on a calendar. Here, you will use ordinal numbers to complete some sentences. Watch for the clue in each sentence.

Julia is sitting at a desk that is (four) rows from the front of the room. Her desk is in the fourth row.

---

1. Kevin is sitting at a desk that is three rows from the front of the room. His desk is in the __________ row.
2. There are five students in line ahead of Luke. He's in the number 6 spot. Luke is the __________ student in line.
3. There are ten students in line ahead of Kim. She is the __________ student in line.
4. No one is in line ahead of Dillon. He is the __________ student in line.
5. Rosa hung her coat on a hook between the first and third hooks on the wall. Her coat is on the __________ hook.
6. Write the missing information in the chart below. Use numbers in the first column; use words in the second column.

Ordinal Numbers	
Number	**Word**
9th	
	eleventh
	fourteenth

7. Circle the third Wednesday of the month.

S	M	T	W	T	F	S
					1	2
3	4	5	6	7	8	9
10	11	12	13	14	15	16
17	18	19	20	21	22	23
24	25	26	27	28	29	30

Name ______________________________

Decision Making

When you know how much time in all you have to get all your activities done, you can make a schedule.

Your karate class lasts for one hour and has four activities: (1) warm-ups, (2) punches and kicks, (3) karate forms, and (4) cool-down.

If each activity lasts the same amount of time, then each activity will last for 15 minutes.

If the class starts at 2:30, then:

the first activity should start at 2:30,

the second activity should start at 2:45,

the third activity should start at 3:00,

and the last activity should start at 3:15.

Complete.

1. You have four activities to fit into a two-hour class.

a. If each activity takes the same amount of time, how long will each one last? __________

b. If the class begins at 5:00 P.M., when will the second activity begin and end? begin: ________ P.M. end: ________ P.M.

2. You have six activities to fit into a one-hour class.

a. If each activity takes the same amount of time, how long will each one last? __________

b. If the class begins at 2:00 P.M., when will the third activity begin and end? begin: ________ P.M. end: ________ P.M.

c. If the class begins at 2:00 P.M., when will the last activity begin and end? begin: ________ P.M. end: ________ P.M.

Name ______________________________

Exploring Addition Patterns

In your book you used basic facts to add greater numbers.
Here is another way to add.

2 ones + 3 ones = 5 ones

2 + 3 = 5

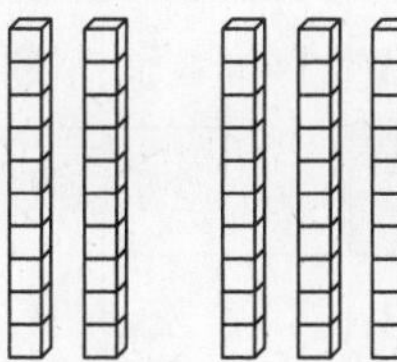

2 tens + 3 tens = 5 tens

20 + 30 = 50

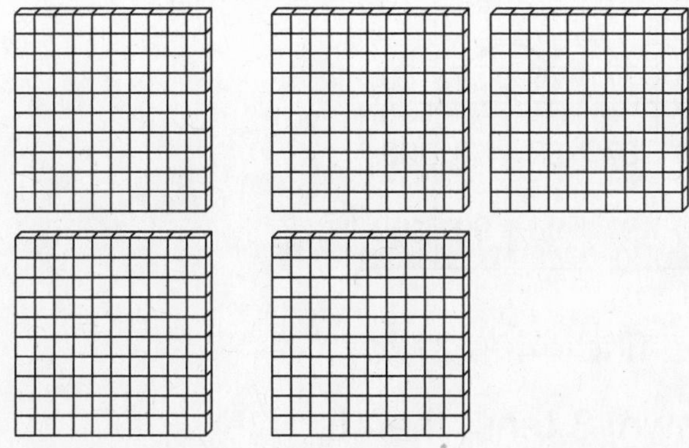

2 hundreds + 3 hundreds = 5 hundreds

200 + 300 = 500

Find each sum. Draw place value blocks to help you.

1. 4 + 5 = ______

2. 40 + 50 = ______

3. 400 + 500 = ______

4. 600 + 700 = ______

Name ______________________________

Exploring Adding on a Hundred Chart

1	2	3	4	5	6	7	8	9	10
11	12	13	14	15	16	17	18	19	20
21	22	23	24	25	26	27	28	29	30
31	32	33	34	35	36	37	38	39	40
41	42	43	44	45	46	47	48	49	50
51	52	53	54	55	56	57	58	59	60
61	62	63	64	65	66	67	68	69	70
71	72	73	74	75	76	77	78	79	80
81	82	83	84	85	86	87	88	89	90
91	92	93	94	95	96	97	98	99	100

You can use a hundred chart to help you find 44 + 37.

Put your finger on 44. Move forward (down) 3 tens, then to the right 7 ones. When you reach the end of the row, go to the first number in the next row.

Your finger is now on the number 81.

44 + 37 = 81

Use a hundred chart to find each sum.

1. 23 + 5 = ________

2. 50 + 8 = ________

3. 30 + 18 = ________

4. 49 + 22 = ________

5. 36 + 19 = ________

6. 27 + 35 = ________

7. 42 + 27 = ________

8. 56 + 29 = ________

9. 73 + 24 = ________

10. 33 + 48 = ________

11. 35 + 52 = ________

12. 64 + 22 = ________

13. 45 + 39 = ________

14. 56 + 22 = ________

Name ______________________________

Another Look 3-3

Exploring Algebra: Missing Numbers

In your book, you found missing numbers using color cubes and workmats. Here is another way to find missing numbers.

1	2	3	4	5	6	7	8	9	10
11	12	13	14	15	16	17	18	19	20
21	22	23	24	25	26	27	28	29	30
31	32	33	34	35	36	37	38	39	40
41	42	43	44	45	46	47	48	49	50
51	52	53	54	55	56	57	58	59	60
61	62	63	64	65	66	67	68	69	70
71	72	73	74	75	76	77	78	79	80
81	82	83	84	85	86	87	88	89	90
91	92	93	94	95	96	97	98	99	100

☐ + 3 = 10

Find the missing number using a hundred chart.

Put your finger on the 3. Move it forward to the 10.

How many spaces did you move to get from the 3 to the 10?

4, 5, 6, 7, 8, 9, 10

You moved 7 spaces from 3 to get to 10.

__7__ + 3 = 10

Use a hundred chart to find the missing numbers.

1. ☐ + 5 = 12

a. Where do you put your finger first? ____________

b. How many spaces do you move to get to 12? ____________

c. What is the missing number? ____________

d. Write it in the number sentence above.

2. 6 + ________ = 18

3. ________ + 13 = 22

Name ________________________________

Another Look
3-4

Estimating Sums

Estimate the sum of 424 and 175.

Which hundred is closer to 424?

Is 424 closer to 400 or 500? __400__

Which hundred is closer to 175?

Is 175 closer to 100 or 200? __200__

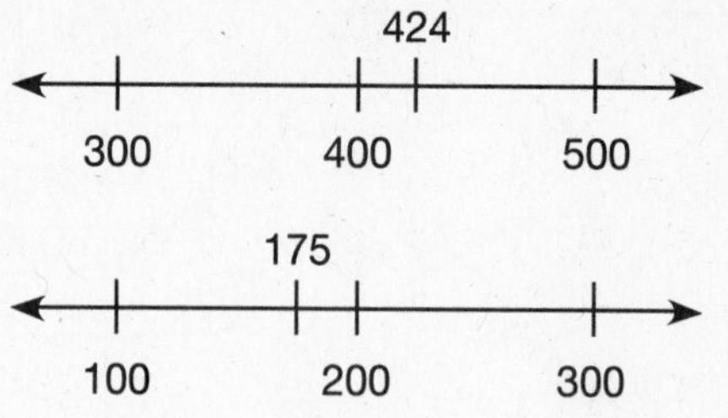

424	→	400
+ 175	→	+ 200
		600

The sum of 424 and 175 is about __600__.

---

1. 327 + 159

a. Is 327 closer to 300 or 400? ________

b. Is 159 closer to 100 or 200? ________

c. ________ + ________ = ________

2. 498 + 111

a. 498 is closer to ________ than 400.

b. 111 is closer to ________ than ________.

c. ________ + ________ = ________

Estimate each sum.

3. 112 + 790 ________

4. 27 + 31 ________

5. 546 + 329 ________

6. 702 + 566 ________

7. 33 + 84 ________

8. 49 + 32 ________

9. 622 + 131 ________

10. 515 + 572 ________

11. 331 + 609 ________

12. 890 + 622 ________

Name ______________________________

Exploring Adding with Regrouping

In your book you added using place-value blocks. Here is another way to add.

Add 26 + 17. Use grid paper.

Show 26 and 17 by shading 26 squares and 17 squares. You can put the two groups together.

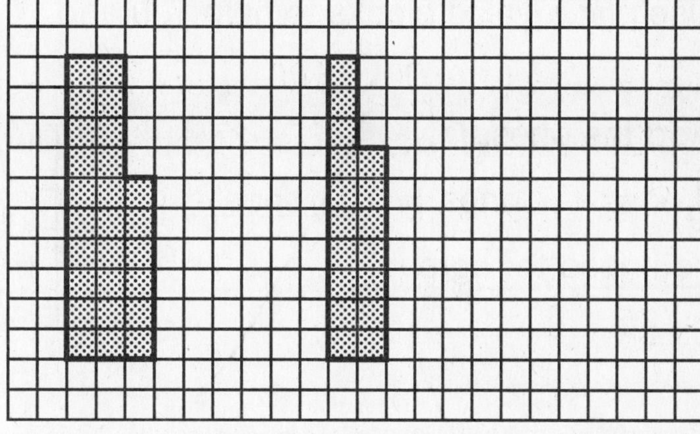

How many ones are there?
13

Regroup 10 ones for 1 ten.

How many tens are there?
4 tens

26 +17 = 43

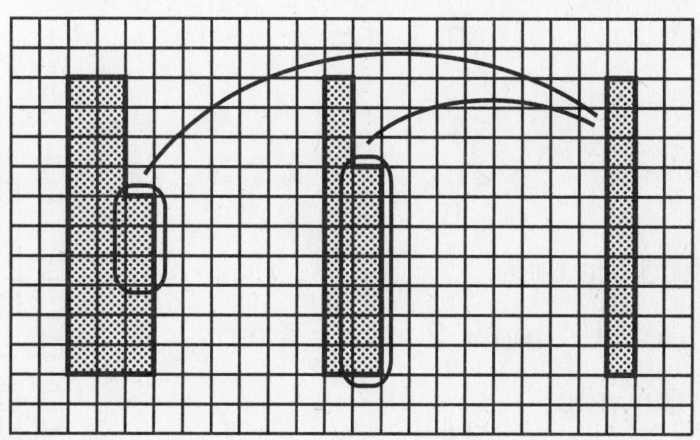

---

1. Use place-value blocks or grid paper to find the sum of 23 + 28.

a. How many ones are there? ______________

b. How many tens are there? ______________

c. What is the sum of 23 + 28? ______________

2. Use place-value blocks or grid paper to find the sum of 35 + 57.

a. How many ones are there? ______________

b. How many tens are there? ______________

c. What is the sum of 35 + 57? ______________

Find each sum.

3. 49 + 28 = ______________ **4.** 21 + 32 = ______________

5. 56 + 18 = ______________ **6.** 47 + 13 = ______________

Name ______________________

Another Look 3-6

Adding 2-Digit Numbers

Add 14 + 27.

Use place-value blocks to help you add.

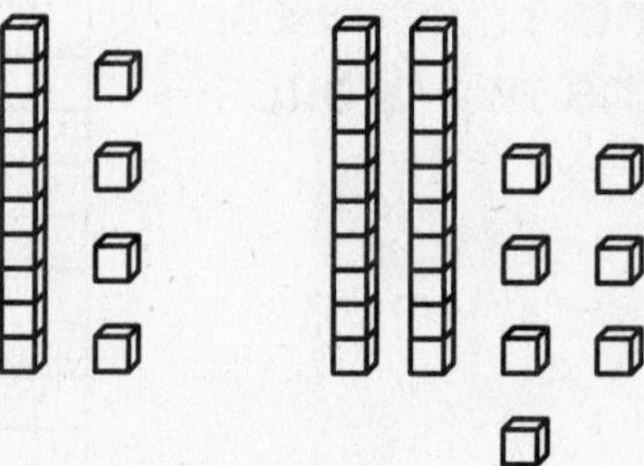

Add the ones.

4 ones + 7 ones = 11 ones

You need to regroup.

11 ones = 1 ten, 1 one

You write:

$$\begin{array}{r} {}^{1} \\ 14 \\ +\ 27 \\ \hline 1 \end{array}$$

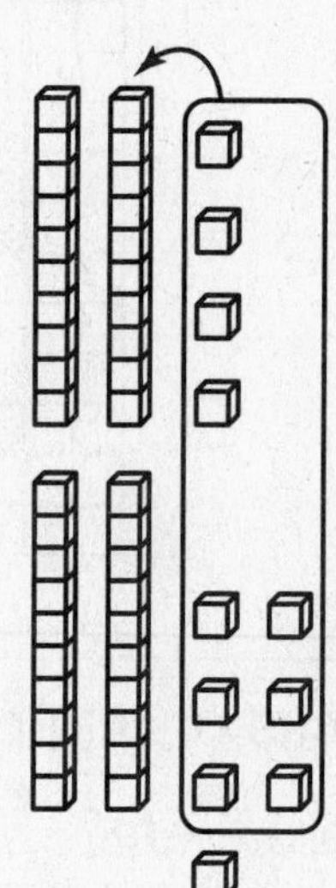

Add the tens.

1 ten + 1 ten + 2 tens = 4 tens

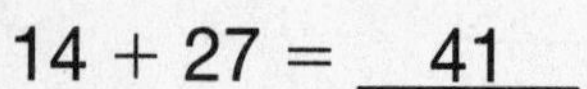

You write:

$$\begin{array}{r} {}^{1} \\ 14 \\ +\ 27 \\ \hline 41 \end{array}$$

14 + 27 = 41

Add. Estimate to check.

1. 23 + 39

a. 3 ones + 9 ones = ______ ones = ______ ten, ______ ones

b. ______ ten + 2 tens + ______ tens = ______ tens

c. 23 + 39 = ______

2. 35 + 18 = ______

3. 52 + 38 = ______

4. 44 + 27 = ______

5. 36 + 42 = ______

6. 78 + 19 = ______

7. 51 + 47 = ______

Name ______________________

Another Look 3-7

Adding 3-Digit Numbers

Place-value blocks can help you find the sum of 274 and 342.

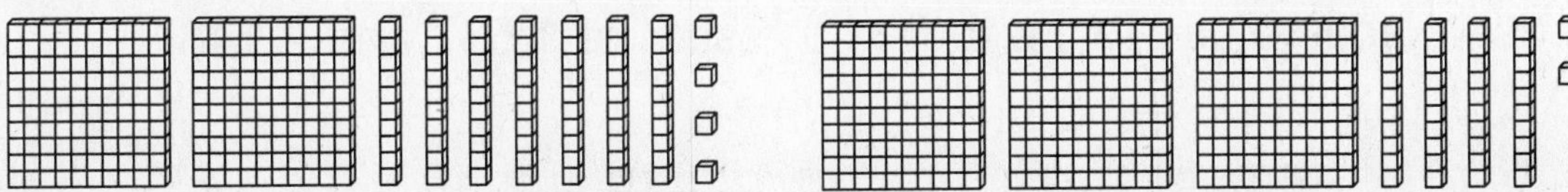

How many ones in all? 6

Do you need to regroup? No ___ ___ 6

How many tens in all? 11

Do you need to regroup? Yes ___ 1 6

Regroup 10 tens as 1 hundred.

How many hundreds in all? 6

Do you need to regroup? No

What is the sum of 274 and 342? 6 1 6

Use the place-value blocks to find each sum. Regroup as needed.

1. 472 + 319

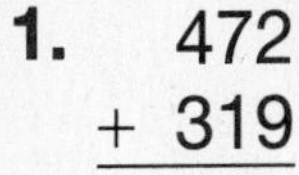

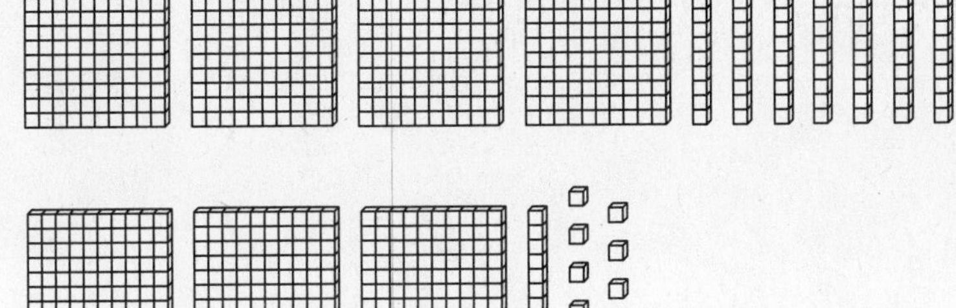

---

2. 568 + 174

3. $709 + 253

4. $386 + 525

5. 364 + 871

6. 494 + 325

7. 688 + 392

8. 434 + 725

9. 207 + 495

Name ____________________

Adding 4-Digit Numbers: Choose a Calculation Method

You can use place-value blocks to find the sum of 1,537 and 2,148.

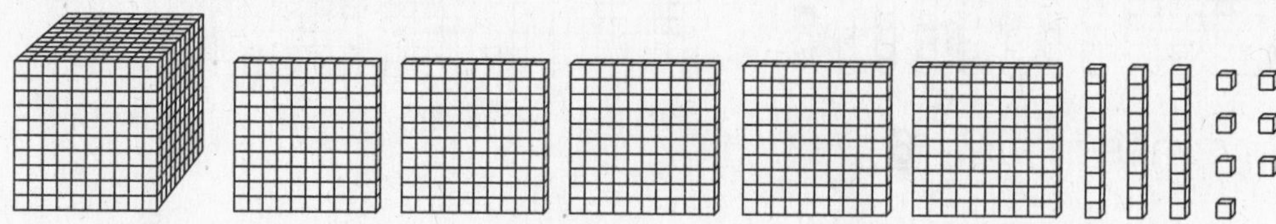

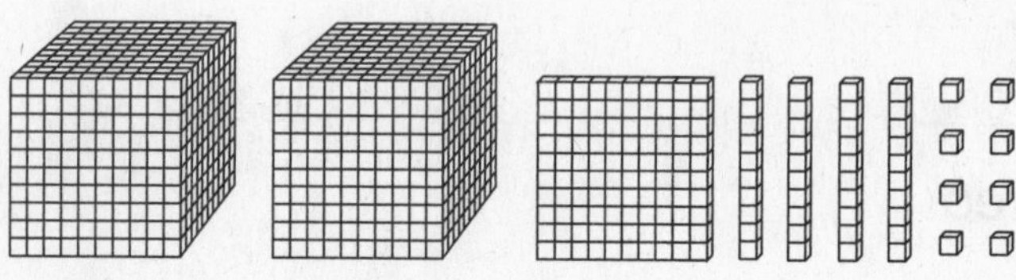

How many ones in all? 15

Do you need to regroup? Yes

The total number of ones is greater than 10, so regroup 10 ones as 1 ten.

How many tens in all? 8 How many hundreds in all? 6

How many thousands in all? 3

```
    1
 1,537
+2,148
 3,685
```

Add.

1. 2,398 + 1,564
2. 3,800 + 650
3. 2,390 + 1,185
4. \$3,326 + 3,748
5. 2,761 + 3,258
6. 5,611 + 1,089
7. 3,505 + 2,706
8. 7,601 + 4,399

Name ______________________________

Another Look 3-9

Column Addition

Number sentences can help you find the sum of three addends.

Find the sum of 78, 24, and 9.

$$\begin{array}{r} 78 \\ 24 \\ +\ \ 9 \\ \hline \end{array}$$

Add the ones.

$$\begin{array}{r} 8 \\ 4 \\ +\ 9 \\ \hline 21 \end{array}$$

Do you need to regroup? Yes

Regroup 20 ones as 2 tens.

Add the tens.

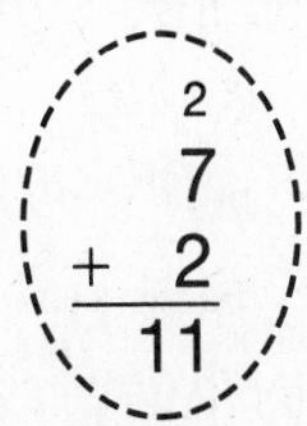

Do you need to regroup? Yes

Regroup 10 tens as 1 hundred.

How many hundreds in all? 1

$$\begin{array}{r} {}^{2} \\ 78 \\ 24 \\ +\ \ 9 \\ \hline 111 \end{array}$$

Find each sum. Regroup as needed.

1. $\begin{array}{r} 261 \\ 119 \\ +\ 25 \\ \hline \end{array}$

2. $\begin{array}{r} 8 \\ 354 \\ +\ 81 \\ \hline \end{array}$

3. $\begin{array}{r} 516 \\ 227 \\ +431 \\ \hline \end{array}$

4. $\begin{array}{r} 326 \\ 219 \\ +\ 28 \\ \hline \end{array}$

5. $\begin{array}{r} 368 \\ 207 \\ +130 \\ \hline \end{array}$

6. $\begin{array}{r} 629 \\ 102 \\ +291 \\ \hline \end{array}$

7. $\begin{array}{r} 57 \\ 347 \\ +223 \\ \hline \end{array}$

8. $\begin{array}{r} 113 \\ 93 \\ +163 \\ \hline \end{array}$

Name ______________________

Another Look
3-10

Analyze Strategies: Guess and Check

Josh needs to record the score of a school baseball game. He knows that the Cubs beat the Hawks by 6 runs and that a total of 24 runs were scored, but he doesn't remember the score!

Josh made a list of what he knows about the game.

The scores are 6 runs apart.
The Cubs won the game.
A total of 24 runs were scored.

Josh picked 2 numbers, 22 and 2, whose sum is 24.

Then he checked to see if the difference of the pair was 6. No
Josh guessed again, picking 12 and 12.

$22 + 2 = 24$	$12 + 12 = 24$
$22 - 2 = 20$	$12 - 12 = 0$
too large ↗	too small ↗

Josh knew that the number of runs for one team was between 22 and 12. He tried a few more guesses until he found numbers that worked.

$18 + \underline{6} = 24$	$18 - 6 = 12$
$16 + \underline{8} = 24$	$16 - 8 = 8$
$15 + \underline{9} = 24$	$15 - 9 = 6$

The Cubs scored 15 runs and the Hawks scored 9 runs.

Follow the same steps to answer these questions.

1. The Hawks lost to the Eagles by 7 runs. A total of 19 runs were scored. How many runs did each team score?

____

2. The Eagles beat the Cubs by 4 runs. A total of 28 runs were scored. How many runs did each team score?

____

3. The Panthers beat the Jaguars by 13 runs. A total of 17 runs were scored. How many runs did each team score?

____

Name ______________________________

Mental Math

Knowing basic addition facts can help you add mentally.

Sam has \$38 saved. He earns \$6 raking leaves. How much money does Sam have now?

\$38 + \$6

Step 1
Rewrite 38. 38 = 30 + 8

Step 2
Add the ones \$8 + \$6 = \$14

Step 3
Add the tens. \$10 + \$30 = \$40

How much money does Sam have? \$44

Use mental math to find each sum.

1. 26 + 5

6 + 5 = ________

________ + 20 = ________

26 + 5 = ________

2. 36 + 21

6 + 1 = ________

30 + 20 = ________

36 + 21 = ________

3. 49 + 8 = ________ **4.** 52 + 11 = ________ **5.** 28 + 41 = ________

6. 84 + 9 = ________ **7.** 47 + 32 = ________ **8.** 64 + 19 = ________

9. 17 + 52 = ________ **10.** 37 + 44 = ________ **11.** 27 + 74 = ________

12. 23 + 57 = ________ **13.** 45 + 27 = ________ **14.** 16 + 79 = ________

15. 49 + 22 = ________ **16.** 34 + 17 = ________ **17.** 36 + 38 = ________

Name ______________________________

Another Look
3-12

Counting Coins

You can find the total value of coins by adding their values mentally.

25¢ + 25¢ = 50¢

50¢ + 10¢ = 60¢

60¢ + 5¢ = 65¢

65¢ + 1¢ = 66¢

The total value of the coins is 66¢.

Write the total value in cents.

1. 

25¢ + 10¢ = ______

______ + 10¢ = ______

______ + 10¢ = ______

______ + 5¢ = ______

2. 

10¢ + 10¢ = ______

______ + 5¢ = ______

______ + 5¢ = ______

______ + 5¢ = ______

______ + 5¢ = ______

______ + 1¢ = ______

______ + 1¢ = ______

______ + 1¢ = ______

3. 

______ + ______ = ______

______ + ______ = ______

______ + ______ = ______

______ + ______ = ______

______ + ______ = ______

4. 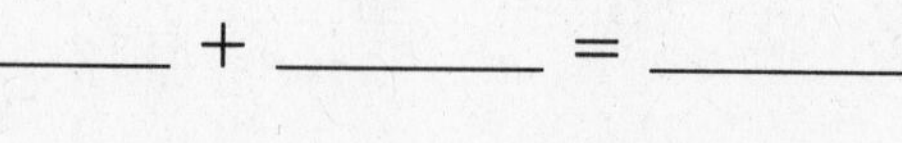

______ + ______ = ______

______ + ______ = ______

______ + ______ = ______

______ + ______ = ______

Name ______________________________

Using Dollars and Cents

Write the value of the coins in dollars and cents.

You can write the value of coins by counting on. Start with the coin having the greatest value. Find the value of the quarters by counting by 25s.

$0.25. . . $0.50
<u>$0.50 in quarters</u>

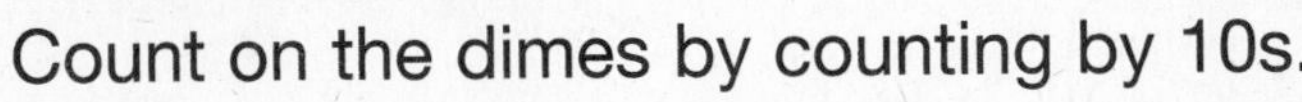

Count on the dimes by counting by 10s.

. . . $0.60 . . . $0.70 . . .$0.80 — <u>$0.80 in quarters and dimes</u>

Count on the nickels by counting by 5s.

. . . $0.85 . . . $0.90 . . . $0.95 . . . $1.00 . . . $1.05 — <u>$1.05 in quarters, dimes and nickels.</u>

Count on the pennies by counting by 1s.

. . . $1.06 . . . $1.07 . . . $1.08 — <u>$1.08 in all.</u>

Write the value of the coins in dollars and cents.

1.

$0.25 . . . __________ . . . $0.60 . . . __________ . . . __________ . . .

__________ . . . __________ . . . $1.00 . . . __________

2.

__________ . . . __________ . . . $0.75 . . . __________ . . . __________

__________ . . . $1.05 . . . __________ . . . __________

Name ______________________________

Another Look
3-14

Exploring Making Change

In your book, you made change using coins and bills. Here is another way to make change.

At an art sale, Robert gives $2.00 for a clay mug that costs $0.28. How much change will he receive?

$2.00 = 200¢ $0.28 = 28¢

200¢ − 28¢ = change owed to Robert

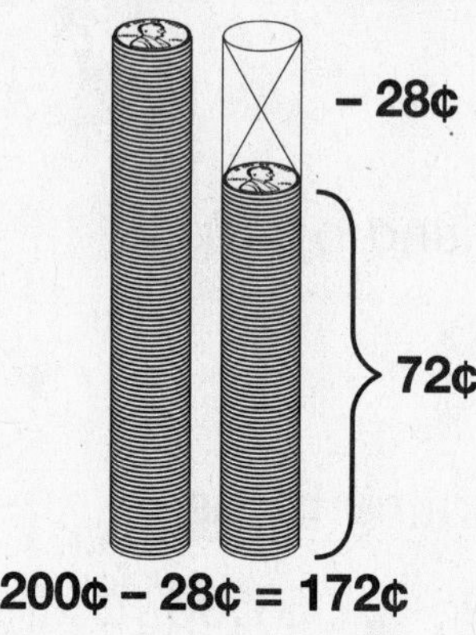

172¢ = $1.72

Follow the steps above to make change. Think of pennies to help you.

1. Keisha gives you $3.00 for a painting that costs $1.54.

   $3.00 = ________ $1.54 = ________

   ________ – ________ = ________ = ________

2. Kelly gives you $5.00 for a clay pot that costs $2.31.

   ____

You can use other coins to make change.

3. What other coins and bills could you use for Keisha's change in **1**?

   ____

4. What other coins could you use for Kelly's change in **2**?

   ____

   ____

Name ____________________

Another Look
3-15

Adding Money

You go to the market. You decide to buy milk and bread.
Milk costs $2.09. Bread costs $1.78.
How much will both items cost?

Since you want to find the total cost, you add $2.09 + $1.78.

Step 1

Change the amounts to cents
$2.09 = 209¢
$1.78 = 178¢

Step 2

Add.

```
   1
  209¢
+ 178¢
------
  387¢
```

Step 3

Change the sum to dollars and cents.

387¢ = $3.87

209¢ + 178¢ = 387¢

$2.09 + $1.78 = $3.87

Use the steps above to add.

1. $4.33 + 0.75

2. $1.45 + 1.96

3. $0.37 + 3.41

4. $0.99 + 3.33

5. $5.59 + 9.23

6. $2.42 + 3.98

7. $1.16 + 2.93

8. $5.63 + 2.28

9. $6.78 + 3.64

10. Find the sum of $2.59 and $1.17. ____________

11. Add $3.42 and $7.21. ____________

Name ______________________

Another Look
3-16

Front-End Estimation

Front-end estimation can help you estimate sums.

Example 1
Make the other digits 0.
Add the front digits.

10	→	10
22	→	20
+ **1**7	→	+ 10
		40

The sum of 10 + 22 + 17 is about __40__.

Example 2
Make the other digits 0.
Add the front digits.

$**2**.40	→	$2.00
4.68	→	$4.00
+ **1**.76	→	$1.00
		$7.00

The sum of $2.40 + $4.68 + $1.76 is about __$7.00__.

Use front-end estimation to estimate each sum.

1. 29 + 42

2. 408 + 263 + 211

3. $9.43 + 5.38 + 1.82

4. $3.09 + 4.24 + 2.49

5. 88 + 92 + 21

6. 775 + 619

7. $6.51 + 8.27 + 3.39

8. 336 + 120 + 291

9. 891 + 117

10. 445 + 286 + 535 ______________

11. $3.01 + $9.12 + $1.46 ______________

Name ______________________________

Another Look
3-17

Analyze Word Problems: Exact Answer or Estimate?

The entire grade is taking a field trip to the county museum. Each bus has 40 seats. Will Ms. D'Angelo's class and Mrs. Smith-Francis' class be able to travel together on one bus?

Teacher	Students
Ms. D'Angelo	23
Mr. Fernandez	21
Mrs. Smith-Francis	14
Mr. Jones	18

You know that there are 40 seats on a bus. Ms. D'Angelo has 23 students. Mrs. Smith-Francis has 14 students.

You can estimate the sum of 23 + 14.

Estimate. 23 is close to 20.

14 is close to _10_

20 + 10 = _30_

Ms. D'Angelo's and Mrs. Smith-Francis' classes _can_ all ride on the same bus.

Follow the model above to solve the problem.

1. Can Mr. Jones' class and Mr. Fernandez's class fit together on one bus?

____

2. How many 40-seat buses will be needed for the entire grade?

____

3. All the students want to ride on one larger bus.

   a. About how many seats should the bus have?

   ____

   b. Find the exact number for all the students. How many seats will be needed?

   ____

Name ______________________________

Reviewing the Meaning of Subtraction

For taking away, comparing, and finding the missing part, clue words are often used. When you see these clue words, you know you have to subtract:

how many more
how many less
how much more
how much of an *-er* word
(such as *larger, smaller, taller, shorter*)
difference
remain
left
fewer
greater

How many more balloons are there in the first group than in the second?

Subtract. $5 - 3 = 2$

There are 2 more balloons in the first group.

Read each problem. Underline the clue words. Then write a number sentence for each and solve.

1. Jack has 9 baseball cards. Sue has 11 baseball cards. How many more baseball cards does Sue have than Jack?

____

2. How much longer is the first truck?

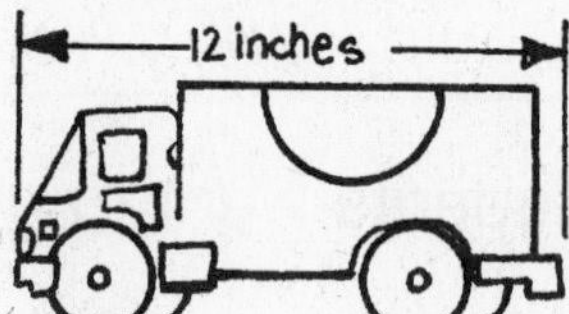

____

3. Marianne has six stamps. She uses two to mail two letters. How many stamps does Marianne have left?

____

4. Four people are in a tent. Two leave the tent. How many people remain in the tent?

____

 Use with pages 150–151.

Name ______________________

Another Look
4-2

Exploring Subtraction Patterns

In your book you used patterns to subtract larger numbers. Here is another way to subtract larger numbers.

Find 900 − 500.

Use a number line.

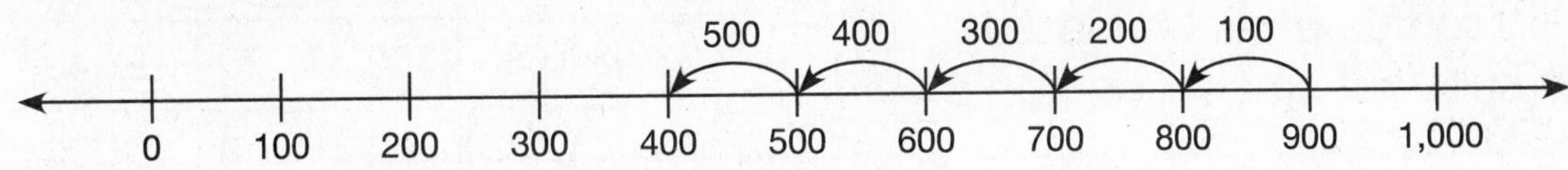

900 − 500 = 400

Find each difference using the number lines.

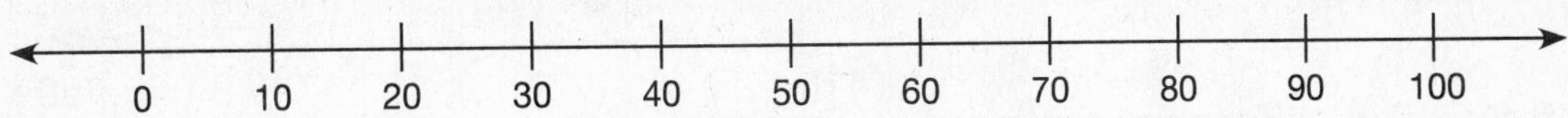

1. 60 − 40 = ______
2. 80 − 40 = ______
3. 70 − 10 = ______
4. 40 − 20 = ______
5. 100 − 30 = ______
6. 90 − 60 = ______
7. 20 − 10 = ______
8. 50 − 30 = ______

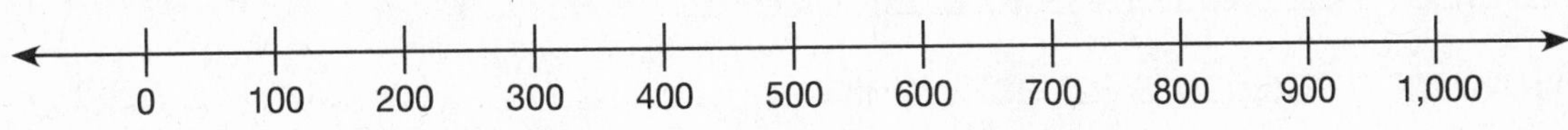

9. 600 − 200 = ______
10. 800 − 600 = ______
11. 700 − 500 = ______
12. 1,000 − 600 = ______
13. 1,000 − 400 = ______
14. 500 − 200 = ______
15. 900 − 300 = ______
16. 700 − 400 = ______

Name ______________________

Another Look
4-3

Exploring Subtracting On a Hundred Chart

In your book you used a hundred chart to explore subtraction. Here is another way to use the hundred chart.

You can use this partial hundred chart to subtract smaller numbers.

1	2	3	4	5	6	7	8	9	10
11	12	13	14	15	16	17	18	19	20
21	22	23	24	25	26	27	28	29	30
31	32	33	34	35	36	37	38	39	40
41	42	43	44	45	46	47	48	49	50

45 − 27

Put your pencil on 45.

Count back 27 squares.

What number is your pencil on?

18

45 − 27 = 18

1	2	3	4	5	6	7	8	9	10
11	12	13	14	15	16	17	18	19	20
21	22	23	24	25	26	27	28	29	30
31	32	33	34	35	36	37	38	39	40
41	42	43	44	45	46	47	48	49	50

You can find the difference without counting all the ones.

Put your pencil on 45 and just count back 7 ones. Then move your pencil up 2 rows to count back 2 tens. Your pencil should be on 18.

---

1. If you subtract by counting back all the ones, how many squares will you count back to subtract 36? ______

Count back by ones and tens to answer each question.

2. a. How many squares (ones) would you count back to subtract 56? ______

   b. How many rows (tens) would you move up to subtract 56? ______

3. a. How many ones would you count back to subtract 41? ______

   b. How many tens would you count back to subtract 41? ______

Find each difference using a hundred chart.

4. 42 − 21 = ______ 5. 34 − 19 = ______ 6. 22 − 7 = ______

7. 49 − 15 = ______ 8. 37 − 28 = ______ 9. 46 − 28 = ______

Name ________________________

Estimating Differences

To estimate, you need to know how to round numbers. The chart lists steps for rounding numbers.

Rounding to the Nearest Tens or Hundreds		
Steps	**Tens**	**Hundreds**
Draw a box around the place to which you will round.	[5]2	[3]71
Is the digit to the right 5 or more? If it is not, make no change. Otherwise, add 1 to the digit in the box.	[5]2 The digit to the right is less than 5, so make no change.	[4]71 The digit to the right is more than 5, so add 1. Change 3 to 4.
Change all the digits to the right to zeros.	50	400

Round each 2-digit number to the nearest 10. Round each 3-digit number to the nearest 100.

1. 28 ________ **2.** 394 ________

3. 67 ________ **4.** 683 ________

5. 881 ________ **6.** 737 ________

7. 42 ________ **8.** 649 ________

9. 11 ________ **10.** 74 ________

Round to the nearest ten. Then estimate the difference.

11. 48 − 36 ________ − ________ = ________

12. 83 − 27 ________ − ________ = ________

13. 38 − 14 ________ − ________ = ________

14. 68 − 26 ________ − ________ = ________

15. 51 − 39 ________ − ________ = ________

Name ______________________________

Another Look
4-5

Exploring Regrouping

In your book you used place-value blocks to explore regrouping. Here is another way to explore regrouping.

1 dime is the same as 10 pennies.
1 ten is the same as 10 ones.

100 pennies or 1 dollar is the same as 10 dimes.
1 hundred is the same as 10 tens.

23¢ is the same as ___1___ dime and ___13___ pennies.

So, 23 is the same as ___1___ ten and ___13___ ones.

Regroup 1 ten for 10 ones. Use the pictures of coins to help.

1.

86¢ is the same as ________ dimes and ________ pennies.

So, 86 is the same as ________ tens and ________ ones.

2.

47¢ is the same as ________ dimes and ________ pennies.

So, 47 is the same as ________ tens and ________ ones.

Name ____________________

Exploring Subtracting 2-Digit Numbers

In your book you used place-value blocks to subtract 2-digit numbers. Here is another way to subtract 2-digit numbers.

27 − 14

You can draw a picture to subtract. Draw a number of objects equal to the first number in the subtraction problem (27). Cross off a number of objects equal to the second number in the subtraction problem (14). Count the remaining objects.

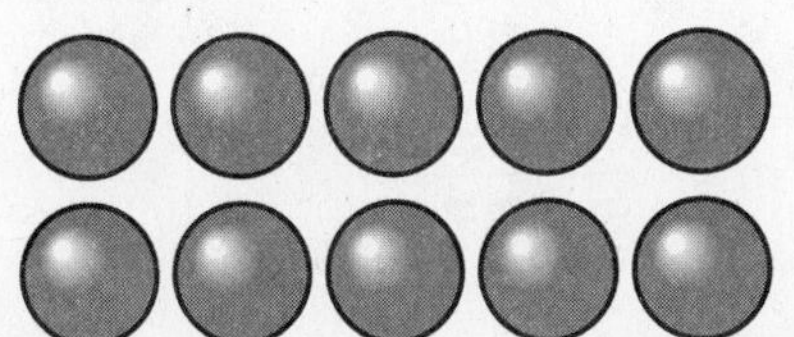
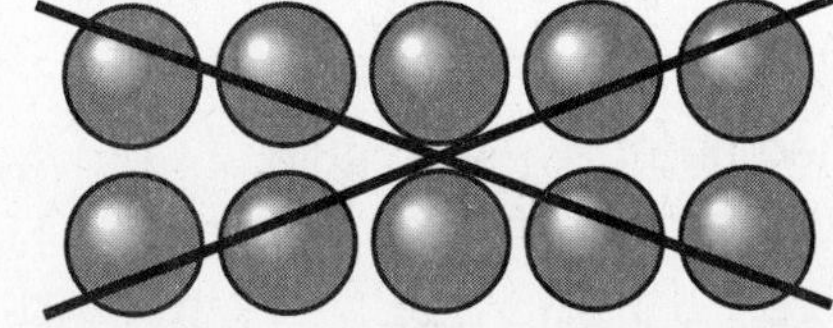
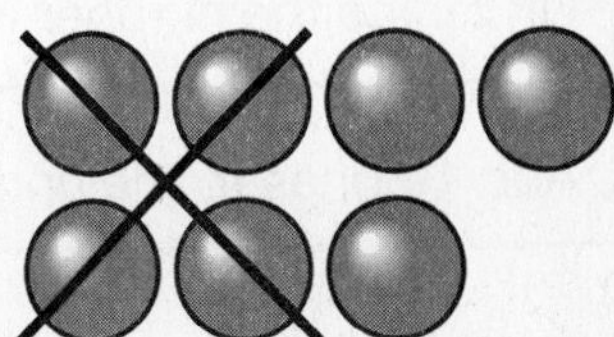

27 − 14 = 13

Find each difference. Draw pictures to help.

1. 18 − 12 = ______

☆☆☆☆☆☆☆☆☆
☆☆☆☆☆☆☆☆☆

2. 24 − 21 = ______

3. 31 − 15 = ______

4. 48 − 31 = ______

5. 57 − 19 = ______

6. 41 − 18 = ______

7. 64 − 21 = ______

8. 37 − 29 = ______

Name ______________________________

Another Look
4-7

Subtracting 2-Digit Numbers

To find the difference between 86 and 29, you cannot take 9 ones from 6 ones. So, you have to regroup. Follow these steps to regroup tens as ones:

Steps	Example
Draw a box around the number in the tens place.	[8]6
Take 1 ten from the boxed number.	7 over [8̸]6
Underline the number in the ones place.	7 over [8̸]<u>6</u>
Add 10 ones to the underlined number.	7 16 over [8̸]6̸

$$\begin{array}{r} {\scriptstyle 7\,16} \\ \not{8}\not{6} \\ -\ 29 \\ \hline 57 \end{array}$$

Now you can subtract ones and tens.

Read each problem. Do you need to regroup 1 ten as 10 ones? Answer yes or no.

1. 48 − 73 ___No___

2. 94 − 36 ________

3. 31 − 41 ________

4. 62 − 27 ________

5. 46 − 67 ________

6. 24 − 12 ________

Read each problem. Do you need to regroup 1 ten as 10 ones? If so, show how you would regroup.

For example: 86 − 68 ___$\overset{7\,16}{\not{8}\not{6}}$___

7. 58 − 54 ________

8. 73 − 15 ________

9. 41 − 26 ________

10. 93 − 52 ________

Subtract. Regroup if necessary.

11. 28 − 17 = ________

12. 52 − 36 = ________

13. 44 − 28 = ________

14. 67 − 45 = ________

15. 82 − 76 = ________

16. 35 − 17 = ________

Name ______________________________

Exploring Subtracting 3-Digit Numbers

In your book you used place-value blocks to subtract 3-digit numbers. Here is another way to subtract 3-digit numbers.

Find 143 − 67.

You can use money to show subtraction.

Show 143 using dollars, dimes, and pennies.
You can think of one dollar as one hundred cents.

You can't take away 7 pennies, so exchange 1 dime for 10 pennies.

Cross off 7 pennies.

You can't take away 6 dimes from 3 dimes, so exchange the dollar for 10 dimes.

Cross off 6 dimes.

Count the amount of change that remains.

143¢ − 67¢ = 76¢

So, 143 − 67 = 76

Find each difference. Use money to help.

1. 261 − 49 = ________

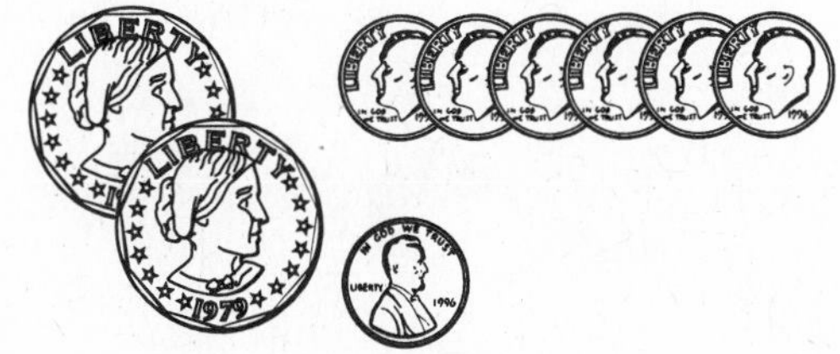

2. 324 − 187 = ________

3. 129 − 37 = ________

4. 382 − 157 = ________

Name ______________________________

Another Look
4-9

Subtracting 3-Digit Numbers

You can use place-value blocks to help you subtract 3-digit numbers.

Subtract 341 − 126.

Show 341 with place-value blocks.

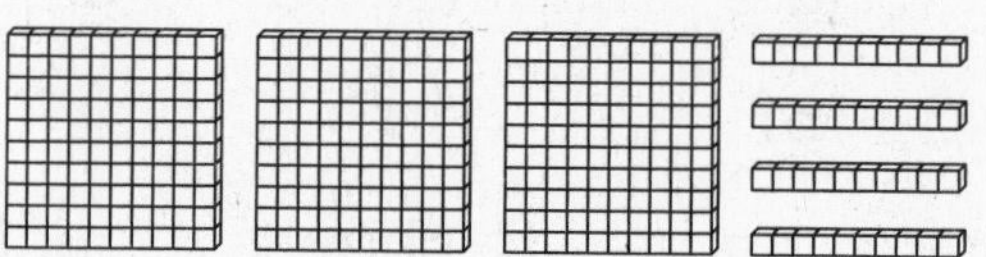

Step 1 First subtract the ones. Do you need to regroup 1 ten for 10 ones? Yes.

Step 2 Regroup 1 tens block for 10 ones blocks.

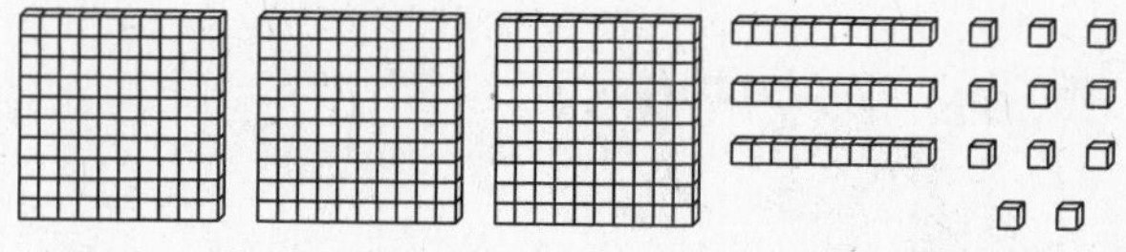

Step 3 Subtract the ones.
Cross off 6 ones blocks.

Step 4 Subtract the tens.
Cross off 2 tens blocks.

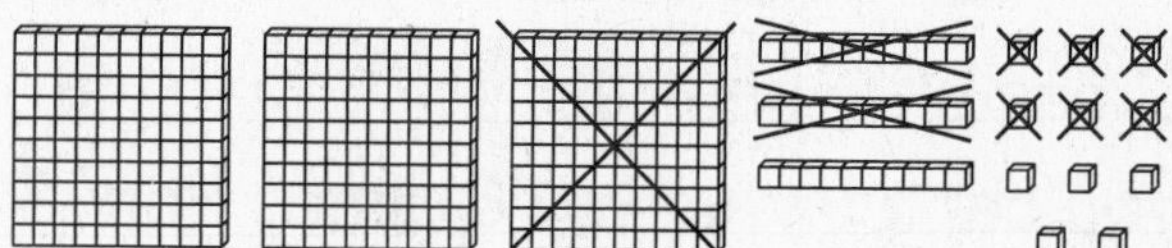

Step 5 Subtract the hundreds.
Cross off 1 hundreds block.

Count the remaining blocks.

341 − 126 = 215.

Subtract. You may use place-value blocks to help.

1. Subtract 459 − 185.

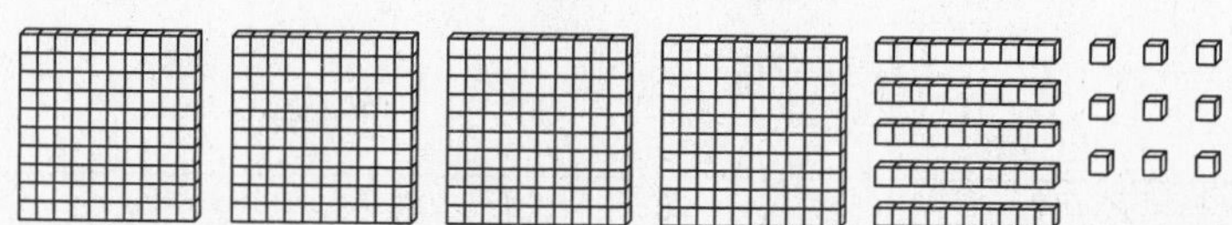

a. Do you need to regroup 1 ten for 10 ones? ________

b. Do you need to regroup 1 hundred for 10 tens? ________

c. 459 − 185 = ________

2. 322 − 217 = ________

3. 548 − 364 = ________

4. 619 − 221 = ________

5. 351 − 191 = ________

Name ____________________

Another Look
4-10

Subtracting with 2 Regroupings

Subtract 234 − 158.

Step 1 Show 234 with place-value blocks.

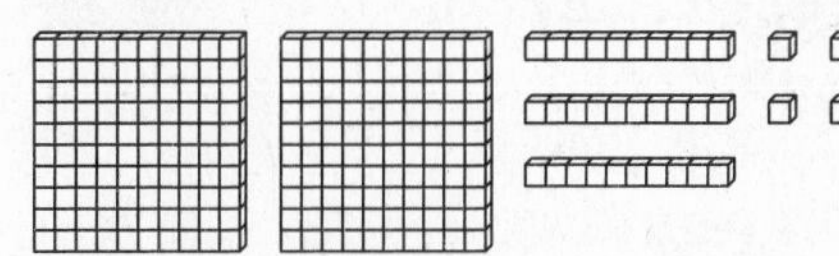

Step 2 First subtract the ones.
Do you need to regroup 1 ten as 10 ones? Yes.
Cross off 8 ones.

$$\begin{array}{r} {\scriptstyle 2\ 14} \\ 2\,\not{3}\,\not{4} \\ -\,1\,5\,8 \\ \hline \end{array}$$

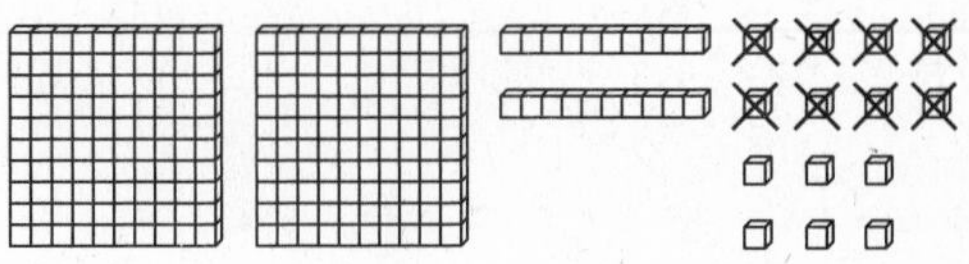

Step 3 Now subtract the tens.
Do you need to regroup 1 hundred as 10 tens? Yes.
Cross off 5 tens.

$$\begin{array}{r} {\scriptstyle 12} \\ {\scriptstyle 1\ \not{2}\ 14} \\ \not{2}\,\not{3}\,\not{4} \\ -\,1\,5\,8 \\ \hline \end{array}$$

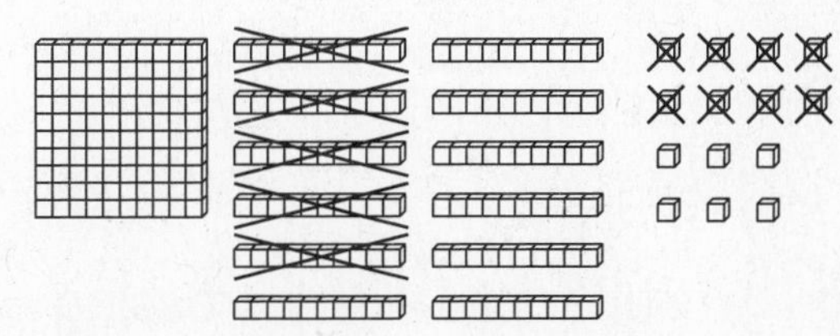

Step 4 Now subtract the hundreds.
Cross off 1 hundred.
Count the remaining blocks.
234 − 158 = 76

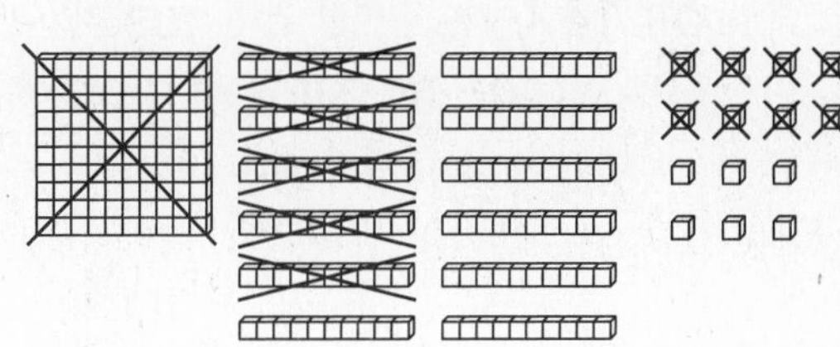

Subtract. You may use place-value blocks to help.

1. Subtract 322 − 164.

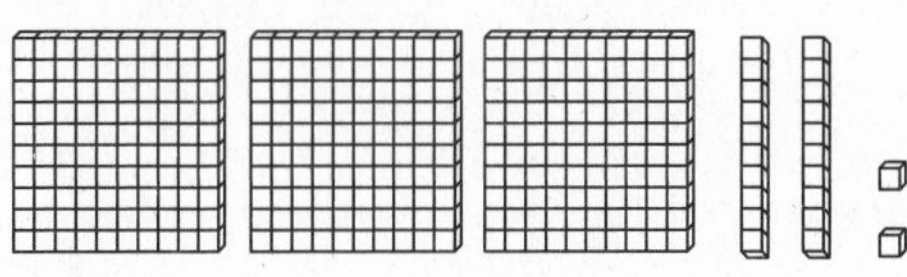

a. Do you need to regroup 1 ten as 10 ones? ________

b. Do you need to regroup 1 hundred as 10 tens? ________

c. 322 − 164 = ________

2. 211 − 76 = ________

3. 556 − 289 = ________

Name ______________________________

Subtracting Across 0

Subtract 203 − 147.

Step 1 Since you can't take 7 ones from 3 ones, you need to regroup. There is a zero in the tens place.

Think: 2 hundreds 3 ones is the same as 20 tens 3 ones.

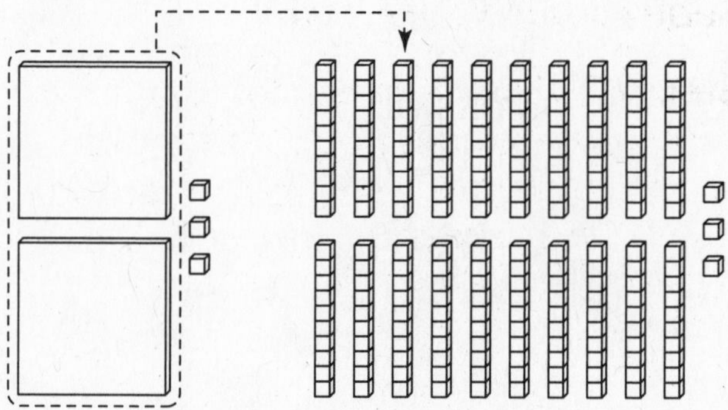

Step 2 Regroup 20 tens 3 ones as 19 tens 13 ones.

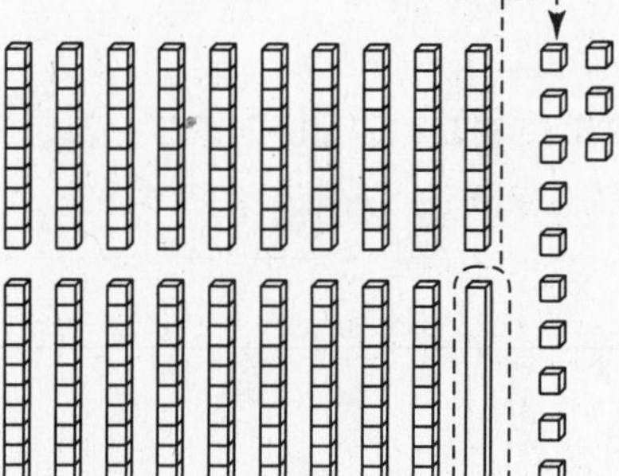

Step 3 Subtract 147 by crossing off 14 tens and 7 ones. Count the remaining blocks.

203 − 147 = 56

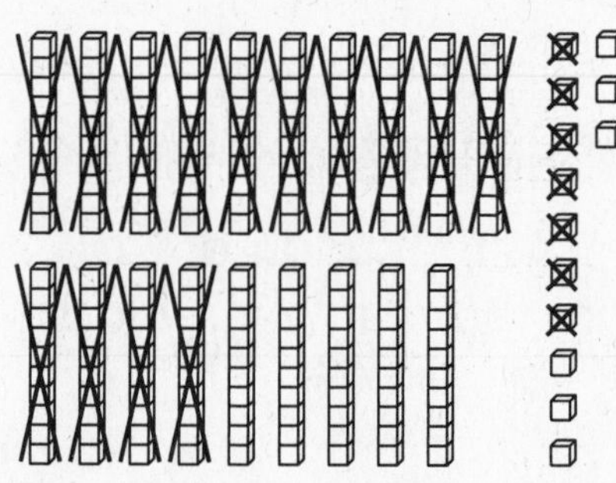

Find each difference. Use place-value blocks to help.

1. 108 − 59 = ________

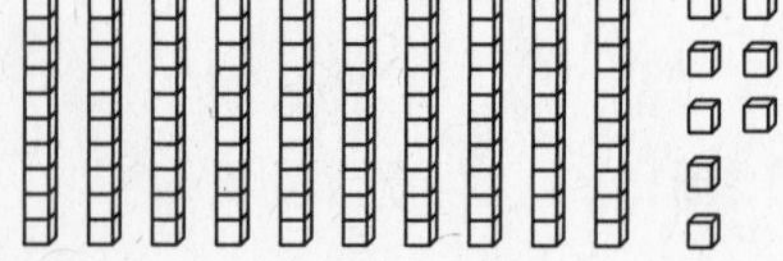

2. 102 − 66 = ________

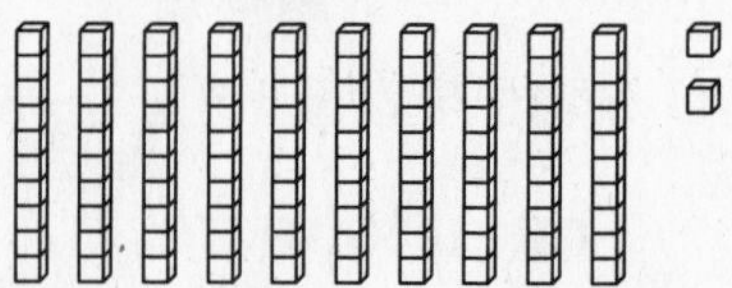

3. 206 − 97 = ________

4. 501 − 222 = ________

5. 703 − 367 = ________

6. 405 − 268 = ________

Name ___________________________

Another Look
4-12

Subtracting 4-Digit Numbers: Choose a Calculation Method

You can use pencil and paper to subtract 4-digit numbers.

Regroup as needed.

Subtract 7,382 − 4,568.

Step 1 First subtract the ones. You can't subtract 8 from 2, so you need to regroup 1 ten as 10 ones.

```
      7 12
  7,3 8 2
− 4,5 6 8
        4
```

Step 2 Now subtract the tens. Since 6 is less than 7, you do not need to regroup.

```
      7 12
  7,3 8 2
− 4,5 6 8
      1 4
```

Step 3 Subtract the hundreds. You can't subtract 5 from 3, so you need to regroup 1 thousand as 10 hundreds.

```
 6 13 7 12
  7,3 8 2
− 4,5 6 8
    8 1 4
```

Step 4 Now subtract the thousands. You do not need to regroup.

```
 6 13 7 12
  7,3 8 2
− 4,5 6 8
  2,8 1 4
```

So, 7,382 − 4,568 = 2,814

Subtract. Use pencil and paper. Regroup when necessary.

1. 3,247 − 1,462

a. Do you need to regroup the ones? ________

b. Do you need to regroup the tens? ________

c. Do you need to regroup the hundreds? ________

d. What is the answer? ________

2.
```
  4,1 4 9
− 2,8 2 6
```

3.
```
  1,3 7 0
−   5 8 0
```

Name ______________________________

Another Look
4-13

Analyze Word Problems: Multiple-Step Problems

Sometimes you need more than one step to solve a problem. Make a plan. Then follow the plan to solve the problem.

Ray has $6. He will get $5 more today. How much more will he need to buy a Fun Park All-Day Ride Pass for $18?

Plan Add to find out how much money Ray has today. Subtract to find out how much more money he needs to buy the pass.

Step 1 Ray has $6 + $5 = $11

Step 2 The pass costs $18. Ray has $11.

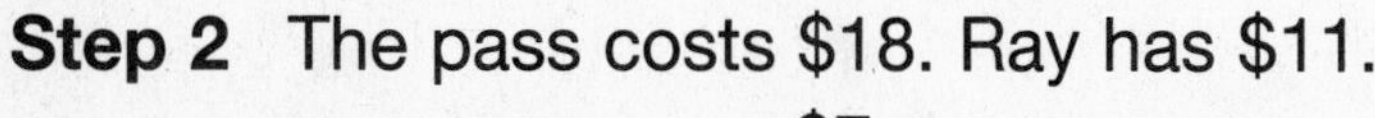

$18 − $11 = $7

Fun Park
All-Day Ride Pass
$18

Ray needs $7 more to buy the All-Day Ride Pass.

Make a plan. Then solve the problem.

Tyler planned 60 minutes for the Fun House before he has to meet friends. He waits in line for 22 minutes and spends 35 minutes in the Fun House. How much time does he have left before he has to meet his friends?

1. Plan

____

2. Step 1

____

3. Step 2

____

4. Answer

____

Name ________________________________

Mental Math

It is easier to add or subtract a multiple of 10. Numbers in problems can be adjusted so you can solve them mentally.

Example 1

34 − 26

Think: What number can I add to 26 to make it a multiple of 10? __4__

But, to keep the problem accurate, add 4 to 34, too.

Think: Add 4. 34 → 38
Think: Add 4. − 26 → − 30
8

So, 34 − 26 = 8.

Example 2

85 − 47

Think: What number can I add to 47 to make it a a multiple of 10? __3__

But, to keep the problem accurate, add 3 to 85, too.

Think: Add 3. 85 → 88
Think: Add 3. − 47 → − 50
38

So, 85 − 47 = 38.

What number would you add to each in order to subtract mentally?

1. 24 − 7 ________

2. 33 − 18 ________

3. 43 − 36 ________

4. 97 − 49 ________

Add 1, 2, 3, or 4 to each number to make it easier to subtract mentally. Then subtract.

5. 46 → □□
− 28 → −□□

So, 46 − 28 = ________

6. 93 → □□
− 79 → −□□

So, 93 − 79 = ________

7. 82 → □□
− 56 → −□□

So, 82 − 56 = ________

8. 71 → □□
− 47 → −□□

So, 71 − 47 = ________

Name ____________________

Another Look 4-15

Subtracting Money

You can use play money to help you subtract money.

Subtract: \$2.75 − \$1.13

Show \$2.75 using dollars, dimes, and pennies.

To subtract, \$1.13, cross off 1 dollar, 1 dime, and 3 pennies.

\$2.75 − \$1.13 = \$1.62

Subtract.

1. \$0.57 − 0.33

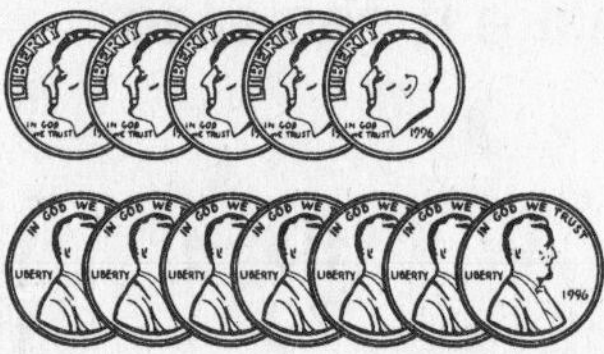

2. \$5.48 − 0.54

3. \$1.87 − 0.59

4. \$0.53 − 0.17

5. \$3.60 − 1.24

6. \$5.00 − 1.37

7. \$6.31 − 2.72

8. \$8.09 − 0.94

Name ______________________________

Another Look
4-16

Analyze Strategies: Use Objects

Jessie counted 7 cycle riders and 19 wheels go past her in the park. How many bicycles and how many tricycles passed her?

What do you know? There are ___7___ cycle riders.

There are ___19___ wheels.

Use two-color counters to show what Jessie saw.

Use 7 red counters to show the cycle riders.

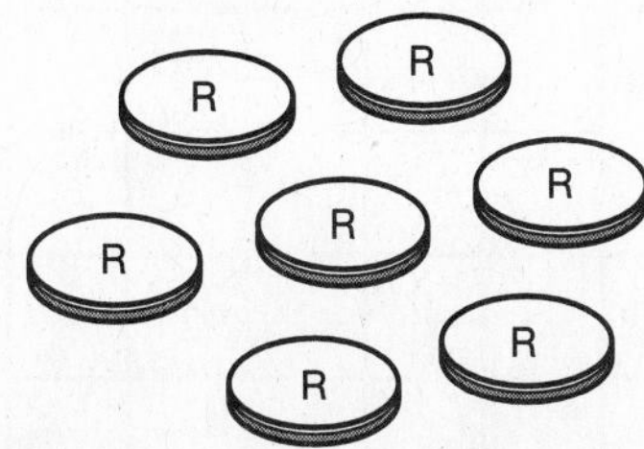

Use 19 yellow counters to show the wheels.

Match each rider with either 2 or 3 wheels until you run out of counters.

    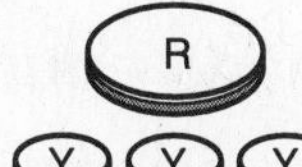  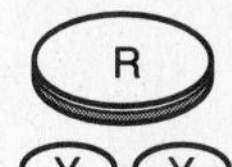

Two bicycles and 5 tricycles passed Jessie.

Solve. Use objects to help.

1. Antonio has 7 coins in his pocket. He has $1.00 in all. What coins does he have in his pocket?

   ____

2. You are riding on an elevator. You get on at the main level. You go up 5 floors, down 3 floors, up 8 floors, and then down 4 floors. Then you get off the elevator. What floor are you on? ____________

3. You are making lunch. You have a choice of tuna or turkey sandwiches. You have a choice of pea, tomato, or chicken soup. How many different ways can you make lunch? ____________

Name ________________________________

Another Look
5-1

Exploring Equal Groups

In your book you explored multiplication using counters or pictures. Here is another way to multiply equal groups.

Suppose Carl has 4 rows of 3 stickers. How many stickers does he have in all?

You can use grid paper to find how many stickers. Shade one row for each row of stickers.

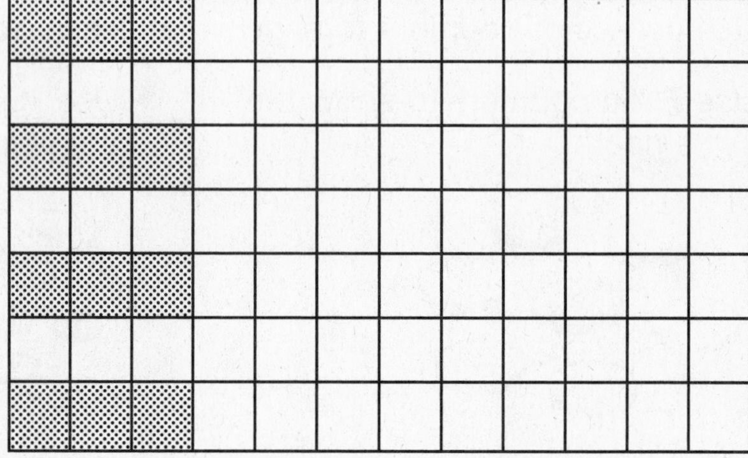

4 rows of 3 equals 12.

So Carl has 12 stickers.

Use grid paper. Shade equal groups. Then write how many.

1. 3 rows of 3 equals ________.

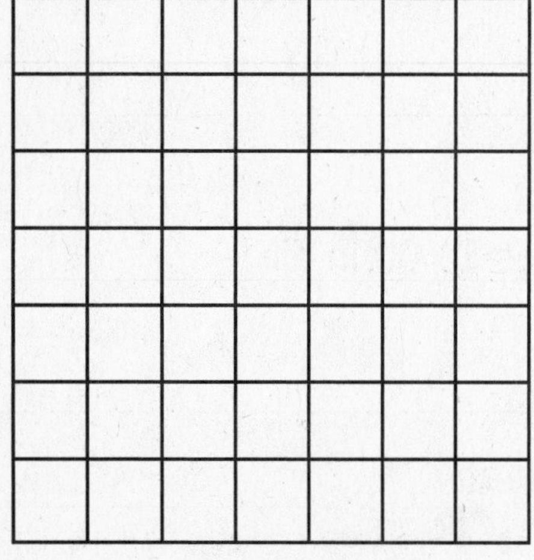

2. 2 rows of 5 equals ________.

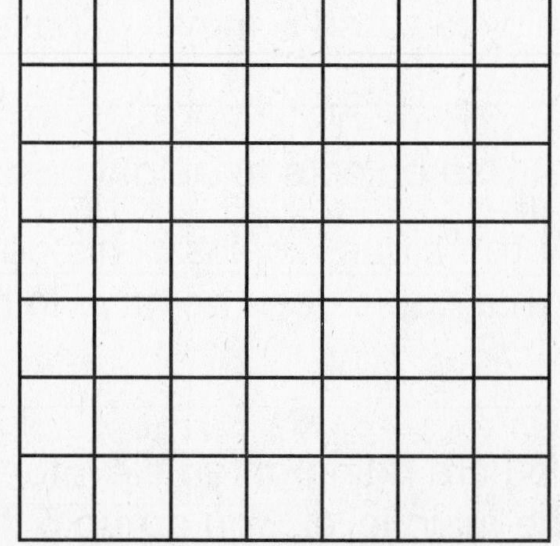

3. 4 rows of 4 equals ________.

4. 6 rows of 2 equals ________.

5. 3 rows of 7 equals ________.

6. 5 rows of 4 equals ________.

7. 4 rows of 6 equals ________.

8. 2 rows of 9 equals ________.

Name ________________________________

Another Look
5-2

Writing Multiplication Sentences

You can use counters to multiply equal groups.

3 groups of 5

3 × 5 = 15
↑ ↑ ↑
factor factor product

Use counters to complete.

1.

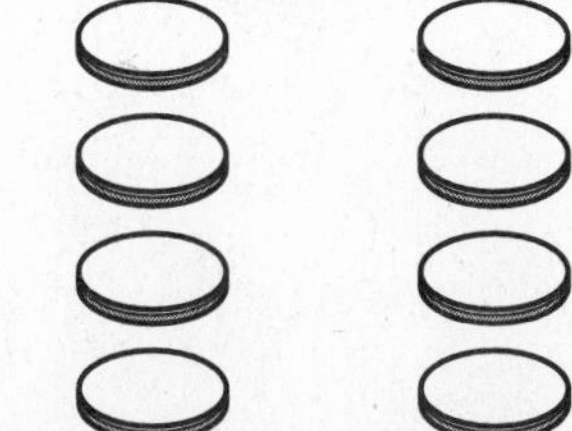

a. 3 groups of ______

b. 4 + ______ + ______ = ______

c. 3 × ______ = ______

2.

a. ______ groups of ______

b. ______ + ______ + ______ + ______ = ______

c. ______ × ______ = ______

3.

a. ______ groups of ______

b. ______ + ______ = ______

c. ______ × ______ = ______

Name ____________________

Another Look 5-3

Exploring Multiplication Stories

Story: Colleen gives each of her aunts 2 bracelets. She has 3 aunts.

Question: How many bracelets does she give? You can draw a picture to solve.

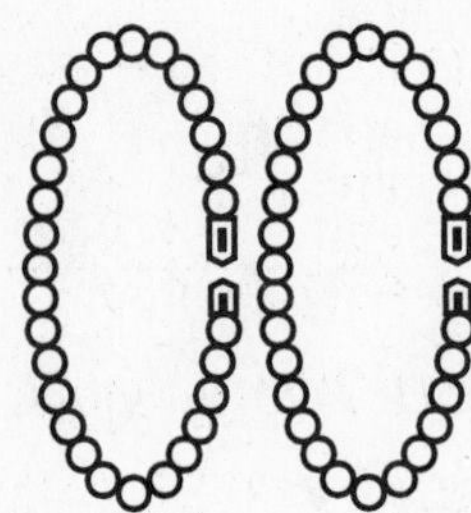

3 aunts
2 bracelets for each aunt

$3 \times 2 = 6$

She gave __6 bracelets__ in all.

Write a multiplication story for each. You may use a picture to solve.

1. $3 \times 5 =$ ______

Story: ____________________

____

Question: ____________________

2. $4 \times 2 =$ ______

Story: ____________________

____

Question: ____________________

Name ______________________

Another Look
5-4

2 as a Factor

You can use a hundreds chart to find products.

The numbers you multiply are **factors**.

The answer is the **product**.

Skip-count by 2s on the chart when 2 is a factor.

To find 7 × 2, start at 2 and shade 7 boxes. You will land on 14. You can shade each box you land on to see patterns.

The product of 7 and 2 is 14.

1	2	3	4	5	6	7	8	9	10
11	12	13	14	15	16	17	18	19	20
21	22	23	24	25	26	27	28	29	30
31	32	33	34	35	36	37	38	39	40
41	42	43	44	45	46	47	48	49	50
51	52	53	54	55	56	57	58	59	60
61	62	63	64	65	66	67	68	69	70
71	72	73	74	75	76	77	78	79	80
81	82	83	84	85	86	87	88	89	90
91	92	93	94	95	96	97	98	99	100

7 × 2 = 14

↑ ↑ ↑

factor factor product

Use the chart. Find each product.

1. 2 × 4 = ______

2. 1 × 2 = ______

3. 9 × 2 = ______

4. 2 × 5 = ______

5. 2 × 3 = ______

6. 8 × 2 = ______

7. 6 × 2

8. 2 × 7

9. 2 × 2

10. 2 × 9

11. 5 × 2

12. 2 × 6

13. 2 × 1

14. 2 × 3

15. 2 × 8

16. 7 × 2

17. 4 × 2

18. 1 × 2

Name ______________________________

Another Look
5-5

5 as a Factor

You can use a hundred chart to find the product when 5 is a factor.

Skip count by 5s on the chart when 5 is a factor and shade in the numbers you land on.

To find 5 × 4, start at 5 and shade 4 boxes. You will land at 20. You can shade the boxes you land on to see patterns.

The product of 5 and 4 is __20__.

5	×	4	=	20
↑		↑		↑
factor		factor		product

1	2	3	4	5	6	7	8	9	10
11	12	13	14	15	16	17	18	19	20
21	22	23	24	25	26	27	28	29	30
31	32	33	34	35	36	37	38	39	40
41	42	43	44	45	46	47	48	49	50
51	52	53	54	55	56	57	58	59	60
61	62	63	64	65	66	67	68	69	70
71	72	73	74	75	76	77	78	79	80
81	82	83	84	85	86	87	88	89	90
91	92	93	94	95	96	97	98	99	100

Use the chart. Find each product.

1. 4 × 5 = ________ **2.** 2 × 5 = ________

3. 3 × 5 = ________ **4.** 5 × 7 = ________

5. 5 × 6 = ________ **6.** 8 × 5 = ________

7. 5 × 5 = ________ **8.** 9 × 5 = ________

9. 7 × 5 **10.** 2 × 5 **11.** 4 × 5 **12.** 5 × 9

13. 5 × 1 **14.** 6 × 5 **15.** 3 × 5 **16.** 5 × 8

17. 9 × 5 **18.** 1 × 5 **19.** 5 × 4 **20.** 5 × 5

Name ______________________________

Another Look
5-6

Exploring Patterns on a Hundred Chart: 2s and 5s

In your book you skip counted to find patterns on a hundred chart. Here's another way to find patterns.

Even numbers are numbers with 0, 2, 4, 6, or 8 as their last digit. Even numbers are multiples of 2. Shade all the even numbers with dots.

1	2	3	4	5	6	7	8	9	10
11	12	13	14	15	16	17	18	19	20
21	22	23	24	25	26	27	28	29	30
31	32	33	34	35	36	37	38	39	40
41	42	43	44	45	46	47	48	49	50

Multiples of 5 always end in 0 or 5. Shade all the multiples of 5 with stripes.

You can use the hundred chart to multiply.

To find the product of 5 and 4, count 4 striped squares starting with 5. Your finger should land on __20__.

To find the product of 2 and 9, count 9 dotted squares starting with 2. Your finger should land on __18__.

Find each product.

1. 5×7

a. How many striped squares should you count? ________

b. On which square do you start? ________

c. $5 \times 7 =$ ________

2. 2×6

a. How many dotted squares should you count? ________

b. On which square do you start? ________

c. $2 \times 6 =$ ________

3. Use the partial hundred chart to complete the table.

×	1	2	3	4	5	6	7	8	9
2									
5									

Name ______________________________

Another Look 5-7

Exploring 0 and 1 as Factors

In your book you looked for patterns in a table. Here's another way to find patterns.

Drawing pictures can help you see patterns.

What does 1 group of 5 look like?

This group can be described in three ways.

1 group of 5   1 × 5   5

Draw pictures to show each grouping.

1. 1 group of 6

2. 6 groups of 1

3. 0 groups of 6

4. 6 groups of 0

5. 1 group of 8

6. 8 groups of 1

7. 0 groups of 8

8. 8 groups of 0

Use the patterns you see to find each product.

9. 5 × 1 = ______   **10.** 9 × 0 = ______   **11.** 1 × 8 = ______

12. 0 × 2 = ______   **13.** 1 × 6 = ______   **14.** 5 × 0 = ______

Name ______________________

9 as a Factor

You can use drawings to help you multiply.

Draw an array to show 6 × 9.

How many rows of 9 did you draw? 6

How many squares in all? 54

What is 6 × 9? 54

---

1. Draw an array to show 3 × 9.

   How many rows of 9 did you draw? ______

   How many squares in all? ______

   What is 3 × 9? ______

2. Draw an array to show 5 × 9.

   How many rows of 9 did you draw? ______

   How many squares in all? ______

   What is 5 × 9? ______

3. Draw an array to show 1 × 9.

   How many rows of 9 did you draw? ______

   How many squares in all? ______

   What is 1 × 9? ______

4. Draw an array to show 2 × 9.

   How many rows of 9 did you draw? ______

   How many squares in all? ______

   What is 2 × 9? ______

Name ______________________________

Analyze Word Problems: Too Much or Too Little Information

Asian elephants have 4 nails on each hind foot. African elephants have 3 nails on each hind foot. How many nails does an Asian elephant have on 2 hind feet?

Underline what you need to find.

Circle the information you need to solve the problem.

Asian elephants have 4 nails on each hind foot. African elephants have 3 nails on each hind foot. How many nails does an Asian elephant have on 2 hind feet?

Since there are 4 nails on one hind foot, there must be 4×2 or 8 nails on 2 hind feet.

Underline what you need to find. Circle the information you need. Then solve if possible. If not possible, tell what information is needed.

1. Cougars can travel 20 feet in one leap and 25 miles in a day. How many feet could a cougar travel in 2 leaps?

   ____

2. Elephants are heavy eaters. They eat 130 pounds of food—hay, fruit, and vegetables—every day. How much hay does an elephant eat in 3 days?

   ____

3. A newborn giraffe can be up to 6 feet tall. An adult giraffe can grow up to 3 times this height. Giraffes do not weigh as much as African elephants. How tall can an adult giraffe grow?

   ____

4. A newborn giraffe is 6 feet tall. How tall is it when it is one year old?

   ____

Name ____________________

Another Look
5-10

Analyze Strategies: Draw a Picture

Draw a picture to solve the problem.

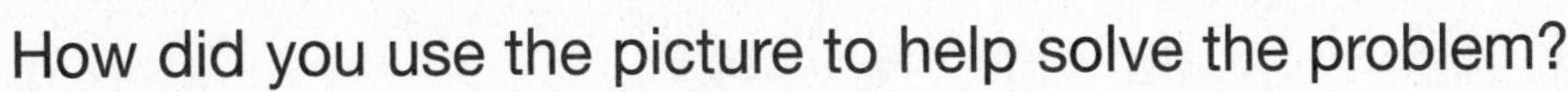

Jason has 15 pepper plants. He wants to plant them in three equal rows. How many plants will each row have? 5

How could you set up your picture?
Start by setting up 3 rows.

How did you use the picture to help solve the problem?
Keep adding one plant to each of the rows until there are 15 plants in all.

Draw a picture to solve each problem.

1. Emily is making a tile tabletop for art class. The tabletop is 4 tiles wide on each side.

a. Finish the picture.

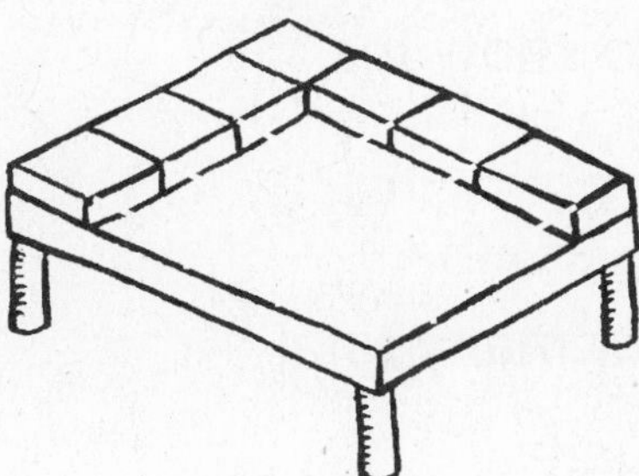

b. How many tiles will she need? ______

2. Robert caught 9 fish today. There were twice as many bass as there were trout. How many trout did Robert catch?

a. Finish the picture.

b. How many trout did Robert catch? ______

Name ______________________

Another Look
6-1

3 as a Factor: Using Known Facts

You can draw an array to find 3 × 5.

Shade one group of 3 squares.

This shows 3 × 1.

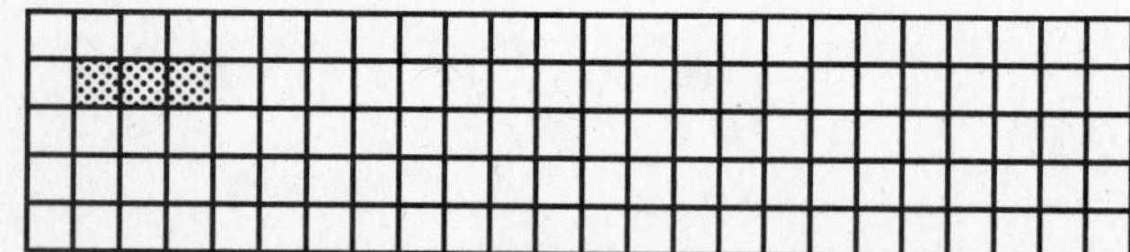

Draw four more groups of 3. Shade all the squares.
This shows 3 × 5.

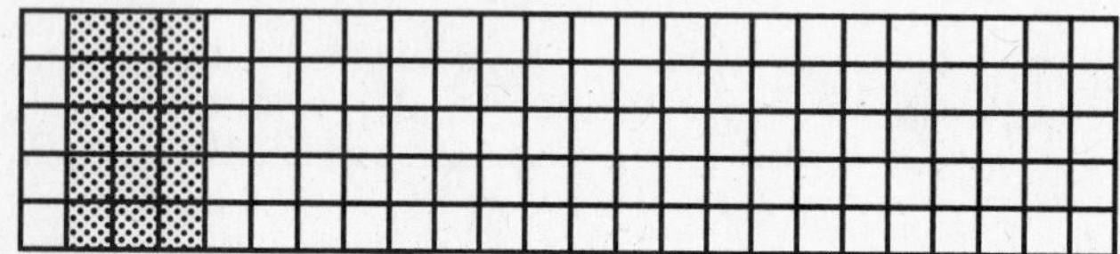

How many total squares are shaded? 15

What is 3 × 5? 15

Draw an array on a separate sheet of paper to show the following. Find each product.

1. 3 × 6

How many total squares? ________

What is 3 × 6? ________

2. 3 × 8

How many total squares? ________

What is 3 × 8? ________

3. 3 × 4

How many total squares? ________

What is 4 × 3? ________

4. 9 × 3

How many total squares? ________

What is 9 × 3? ________

5. How could you add to the array for 3 × 4 to show 3 × 5?

____

Name ______________________

4 as a Factor: Doubling

To multiply by 4, first multiply by 2. Then double the product. You can draw an array to find 4 × 6.

Draw 6 on a grid. Shade the squares.

This shows 1 × 6.

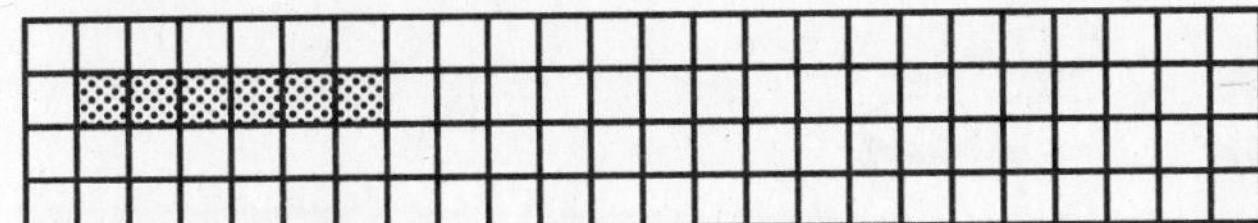

Draw the same number of squares again. Shade the squares. This shows 2 × 6.

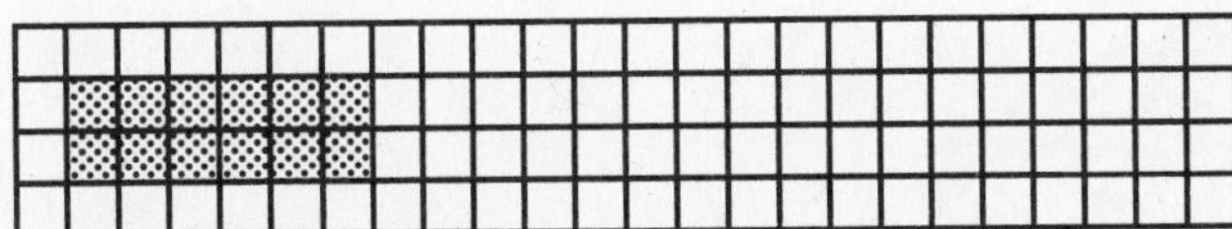

How many total squares are shaded? 12

What is 2 × 6? 12

Double this product. What is 4 × 6? 24

---

1. What is the product of 4 and 3?

   Draw an array to find the product of 2 and 3.

   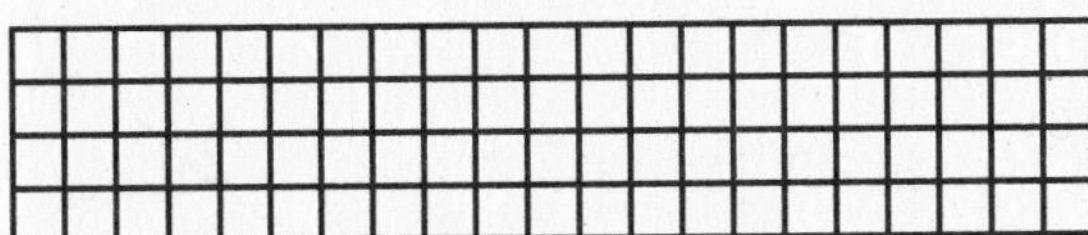

   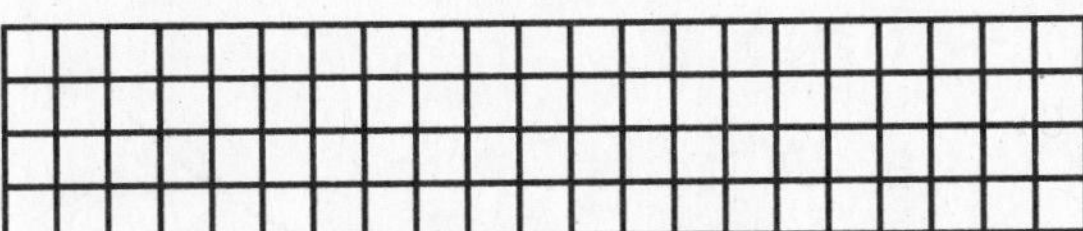

   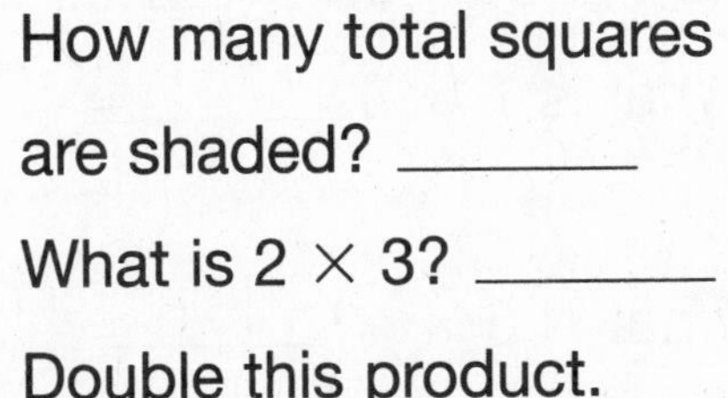

   How many total squares are shaded? ______

   What is 2 × 3? ______

   Double this product.

   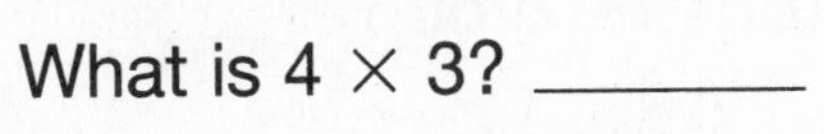

   What is 4 × 3? ______

2. What is the product of 4 and 9?

   Draw an array to find the product of 2 and 9.

   How many total squares are shaded? ______

   What is 2 × 9? ______

   Double this product.

   What is 4 × 9? ______

Name ____________________

6 as a Factor: Using Known Facts

You can use what you know about multiplying by 5 to multiply by 6.

Find 6 × 6.

What is 5 × 6? 30

Now add one more group of 6.

How many total counters are there? 36

What is 6 × 6? 36

Use what you know about multiplying by 5 to find each product.

1. 6 × 3

a. What is 5 × 3? ______

Add one group of 3.

b. What is 6 × 3? ______

2. 6 × 8

a. What is 5 × 8? ______

Add one group of 8.

b. What is 6 × 8? ______

3. 6 × 5

a. What is 5 × 5? ______

b. Add one group of ______.

c. What is 6 × 5? ______

4. 7 × 6

a. What is 7 × 5? ______

b. Add one group of ______.

c. What is 7 × 6? ______

5. 9 × 6

a. What is 9 × 5? ______

b. Add one group of ______.

c. What is 9 × 6? ______

6. 6 × 4

a. What is 5 × 4? ______

b. Add one group of ______.

c. What is 6 × 4? ______

Name ______________________

Another Look 6-4

7 and 8 as Factors

You can use basic facts of 5 and 2 to find 7×7.

What is the product of 5 and 7? 35

What is the product of 2 and 7? 14

What is the sum of these products? 49

What is the product of 7 and 7? 49

Draw a picture that shows how you can use basic facts of 5 and 2 to find each product.

1. You can use basic facts of 5 and 2 to find 7×9.

What is the product of 5 and 9? ______

What is the product of 2 and 9? ______

What is the sum of these products? ______

What is the product of 7 and 9? ______

2. What is the product of 7 and 8? ______

5 Fact ____________ 2 Fact ____________

3. What is the product of 7 and 6? ______

5 Fact ____________ 2 Fact ____________

Name ___________________________

Another Look
6-5

Decision Making

Multiplication can help you solve problems when you have groups of equal numbers.

Seven people are going on a hiking trip. Each person will carry five pounds of food. What is the total weight of the food the group can carry?

7 backpacks each with 5 pounds of food

7 groups of 5 = 7 × 5 = 35 pounds

Use multiplication to help you solve each problem.

A well-balanced diet includes 3 servings of fruit a day. How many servings of fruit should a person eat in a 7-day week?

1. What do you know?

____

2. What do you need to know?

____

3. What basic fact can you use to find the answer?

____

4. How many servings of fruit should a person eat in a 7-day week?

____

A well-balanced diet also includes 4 servings of vegetables a day. How many servings of vegetables should a person eat in a 7-day week?

5. What do you know?

____

6. What do you need to know?

____

7. Write a number sentence and solve the problem.

____

Name ________________________

Another Look
6-6

Exploring Patterns on a Hundred Chart: 3s and 6s

In your book you looked for patterns on a hundred chart to help you multiply with 3 and 6 as factors.

1	2	3	4	5	6	7	8	9	10
11	12	13	14	15	16	17	18	19	20
21	22	23	24	25	26	27	28	29	30

Find the product of 3 and 6 on the hundred chart. 3 groups of 6

Use your finger to skip count 3 sixes. Your finger should land on 6, 12, and 18. The last number you land on is the product.

3 × 6 = 18

Use the hundred chart to find each product. You can point to multiples as you skip count to help you multiply.

1. 5 × 6 = ______

a. 5 groups of ______

b. Your finger lands on ______, ______, ______, ______, ______

2. 9 × 3 = ______

a. 9 groups of ______

b. Your finger lands on ______, ______, ______, ______, ______, ______, ______, ______, ______

3. 7 × 3 = ______

4. 4 × 6 = ______

5. 5 × 3 = ______

6. 3 × 6 = ______

7. 7 × 6 = ______

8. 3 × 4 = ______

9. 3 × 8 = ______

10. 6 × 6 = ______

Name ____________________

Another Look
6-7

Exploring Patterns on a Fact Table

In your book you found patterns in a fact table to help you remember multiplication facts. Here is another way you can use a fact table.

×	1	2	3	4	5	6	7	8	9	10	11	12
1	1	2	3	4	5	6	7	8	9	10	11	12
2	2	4	6	8	10	12	14	16	18	20	22	24
3	3	6	9	12	15	18	21	24	27	30	33	36
4	4	8	12	16	20	24	28	32	36	40	44	48
5	5	10	15	20	25	30	35	40	45	50	55	60
6	6	12	18	24	30	36	42	48	54	60	66	72
7	7	14	21	28	35	42	49	56	63	70	77	84
8	8	16	24	32	40	48	56	64	72	80	88	96
9	9	18	27	36	45	54	63	72	81	90	99	108
10	10	20	30	40	50	60	70	80	90	100	110	120
11	11	22	33	44	55	66	77	88	99	110	121	132
12	12	24	36	48	60	72	84	96	108	120	132	144

Find the product of 8 and 7 in the fact table. Look for 8 in the first row. Draw a line down from 8. Look for 7 in the first column. Draw a line to the right from 7. Where do the lines cross? This is the product of 8 and 7.

8 × 7 = 56

Use the table to find each product.

1. 2 × 7 = ________
2. 8 × 10 = ________
3. 9 × 4 = ________
4. 11 × 5 = ________
5. 6 × 12 = ________
6. 6 × 8 = ________
7. 11 × 12 = ________
8. 7 × 7 = ________
9. 11 × 4 = ________
10. 6 × 10 = ________
11. 12 × 6 = ________
12. 10 × 10 = ________
13. 6 × 9 = ________
14. 9 × 9 = ________
15. 11 × 11 = ________
16. 12 × 8 = ________

Name ______________________________

Multiplying with 3 Factors

Parentheses show you which pair of numbers to multiply first.

4 × (2 × 3) =

4 × __6__ = __24__

If there are no parentheses, you can choose which pair of numbers to multiply first.

4 × 2 × 6 =

__8__ × 6 = __48__

---

1. Find the product of 6 × (2 × 3).

   6 × ________ = ________

2. Find the product of 3 × 5 × 2. Multiply the two lesser numbers first.

   3 × 2 × 5 =

   ________ × 5 = ________

Find each product.

3. (4 × 2) × 6

   ________ × 6 = ________

4. 5 × (5 × 2)

   5 × ________ = ________

5. 8 × 1 × 9

   ________ × 9 = ________

6. (7 × 0) × 8

   ________ × 8 = ________

7. 3 × (3 × 1)

   3 × ________ = ________

8. 2 × 6 × 3

   ________ × 6 = ________

9. (1 × 6) × 6

   ________ × 6 = ________

10. 6 × 2 × 2

    6 × ________ = ________

11. (3 × 9) × 0

    ________ × 0 = ________

12. 5 × 4 × 2

    5 × ________ = ________

13. Find the product of 9, 3, and 1. ________

14. Find the product of 2, 5, and 4. ________

15. Find the product of 6, 7, and 1. ________

16. Find the product of 5, 3, and 2. ________

Name ______________________________

Another Look
6-9

Compare Strategies: Look for a Pattern and Draw a Picture

Plan a party! You must decide how many tables to set up. Each table seats 6 people. If there are 34 people coming, how many tables do you need?

Each table seats 6 people. 34 people are coming.
I need to find out how many tables will seat 34 people.

You can draw a picture to find the answer.

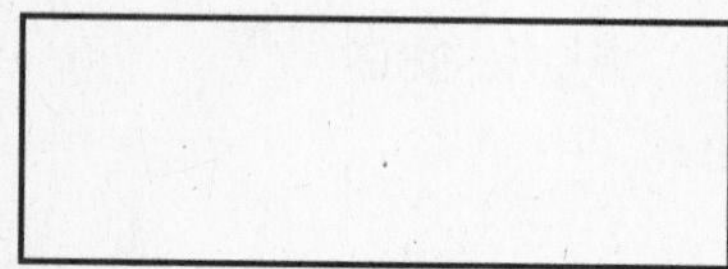

Each **x** is one person. Draw 6 **x**s on each table until you have 34 **x**s. Count to see how many tables are used.

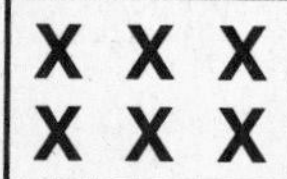

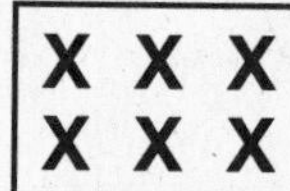

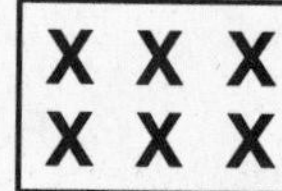

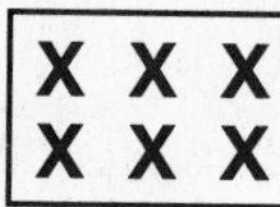

X X X
X X X

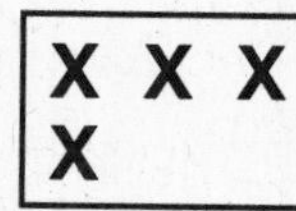

6 tables are needed for 34 people.

You can also look for a pattern to solve the problem.

Tables	1	2	3	4	5	6
People	6	12	18	24	30	36

6 tables for 34 people

Look for a pattern or draw a picture to solve each problem.

1. You are planning a picnic and you must decide how many blankets to bring. Five people can sit on each blanket. How many blankets will you need if 27 people are coming?

____

2. One package of muffins contains 4 muffins. If each person gets 1 muffin, how many packages will you need to feed 14 people?

____

Name ______________________________

Exploring Division As Sharing

In your book you used counters to explore division. Here is another way to understand division.

A road construction crew boss has 18 people in his crew. There are 3 jobs that need to be done. He's going to divide up the crew equally. Draw pictures to show how many people will do each job. Draw one picture in each box until all the workers have a job.

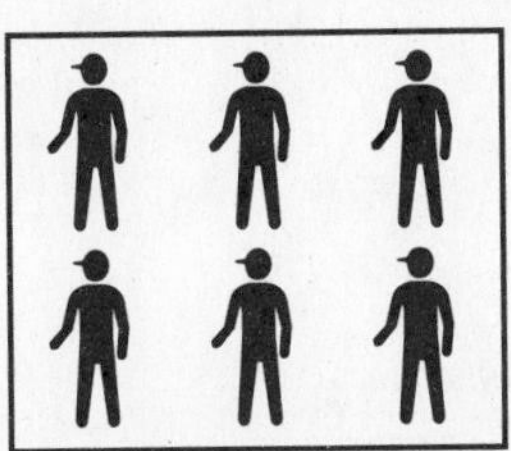
Job 1

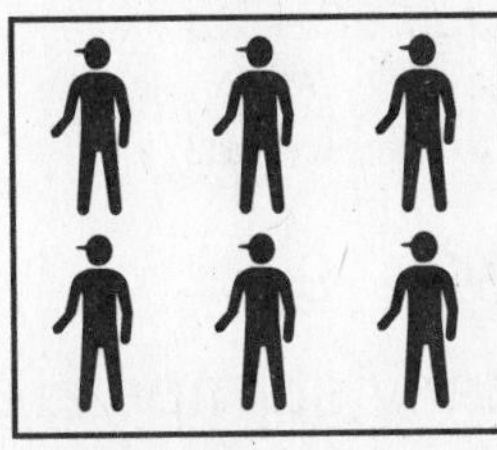
Job 2

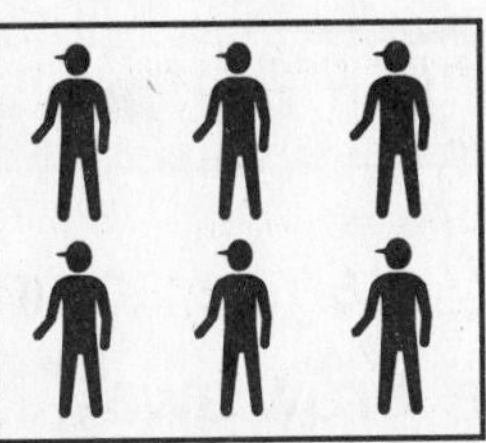
Job 3

---

1. On the second day of the job, 3 workers are absent. The crew boss still wants to divide the work equally among the 15 workers. Draw stick figures in the boxes below to show how many people will be assigned to each job.

Job 1

Job 2

Job 3

2. By the third day of the job, everyone is back at work. Job 1 is finished. So the crew boss decides to divide the 18 workers into 2 groups in order to finish the 2 remaining jobs. Draw pictures in the boxes below to show how many people will be assigned to each job.

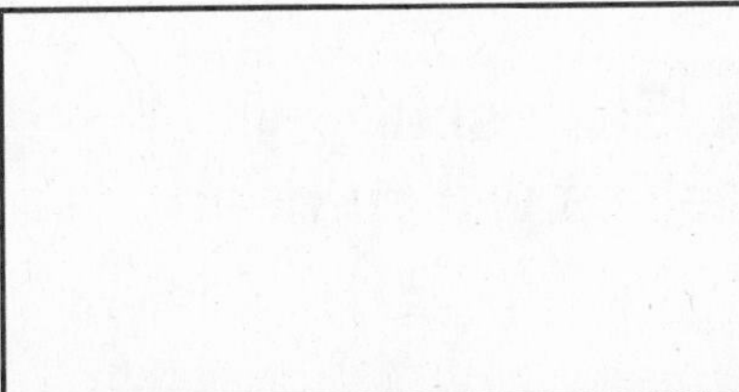
Job 2

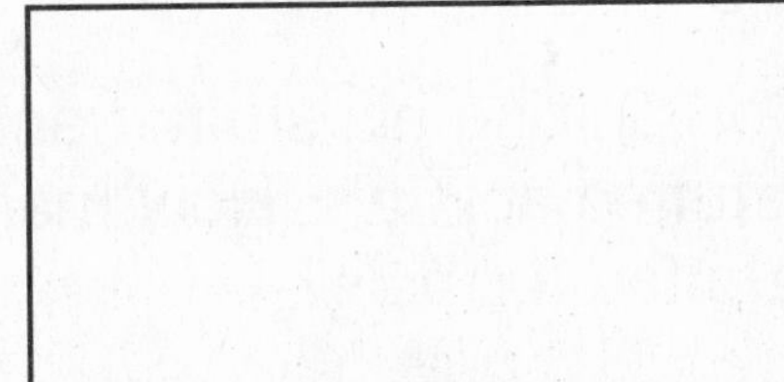
Job 3

Name ______________________________

Another Look 7-2

Exploring Division as Repeated Subtraction

In your book you used counters to explore division. Here is another way to understand division.

You can use an array. This array shows 27 stamps.

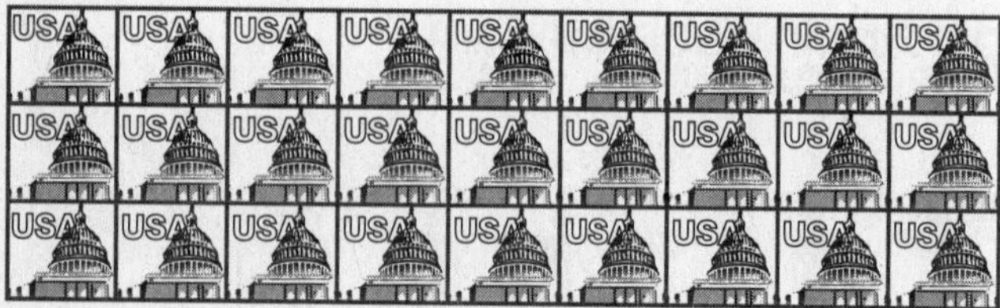

How many stamps are in 1 row? 9

If you take 1 row away, how many stamps are left? 18

If you take another row away, how many stamps are left? 9

How many rows of stamps can you take away? 3

27 ÷ 9 = 3

---

1. Sam is packing his toy cars into boxes. Each row has 8 cars. How many rows are needed for 24 cars?

a. Draw a box around each set of 8 cars.

b. How many boxes did you draw? ______

c. 24 ÷ 8 = ______

2. Sam is organizing his stuffed animals. Each shelf will hold 5 stuffed animals. How many shelves will he need for 10 stuffed animals?

______

Name ______________________

Exploring Division Stories

A round pizza has been cut into 6 equal slices.

There are 3 people.

How many slices does each person get?

Take away one for each of the three people.

Take away another for each of the three people.

$6 \div 3 = 2$

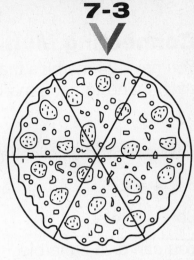

1. Look at how the muffins are arranged in the box. There are three rows, each with four muffins.

a. How would four children share the muffins?

____

b. How would three children share the muffins?

____

Write a division story for each. Use counters or drawings to help.

2. $24 \div 8$

____

____

3. $16 \div 4$

____

____

4. $18 \div 3$

____

____

Name ______________________________

Another Look 7-4

Connecting Multiplication and Division

You have 24 marbles that you want to give away to your friends. You want each friend to get 6 marbles. To how many friends can you give marbles?

24 ÷ 6

Think: What multiplication fact do you know that includes 24 and 6?

6 × 4 = 24

So, 24 ÷ 6 = __4__

You can give 6 marbles to 4 friends.

---

1. 36 ÷ 4

a. What multiplication fact includes 36 and 4? ______________

b. 36 ÷ 4 = ______

2. 28 ÷ 7

a. What multiplication fact includes 28 and 7? ______________

b. 28 ÷ 7 = ______

Complete. You may use counters to help.

3. 14 ÷ 7 = ______
7 × ______ = 14

4. 32 ÷ 4 = ______
4 × ______ = 32

5. 30 ÷ 5 = ______
5 × ______ = 30

6. 18 ÷ 6 = ______
6 × ______ = 18

7. 27 ÷ 9 = ______
9 × ______ = 27

8. 24 ÷ 8 = ______
8 × ______ = 24

9. 15 ÷ 3 = ______
3 × ______ = 15

10. 16 ÷ 4 = ______
4 × ______ = 16

11. 28 ÷ 4 = ______
4 × ______ = 28

12. 18 ÷ 2 = ______
2 × ______ = 18

Name ______________________________

Another Look
7-5

Dividing by 2

There are 18 students in Mr. Tang's third grade class. The class is evenly divided between girls and boys.

Draw a line to divide the class into 2 groups with the same number of students in each. How many are in each group? 9

18 ÷ 2 = 9

Divide each group into 2 groups with the same number of items.

1. 12 ÷ 2 = ______

2. 10 ÷ 2 = ______

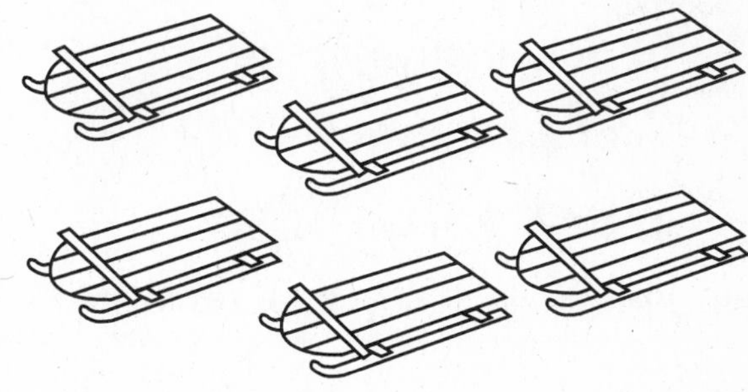

3. 14 ÷ 2 = ______

4. 6 ÷ 2 = ______

5. Draw a picture to show 16 ÷ 2.

Name ________________________________

Another Look
7-6

Dividing by 5

Find $5\overline{)20}$

Take away groups of 5 from 20 to find the answer. Stop subtracting when you get to 0.

$$\begin{array}{r}20\\-\ \ 5\\\hline 15\end{array}\qquad\begin{array}{r}15\\-\ \ 5\\\hline 10\end{array}\qquad\begin{array}{r}10\\-\ \ 5\\\hline 5\end{array}\qquad\begin{array}{r}5\\-\ 5\\\hline 0\end{array}$$

You had to subtract 5 **four** times to get to 0.

So, 20 ÷ 5 = __4__

Take away groups of 5 to find each quotient.

1. $5\overline{)30}$

a. Begin subtracting. 30 − 5 = ________

b. Keep subtracting until you get to 0. How many times did you subtract 5? ________

c. 30 ÷ 5 = ________

2. Draw lines to divide the cars into equal groups of 5.

a. How many cars are there? ________

b. How many groups of 5 are there? ________

c. So, 25 ÷ 5 = ________

Find each quotient. Use taking away or equal groups if you need to.

3. 45 ÷ 5 = ________

4. 10 ÷ 5 = ________

5. $5\overline{)35}$

6. $5\overline{)15}$

7. $5\overline{)5}$

8. $5\overline{)40}$

Name ______________________________

Another Look
7-7

Dividing by 3 and 4

Find $3\overline{)12}$.

Take away groups of 3 from 12 to find the answer. Stop subtracting when you get to 0.

$$\begin{array}{r}12\\-\ 3\\\hline 9\end{array}\qquad\begin{array}{r}9\\-\ 3\\\hline 6\end{array}\qquad\begin{array}{r}6\\-\ 3\\\hline 3\end{array}\qquad\begin{array}{r}3\\-\ 3\\\hline 0\end{array}$$

You had to subtract 3 **four** times to get to 0.

So, 12 ÷ 3 = __4__

Take away equal groups to find each quotient.

1. $4\overline{)16}$

a. Begin subtracting. 16 − 4 = ________

b. Keep subtracting until you get to 0. How many times did you subtract 4? ________

c. 16 ÷ 4 = ________

2. Divide the fish into equal groups of 3.

a. How many fish are there? ________

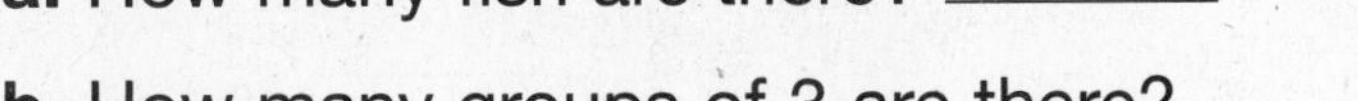

b. How many groups of 3 are there? ________

c. So, 6 ÷ 3 = ________

Find each quotient. Use taking away or equal groups if you need to.

3. 21 ÷ 3 = ________ **4.** 24 ÷ 4 = ________

5. 24 ÷ 3 = ________ **6.** 12 ÷ 4 = ________

7. $3\overline{)27}$ **8.** $4\overline{)32}$

9. $4\overline{)28}$ **10.** $3\overline{)21}$

11. $4\overline{)8}$ **12.** $3\overline{)9}$

13. $4\overline{)20}$ **14.** $4\overline{)36}$

Name ________________________________

Exploring Dividing With 0 and 1

In your book you divided using a calculator. Here is another way to divide.

Find $3 \div 1$.

Think: 1 times what number equals 3?

$1 \times \mathbf{3} = 3$

So, $3 \div 1 = \mathbf{3}$

Find $3 \div 3$.

Think: 3 times what number equals 3?

$3 \times \mathbf{1} = 3$

So, $3 \div 3 = \mathbf{1}$

Find $0 \div 4$.

Think: 4 times what number equals 0?

$4 \times \mathbf{0} = 0$

So, $0 \div 4 = \mathbf{0}$

(You cannot divide by 0.)

Find each quotient.

1. $5 \div 1$

a. 1 times what number equals 5? ______

b. $5 \div 1 =$ ______

2. $0 \div 3$

a. 3 times what number equals 0? ______

b. $0 \div 3 =$ ______

3. $5 \div 5 =$ ______

4. $0 \div 5 =$ ______

5. $6 \div 1 =$ ______

6. $4 \div 4 =$ ______

7. $7\overline{)7}$

8. $1\overline{)9}$

9. $1\overline{)4}$

10. $3\overline{)3}$

11. Divide the cups into groups of 1.

a. How many cups are there? ______

b. How many groups of 1 are there? ______

c. So, $7 \div 1 =$ ______

 Use with pages 292–293.

Name ____________________

Another Look
7-9

Analyze Word Problems: Choose an Operation

Solve the problem.

Ann works at a local grocery store on Saturdays. She is paid $4 for every hour that she works. If she works for 3 hours, how much will she be paid?

What do you know?

Ann is paid $4 for each hour she works. Ann works for 3 hours.

What do you need to find out?

How much money Ann will be paid.

What operation could you choose to solve the problem?

Since you need to put together equal groups of $4, multiply.

Multiply.	$4	×	3	=	$12
	amount each hour		hours		total amount

So, Ann will be paid $12.

Does your answer make sense?

Yes, because 12 ÷ 4 = 3 and 12 ÷ 3 = 4.

1. Rhonda bought 18 bagels. If there are 6 bagels in each package, how many packages did she buy?
   a. How many bagels are in a package? ____________
   b. How many bagels does Rhonda have? ____________
   c. What operation could you use to solve the problem?

      ____
   d. Write the number sentence. What is the answer?

      ____

Write the operation, then solve each problem.

2. Pete had 8 marbles. Then John gave him 5 marbles.
   How many marbles does Pete have? ____________
3. Fiona bought 9 treats for her dog Spot. If Spot ate 2 treats, how many treats are left? ____________

Name ______________________________

Another Look 7-10

Dividing by 6 and 7

Suppose you are given a page of 30 animal stickers for your collection. Your sticker album holds 6 stickers on each page. How many pages do you need for your animal stickers?

Find 30 ÷ 6.

You can solve this problem using counters.

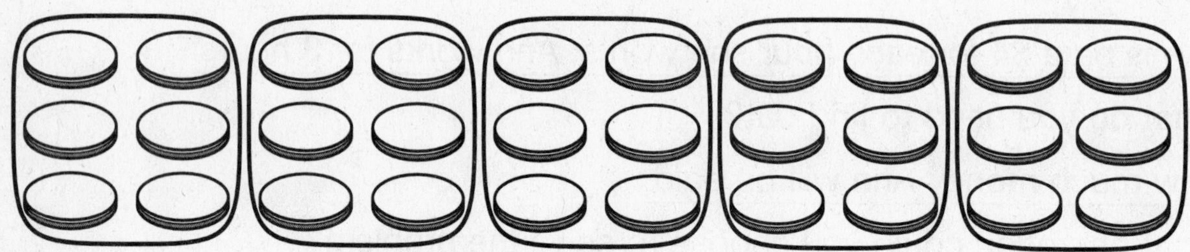

Draw boxes around groups of 6 counters.

How many boxes did you draw? 5

30 ÷ 6 = 5

You need 5 pages for your animal stickers.

Find each quotient. Use counters or draw a picture to help you.

1. Find 35 ÷ 7.

Draw or set out 35 counters.
Sort counters into groups of 7.

a. How many groups do you have? ______

b. So, 35 ÷ 7 = ______

2. Find 42 ÷ 6.

Draw or set out 42 counters.
Sort counters into groups of 6.

a. How many groups do you have? ______

b. So, 42 ÷ 6 = ______

Find each quotient.

3. $7\overline{)28}$ **4.** $6\overline{)54}$ **5.** $7\overline{)49}$

6. 18 ÷ 6 = ______ **7.** 56 ÷ 7 = ______ **8.** 28 ÷ 7 = ______

9. If you wanted to share 18 crackers between 3 friends, how many crackers would you give to each friend? ______

10. Divide 14 counters into 7 groups. How many are in each group? ______

Name ______________________________

Another Look
7-11

Dividing by 8 and 9

Find 40 ÷ 8 by drawing a picture.

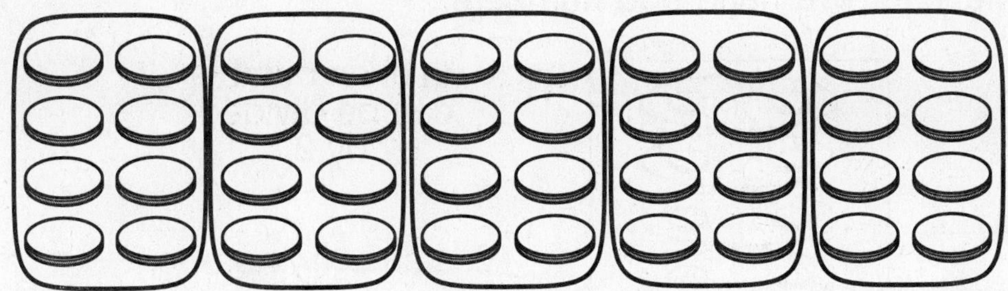

Draw a ring around groups of 8 circles.

How many groups of 8 are there? 5

So, 40 ÷ 8 = 5

Find each quotient. Use counters or draw a picture to help you.

1. Find 24 ÷ 8

Draw 24 stars.

Ring groups of 8 stars.

a. How many groups are there?

______

b. So, 24 ÷ 8 = ______

2. Find 27 ÷ 9

Draw 27 squares.

Ring groups of 9 squares.

a. How many groups are there?

______

b. So, 27 ÷ 9 = ______

Find each quotient.

3. $8\overline{)40}$ **4.** $9\overline{)36}$ **5.** $8\overline{)56}$

6. 48 ÷ 8 = ______ **7.** 72 ÷ 9 = ______ **8.** 45 ÷ 9 = ______

9. Divide the flowers into groups of 8.

❀ ❀ ❀ ❀ ❀ ❀ ❀ ❀ ❀ ❀ ❀ ❀ ❀ ❀ ❀ ❀

a. How many flowers are there? ______

b. How many groups of 8 are there? ______

c. So 16 ÷ 8 = ______

Name ______________________________

Another Look
7-12

Exploring Even and Odd Numbers

In your book you used division to test for even and odd numbers. Here is another way to check for even and odd numbers.

Here is a picture of 10 counters.

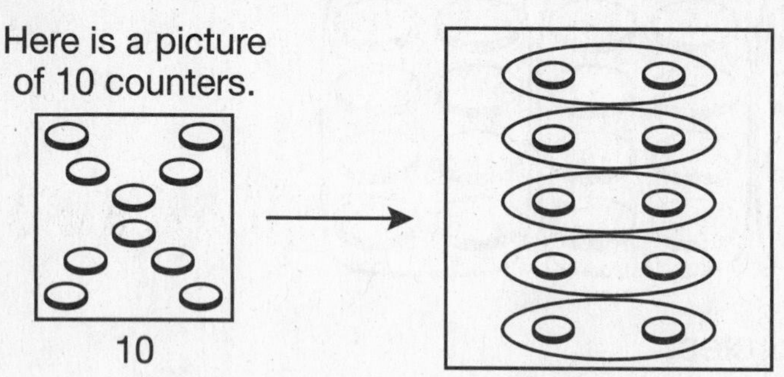

An *even* number can be divided by 2.

10 is an *even* number.

Here is a picture of 11 counters.

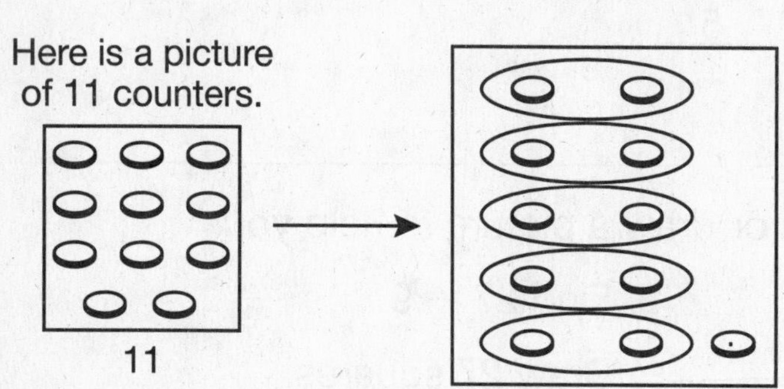

An *odd* number has one left over when it is divided by 2.

11 is an *odd* number.

On a separate sheet of paper, draw a picture of counters to determine if each number is even or odd. Then answer each question.

1. 12

a. Circle groups of 2 counters. How many counters are left over? __________

b. Is 12 even or odd? __________

2. 27

a. Circle groups of 2 counters. How many counters are left over? __________

b. Is 27 even or odd? __________

Write even or odd for each number.

3. 22 __________ **4.** 17 __________ **5.** 21 __________

6. 30 __________ **7.** 4 __________ **8.** 1 __________

 Use with pages 306–307.

Name ______________________________

Another Look 7-13

Compare Strategies: Use Objects and Make an Organized List

Denise and Robert are making a poster with 6 pictures of endangered animals. They want the pictures in equal rows. What are all the ways to arrange the pictures?

You can make arrays to find all the possible ways.

If you make an array of 1 row
how many pictures will be in each row? 6

If you make an array of 2 rows
how many pictures will be in each row? 3

If you make an array of 3 rows
how many pictures will be in each row? 2

If you make an array of 6 rows
how many pictures will be in each row? 1

---

1. Suppose Denise and Robert want to use 18 pictures of animals for their poster. What are all the possible ways to arrange the pictures in rows?

Rows	Pictures in Each Row	Total
1		
6		
18		

2. Denise and Robert decide to use 16 pictures. Take a square piece of paper and arrange 16 counters on it in rows. How many rows fit best on the paper?

____

3. In an album, Ann, Bob, Cal, and Dee's pictures are in a row. From the left, Bob's picture is after Ann's and Dee's but before Cal's. Dee's picture is before Ann's. List the order of the students from left to right.

____

Name ______________________________

Another Look
7-14

Exploring Algebra: Balancing Scales

In your book you made tables to balance scales. Here is another way to balance scales. A scale is balanced when the same amount is on both sides. Find all the ways to balance this scale.

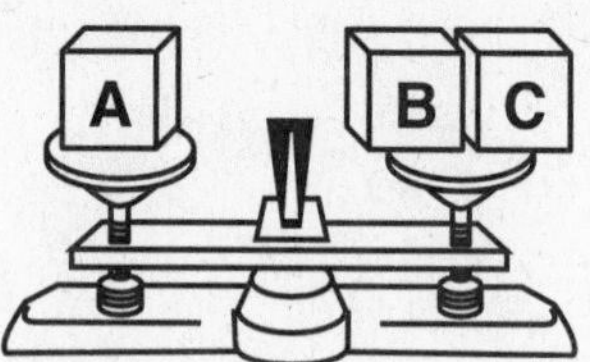

A	=	B	+	C
4	=	4	+	0
4	=	3	+	1
4	=	2	+	2
4	=	1	+	3
4	=	0	+	4

Box A has 4 cubes inside. You can find how many cubes can be placed in boxes B and C by finding all the pairs of numbers with a sum of 4.

---

1. Box A has 3 cubes inside.

a. The number of cubes in boxes B and C must have a sum of ______.

b. How many cubes can be in boxes B and C? Complete the table to record each way.

A	B	C
3	3	0
3		1

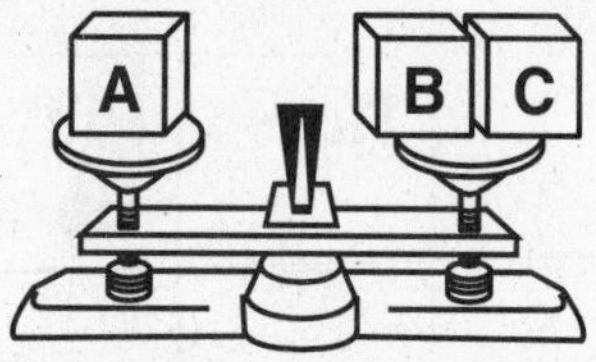

2. Each box A has 3 cubes inside.

a. The number of cubes in boxes B and C must have a sum of ______.

b. How many cubes can be in boxes B and C? Make a table to record each way.

A	A+A	B	C
3	6	0	
3	6	1	
3	6	2	
3	6		3
3	6		2
3	6		
3	6		

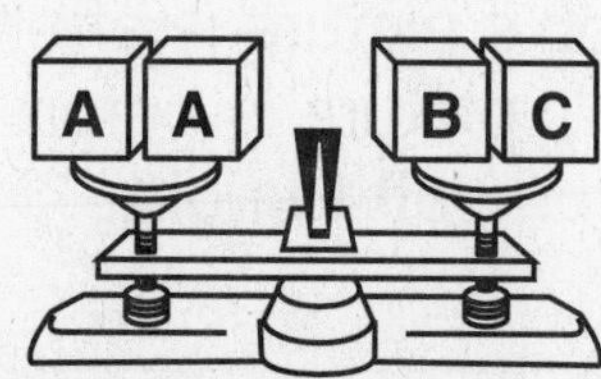

 Use with pages 310–311.

Name ______________________

Another Look 8-1

Exploring Solids

In your book you matched classroom objects with solid figures. Here is another way to explore solid figures. Read the chart to find out about each solid figure.

Solid Figure	It can roll	It has faces	It matches
cube		✓	connecting cubes
rectangular prism		✓	margarine box
pyramid		✓	pyramid block
sphere	✓		spherical balloon
cylinder	✓	✓	soup can
cone	✓	✓	ice-cream cone

Circle the shape name that matches each object. Use the chart to help.

1. 

sphere
cylinder
cone

2. 

cube
pyramid
cylinder

3. 

cube
cylinder
pyramid

Name ______________________________

Another Look
8-2

Exploring Solids and Shapes

In your book you connected solids and shapes by tracing the faces of solid figures and naming the shape you drew. Here is another way to explore solids and shapes. Look at the shape you can make from each solid figure.

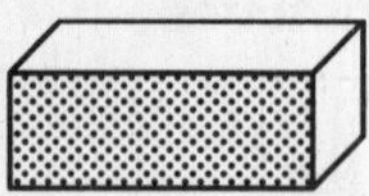

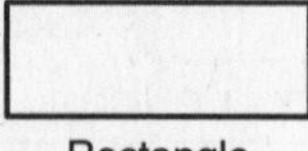

Rectangle

- 4 sides
- 4 corners

Square

- 4 equal sides
- 4 equal corners

Triangle

- 3 sides
- 3 corners

Circle

- 0 sides
- 0 corners

1. What are these shapes?

____

2. What shapes can you trace from this cube?

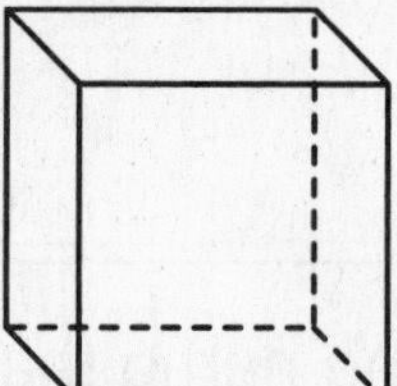

____

3. What are these shapes?

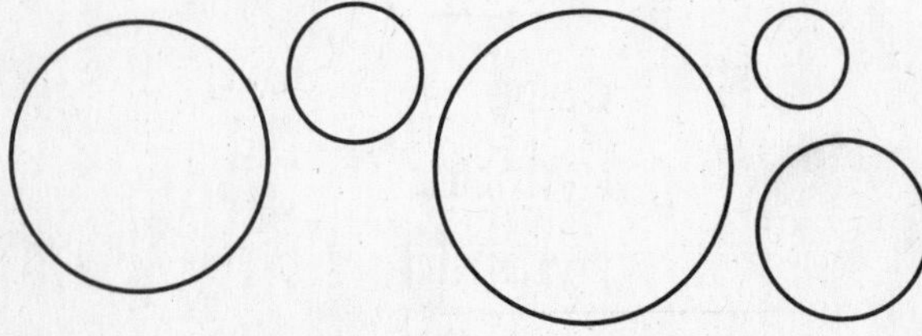

____

4. What shapes can you trace from this pyramid?

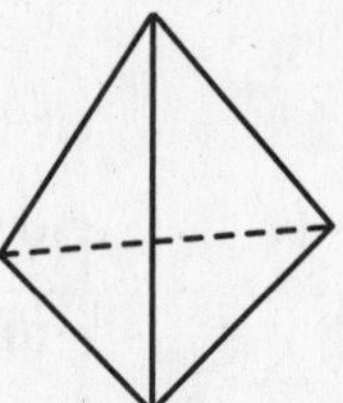

____

Name ______________________________

Another Look
8-3

Lines and Line Segments

Follow the directions to learn about lines.

1. This is a line. Draw a line in the box.

2. This is a point. Draw a point that is not on your line.

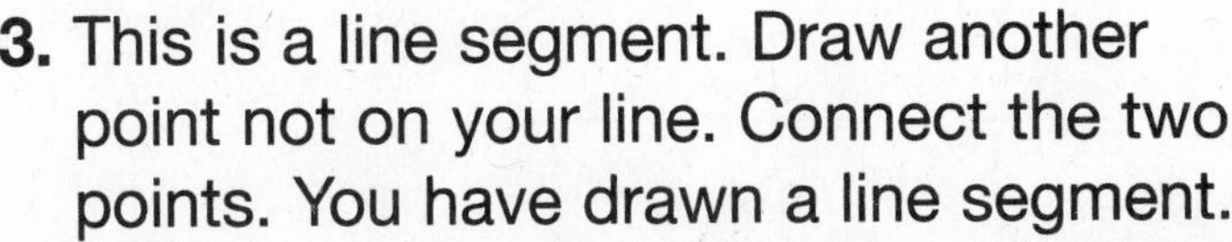

3. This is a line segment. Draw another point not on your line. Connect the two points. You have drawn a line segment.

4. This is a ray. Draw a ray coming from your line.

5. These lines are parallel. Parallel lines do not cross. Draw a line that is parallel to your line.

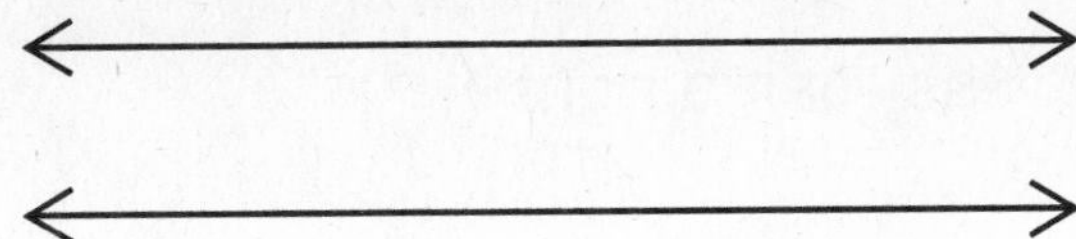

6. These lines intersect. Intersecting lines cross. Draw a line that intersects your line.

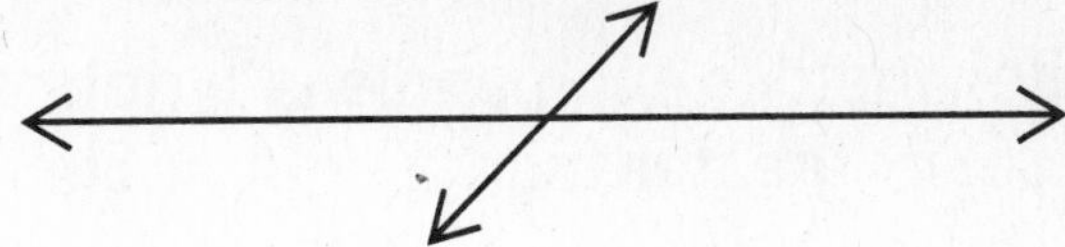

Circle the word that names each picture.

7. •

line
point
line segment
ray

8.

line
point
line segment
ray

9.

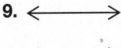

parallel lines
intersecting lines
line
line segment

Name ______________________________

Exploring Angles

In your book, you used Power Polygons to find angles. Here is another way to explore angles.

Each corner of a polygon forms an angle. Angles are many different sizes.

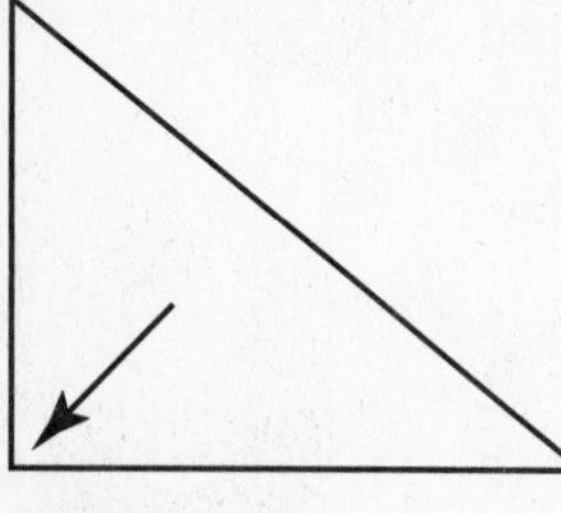

This is a right angle.

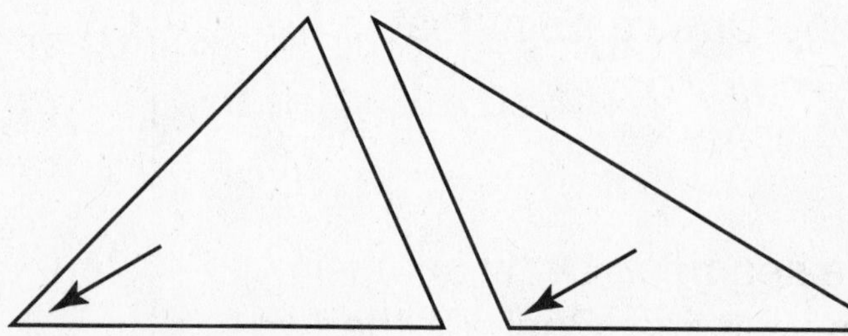

This angle is less than a right angle.

This angle is more than a right angle.

Can you identify these angles?

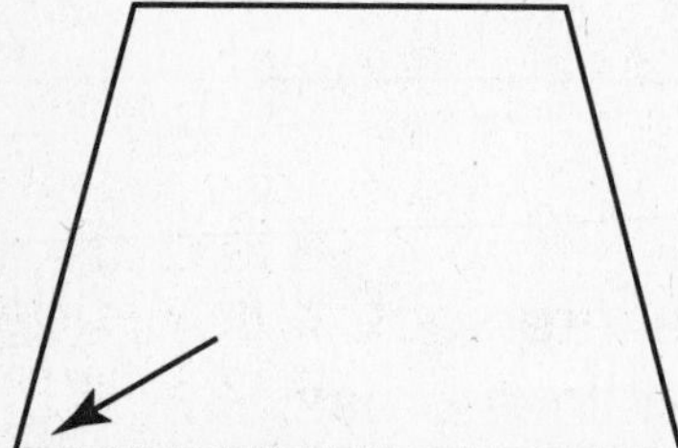

This angle is less than a right angle.

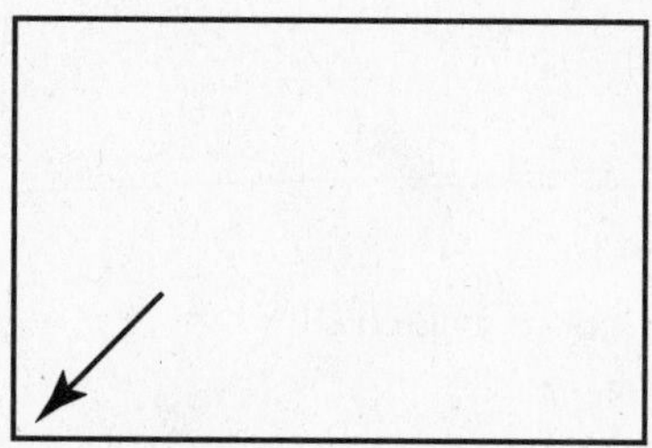

This angle is a right angle.

Write whether each angle is a right angle, less than a right angle, or greater than a right angle.

1. 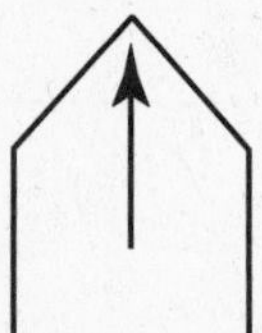

____

____

2. 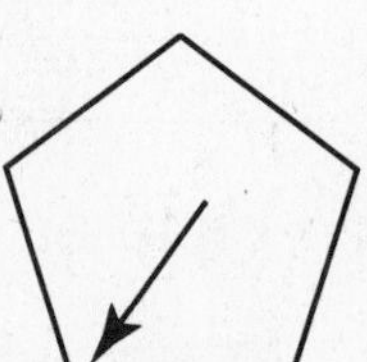

____

____

3. 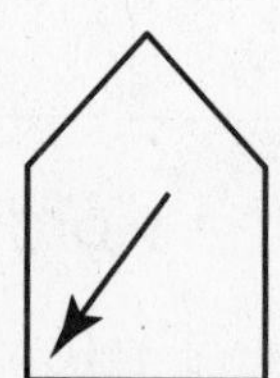

____

____

4. Give an example of a right angle in your classroom.

____

 Use with pages 328–329.

Name ______________________________

Exploring Slides, Flips, and Turns

In your book, you used power polygons to show slides, flips, and turns. Here is another way to explore slides, flips, and turns.

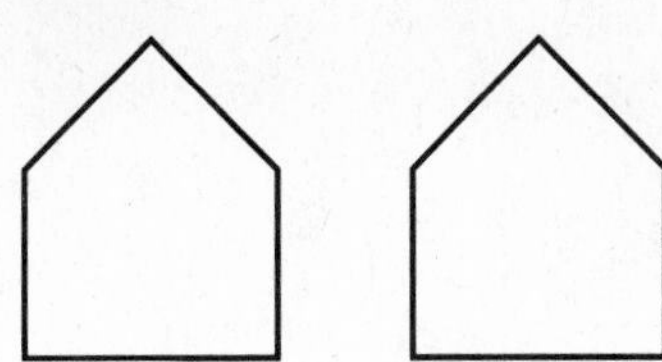

These two figures are the same size and shape. They are congruent.
Moving a figure does not change its shape.
Can you tell which pairs are congruent?

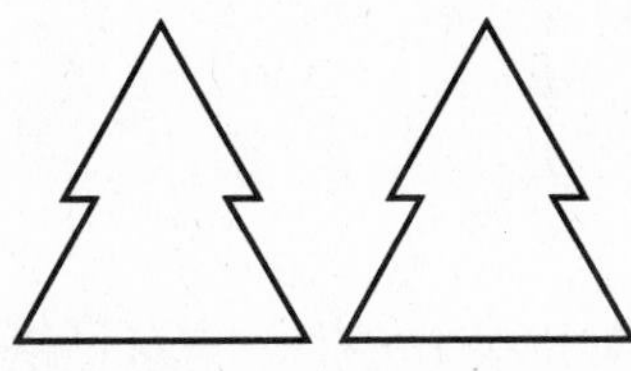

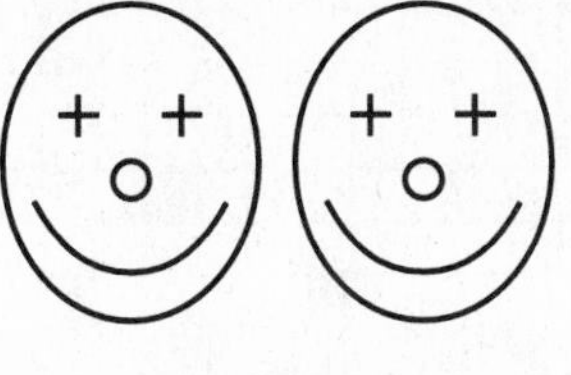

a **b** **c**

a and **b** are congruent pairs.

You can move a figure many ways. You can slide it, flip it, or turn it. Can you tell which is a flip? Which is a slide? Which is a turn?

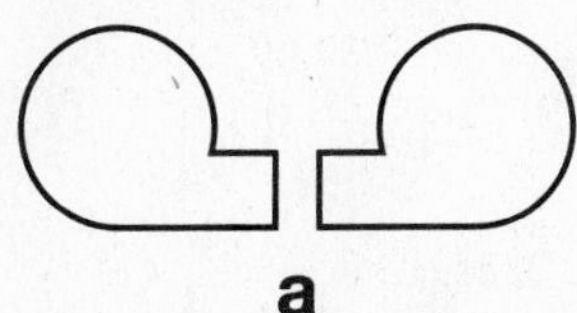

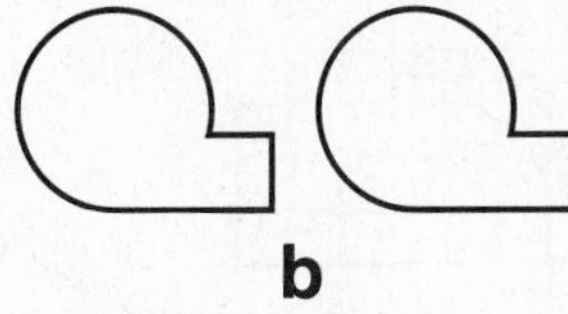

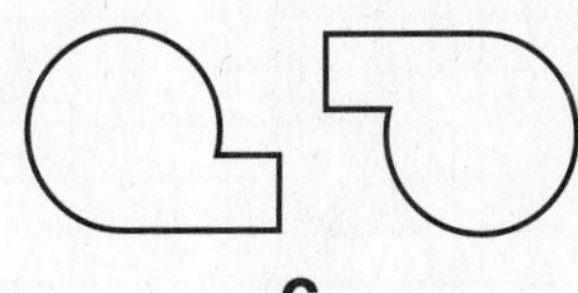

a **b** **c**

a is a flip
b is a slide
c is a turn

---

1. Circle each congruent pair.

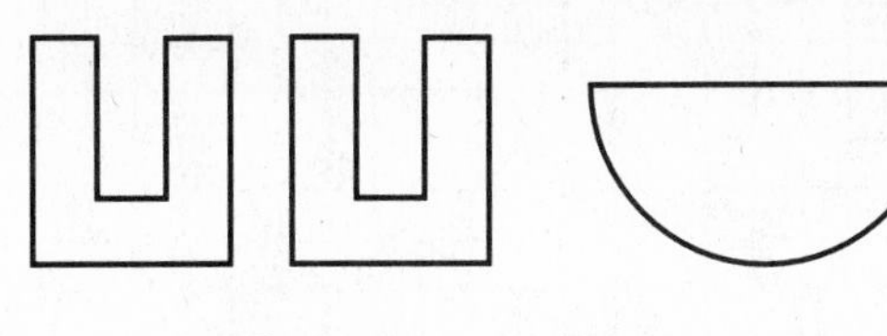

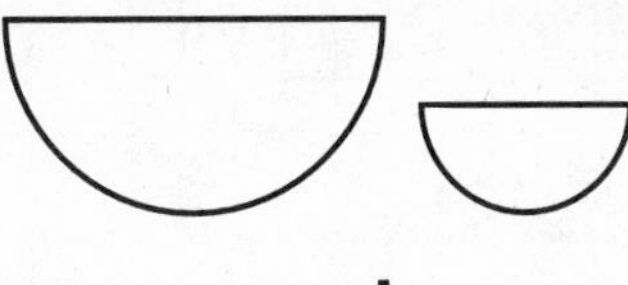

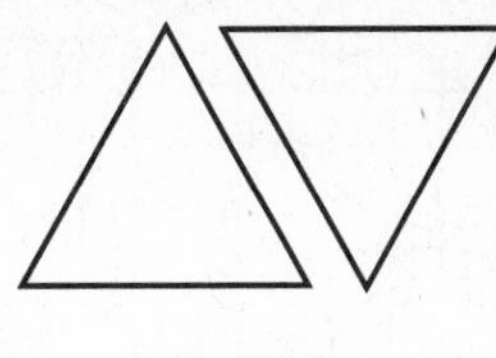

a **b** **c**

2. Write flip, slide, or turn for each.

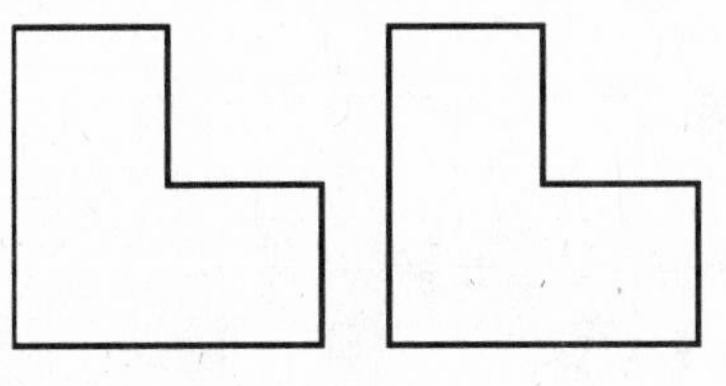

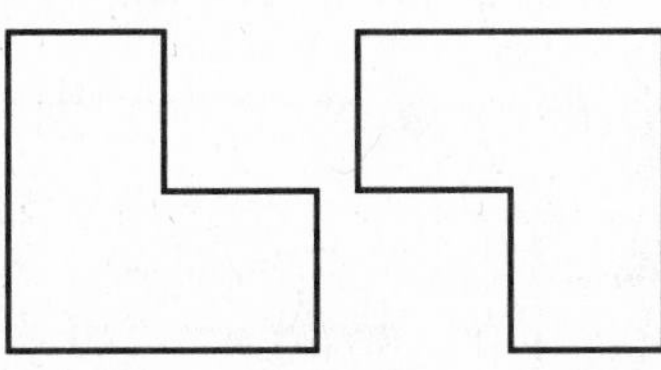

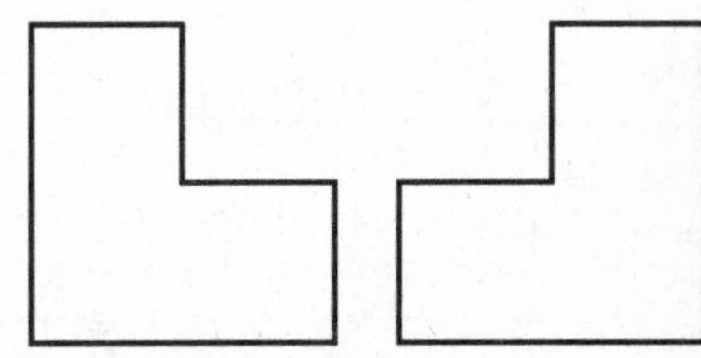

a. __________ **b.** __________ **c.** __________

Name ______________________________

Another Look
8-6

Exploring Symmetry

In your book, you folded sheets of paper to find lines of symmetry. Here is another way to explore symmetry.

Each shape below has a line of symmetry. It divides the shape into two equal parts. A grid helps you see that the parts match.

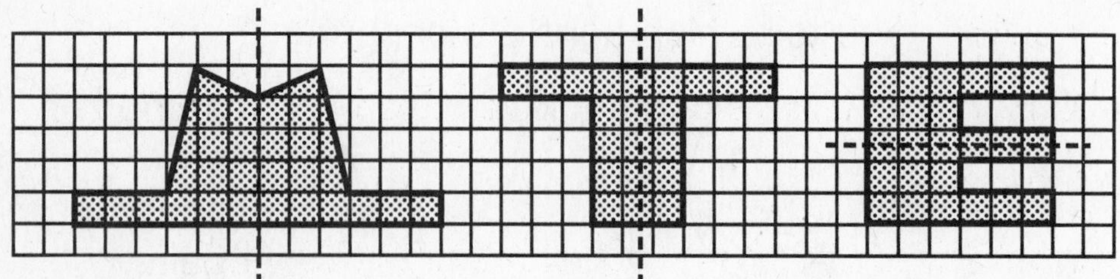

Shapes can have more than one line of symmetry. Each shape below has two lines of symmetry. All of the parts match.

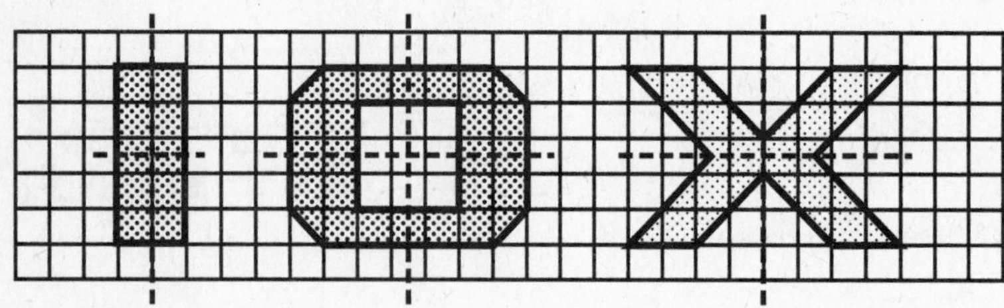

Which shapes have one or more lines of symmetry?

A.

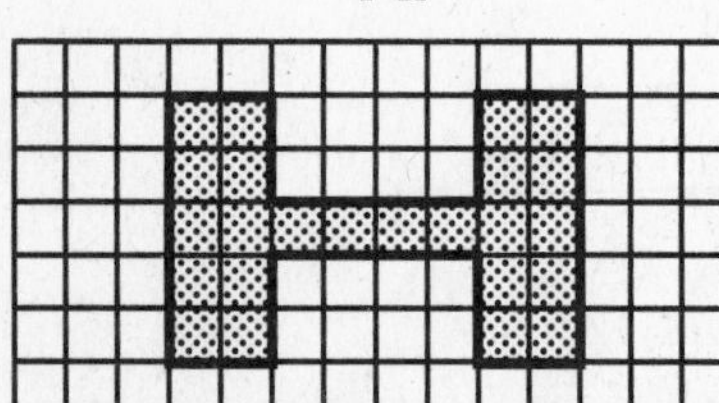

B.

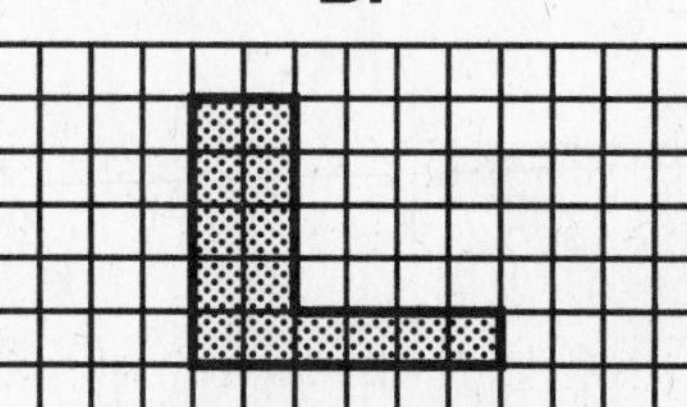

C.

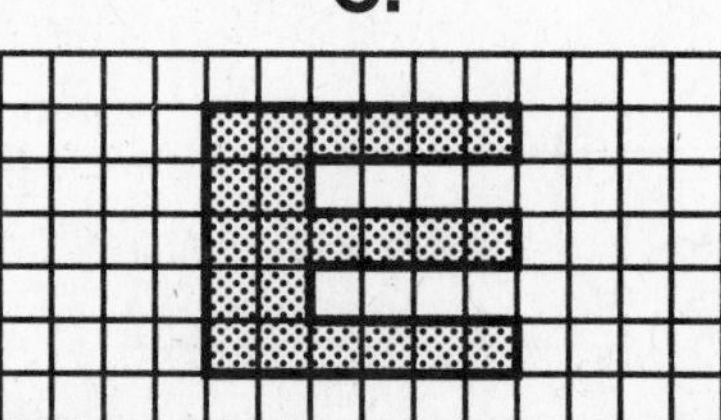

A has two lines of symmetry. **C** has one line of symmetry.

Color in each shape that has one or more lines of symmetry.

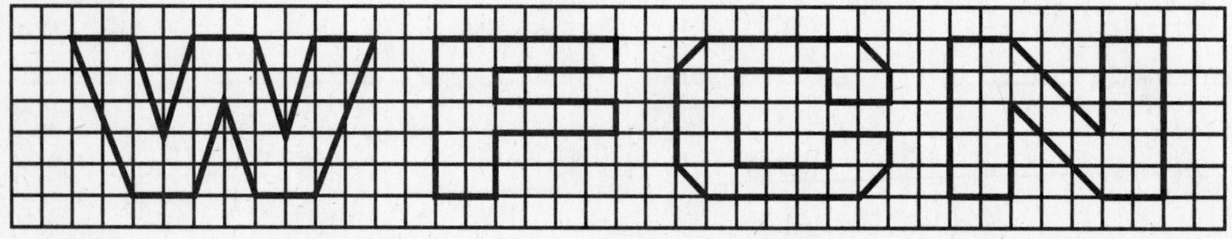

Name ____________________

Analyze Strategies: Solve a Simpler Problem

Sue Ellen North wants to use her initials in her Internet address. How many different combinations are possible if each letter is used only once?

If S is the first letter, how many ways can the other two letters be written?

SEN SNE Two ways

If E is the first letter, how many ways can the other two be written?

ESN ENS Two ways

What are the combinations using N as the first letter? NES NSE

How many different combinations are there? 6

---

1. Mark is arranging his model cars on a shelf. He has 1 blue, 2 red, and 1 black car. He wants to put the 2 red cars as the first and last cars on the shelf. How many ways can he arrange the cars?

   a. Which cars can be put second? ____________

   b. Which cars can be put third? ____________

   c. How many arrangements are there all together? ________

2. Kira has 3 different plants.

   a. If she wants to put the pink tulips first, how many ways can she arrange the plants on a window sill? ________

   b. Kira buys another plant, but she still wants to keep the pink tulips first. How many ways can she arrange her plants now? ________

3. Kevin has flower pots that hold 1 or 3 bulbs. He has 18 bulbs. How many ways can he plant the bulbs? ________

Name ___________________________

Exploring Perimeter

In your book you used grid paper to measure perimeter. Here is another way to find perimeter. Count the edges of the tiles around the outside of the rectangle. The distance around is 14 units, since 5 + 2 + 5 + 2 = __14__.

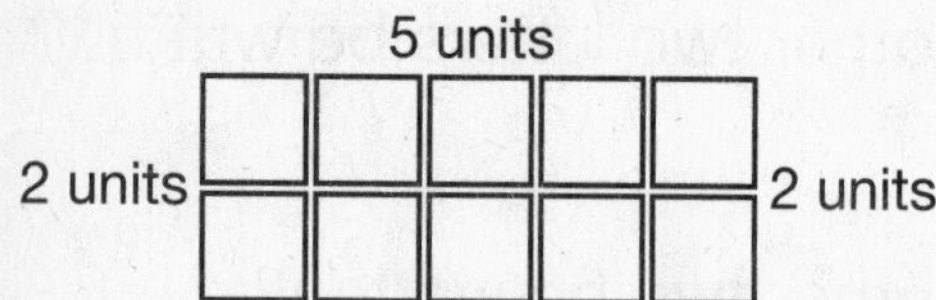

---

1. Find the distance around the rectangle made of tiles.

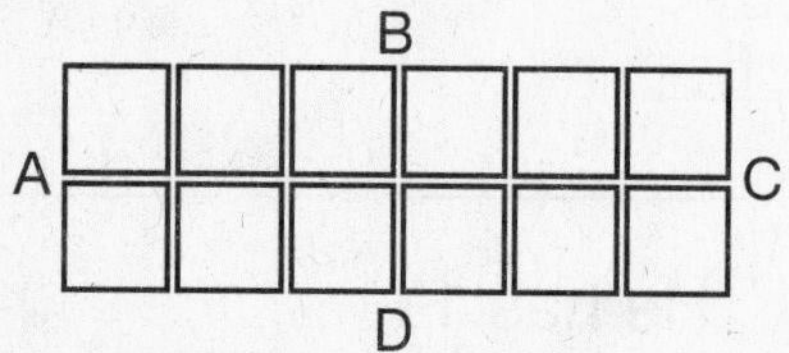

a. What is the length of side A? __________

b. What is the length of side B? __________

c. What is the length of side C? __________

d. What is the length of side D? __________

e. What is the distance around the shape? __________

2. Find the distance around the shape.

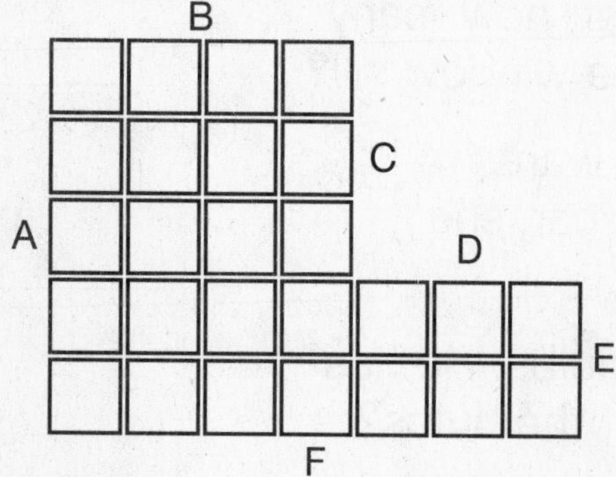

a. What is the length of each side?

A __________ B __________ C __________

D __________ E __________ F __________

b. What is the distance around the shape? __________

 Use with pages 340–341.

Name ______________________

Exploring Area

In your book you explored area using grid paper. Here is another way to explore area.

You can use square counters to measure the area of a shape in square units.

Make a 1 × 5 array with square counters.

Make two more 1 × 5 arrays and line them up with the first array.

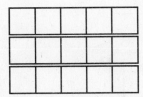

What is the width of the array? 3 units

What is the length of the array? 5 units

How many counters are in the array? 15

The 3 × 5 rectangle is 15 square units in size.

Use square counters to build arrays.

1. Make a 3 × 3 square array.

a. How many counters did you use? ________

b. What is the area in square units of a 3 × 3 square?

____

2. Make a 4 × 6 rectangular array.

a. What is the width of the array? ______________________

b. What is the length? ______________________

c. How many counters did you use to make the array? ________

d. What is the area in square units of a 4 × 6 rectangle?

____

Name ___________________________

Another Look
8-10

Decision Making

Carrie wants to put a new desk in her room. She drew a picture of her room to help figure out where it will fit.

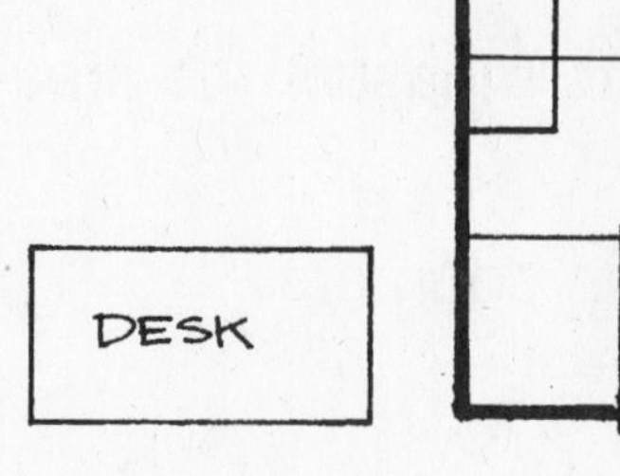

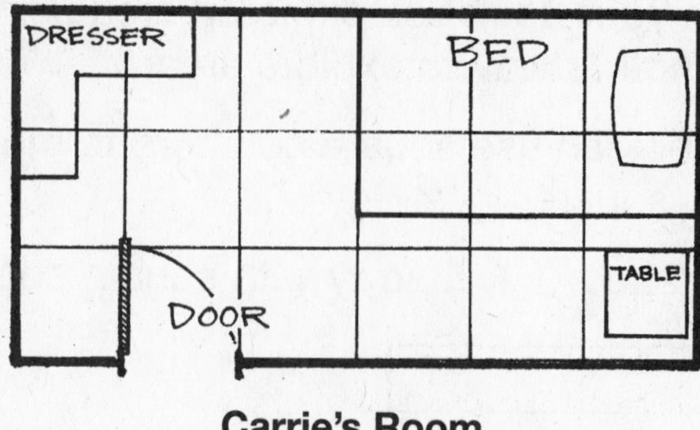

Carrie's Room

Does Carrie have space for her new desk? Yes

Where could she put it? Along the same wall as the door

Carrie wants to put her new chair in front of the desk. Look at the drawing. Do you think she has room for the chair?

Possible answer: No, the bed would be too close.

Can Carrie rearrange her room so both the desk and the chair fit?

1. Trace and cut out the pieces of furniture above that Carrie would like in her room.
2. Arrange the furniture on the diagram of Carrie's room. Tape the furniture in place when you find an arrangement that works.

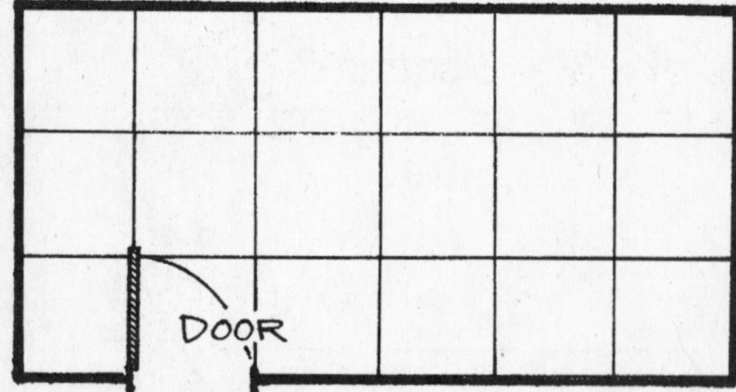

3. Suppose Carrie's closet is right behind the bedroom door. Will your arrangement still work? Explain.

Name ______________________________

Exploring Volume

In your book you used cubes to find the volume of figures. Here is another way to find volume.

Volume can be found by using multiplication.

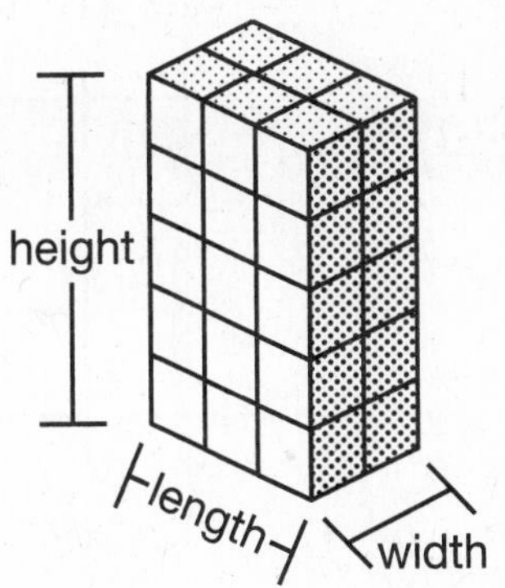

Count the number of cubes in each dimension.

Width: 2 cubes
Length: 3 cubes
Height: 5 cubes

Multiply the 3 dimensions.

$2 \times 3 \times 5 = 6 \times 5 =$ 30

The volume is 30 cubic units.

Use multiplication to find the volume of each shape.

1. a. Width: ________

b. Length: ________

c. Height: ________

d. Volume: ________ cubic units

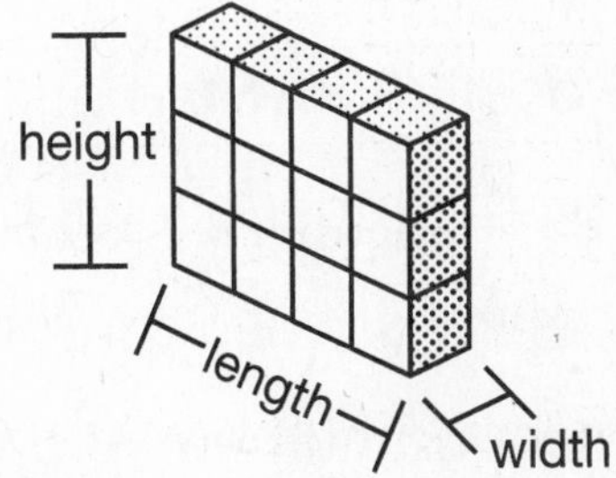

2. a. Width: ________

b. Length: ________

c. Height: ________

d. Volume: ________ cubic units

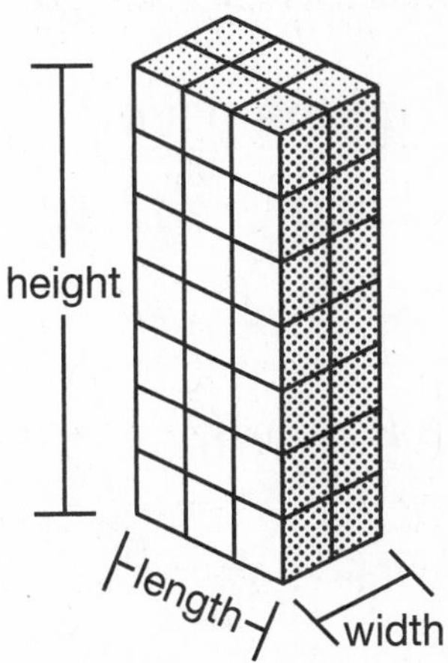

Name ______________________________

Another Look
8-12

Coordinate Grids

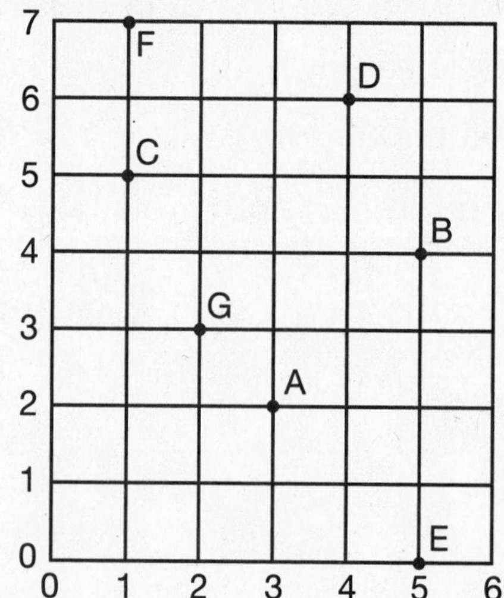

A **coordinate grid** is a special map. On this grid there are lines that go up and down, and some that go across. When the lines cross, or **intersect**, they form a point or **ordered pair**.

Find point (3,2). Start at 0.

The first number shows how many spaces you move to the right.

How many spaces do you move along the bottom of the grid? __3__

The second number shows how many spaces you move up.

How many spaces do you move up the grid? __2__

What is this point labeled on the grid? __A__

Use the grid. Write the letter located at each ordered pair.

1. To find the point at (1,7) move ______ space to the right and ______ up. The point is labeled ______.

2. (2,3) ______ **3.** (4,6) ______ **4.** (5,4) ______

Use the grid. Write the ordered pair for each point.

5. G ________ **6.** B ________ **7.** F ________

8. C ________ **9.** E ________ **10.** D ________

Name ____________________

Another Look 9-1

Exploring Multiplying Tens

In your book you multiplied tens using place-value blocks. Here is another way. You can think of a symbol to represent 10, like you did with a pictograph.

To multiply by 10, you can think of basic facts.

To find 4 × 80, think about 4 × 8

4 × 8 = 32
4 × 8 tens = 32 tens
32 tens = 320
So, 4 × 80 = 320.

❀ = 10

---

1. 3 × 50

a. 3 groups of ☐ tens

b. 3 × ☐ tens = ☐ tens

c. 3 × 50 = ☐

❀ = 10

2. 6 × 30

a. 6 groups of ☐ tens

b. 6 × ☐ tens = ☐ tens

c. 6 × 30 = ☐

❀ = 10

3. 4 × 7 tens = ☐ tens

a. 4 × 70 = ☐

4. 5 × 4 tens = ☐ tens

a. 5 × 40 = ☐

5. 6 × 8 tens = ☐ tens

a. 6 × 80 = ☐

6. 7 × 2 tens = ☐ tens

a. 7 × 20 = ☐

7. 8 × 9 tens = ☐ tens

a. 8 × 90 = ☐

8. 5 × 6 tens = ☐ tens

a. 5 × 60 = ☐

Name ______________________________

Another Look
9-2

Exploring Multiplication Patterns

In your book you used a calculator to help you multiply by tens and hundreds. Here are two rules you can follow to multiply by tens and hundreds.

To multiply by tens, write a zero in the ones place. Then multiply the non-zero digits

4 × 5 = 20

4 × 5<u>0</u> = 20<u>0</u>

To multiply by hundreds, write *two* zeros, one in the ones place, and one in the tens place. Then multiply the non-zero digits.

4 × 5 = 20

4 × 5<u>00</u> = 2,0<u>00</u>

Complete.

1. 3 × 6 = ☐☐
   3 × 60 = ☐☐0
   3 × 600 = ☐,☐00

2. 2 × 3 = ☐
   2 × 30 = ☐0
   2 × 300 = ☐00

3. 5 × 3 = ________
   5 × 30 = ________
   5 × 300 = ________

4. 3 × 8 = ________
   3 × 80 = ________
   3 × 800 = ________

5. 4 × 8 = ________
   4 × 80 = ________
   4 × 800 = ________

6. 2 × 6 = ________
   2 × 60 = ________
   2 × 600 = ________

7. 1 × 7 = ________
   1 × 70 = ________
   1 × 700 = ________

8. 3 × 7 = ________
   3 × 70 = ________
   3 × 700 = ________

9. 5 × 4 = ________
   5 × 40 = ________
   5 × 400 = ________

10. 4 × 7 = ________
    4 × 70 = ________
    4 × 700 = ________

 Use with pages 362–363.

Name ____________________

Another Look 9-3

Estimating Products

An estimate tells *about* how many. To estimate a product, round the greater factor to the nearest ten or hundred. Then multiply.

You can use a number line to help you round.

Example 1 Estimate 3 × 22.

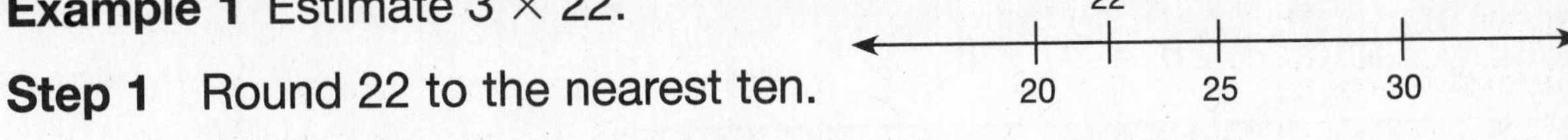

Step 1 Round 22 to the nearest ten.

22 is closer to 20 than 30, so 22 rounds to <u>20</u>.

Step 2 Multiply the factors.

3 × 20 = <u>60</u>

3 × 22 is about 60.

Example 2 Estimate 8 × 389.

389, 300, 350, 400

Step 1 Round 389 to the nearest hundred.

389 is closer to 400 than 300, so 389 rounds to <u>400</u>.

Step 2 Multiply the factors.

8 × 400 = <u>3,200</u>

8 × 389 is about 3,200.

Circle the better estimate.

1. 5 × 34 **a.** 5 × 30 = 150 **b.** 5 × 40 = 200

2. 6 × 57 **a.** 6 × 50 = 300 **b.** 6 × 60 = 360

3. 4 × 416 **a.** 4 × 400 = 1,600 **b.** 4 × 500 = 2,000

4. 3 × 345 **a.** 3 × 300 = 900 **b.** 3 × 200 = 600

5. 8 × 678 **a.** 8 × 600 = 4,800 **b.** 8 × 700 = 5,600

6. 2 × 729 **a.** 2 × 700 = 1,400 **b.** 2 × 600 = 1,200

Name ______________________________

Another Look
9-4

Exploring Multiplication with Arrays

In your book you used place-value blocks to show an array. Here is another way to show an array.

When multiplying 2-digit numbers, break apart the number into tens and ones. You can use grid paper to help.

Multiply 2 and 28. $28 = 20 + 8$

Step 1 Shade 2 rows of 20.

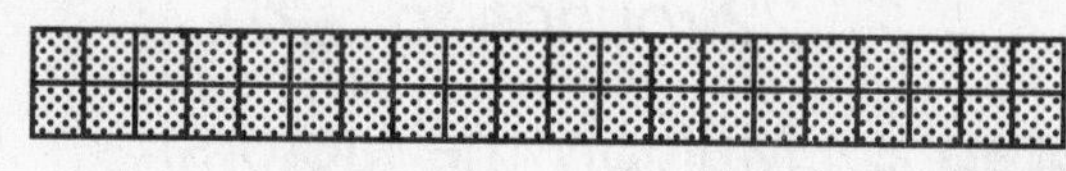

$2 \times 20 =$ 40

Step 2 Shade 2 rows of 8 next to the 2 rows of 20.

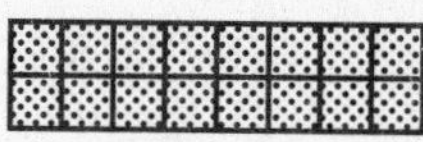

$2 \times 8 =$ 16

Step 3 Add the number of squares in the 2 pieces you shaded. This is the product.

$(2 \times 20) + (2 \times 8) = 40 + 16 =$ 56

Step 4 $2 \times 28 =$ 56

Find each product. You may use place-value blocks or grid paper to help.

5. Find 3×29.

a. $3 \times 20 =$ ______

b. $3 \times 9 =$ ______

c. ______ + ______ = ______

6. Find 2×43.

a. $2 \times 40 =$ ______

b. $2 \times 3 =$ ______

c. ______ + ______ = ______

7. Find 4×17.

a. $4 \times$ ______ = ______

b. $4 \times$ ______ = ______

c. ______ + ______ = ______

8. Find 2×37.

a. $2 \times$ ______ = ______

b. $2 \times$ ______ = ______

c. ______ + ______ = ______

Name ______________________________

Another Look 9-5

Multiplying: Partial Products

You can draw rectangles to help you multiply.

Find 4×27.

Draw a rectangle 27 squares long by 4 squares wide. Divide the rectangle into smaller rectangles by 10s. Find the sum of the number of squares in each section.

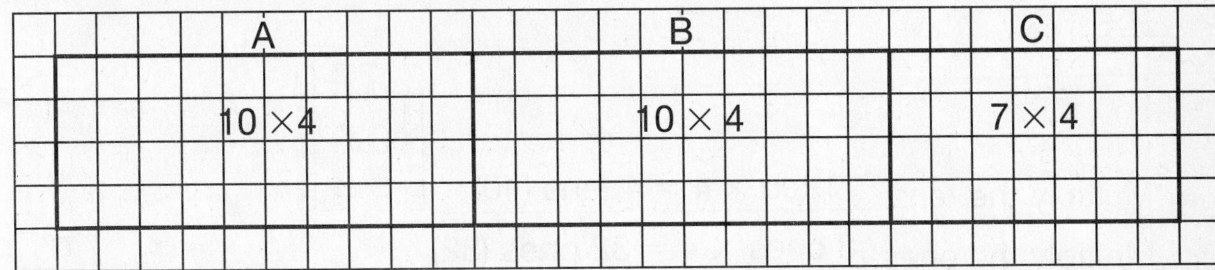

Section A $10 \times 4 = 40$ Section B $10 \times 4 = 40$ Section C $7 \times 4 = 28$

$40 + 40 + 28 = 108$

$4 \times 27 = 108$

Find each product. Use grid paper to help you.

1. 6×23

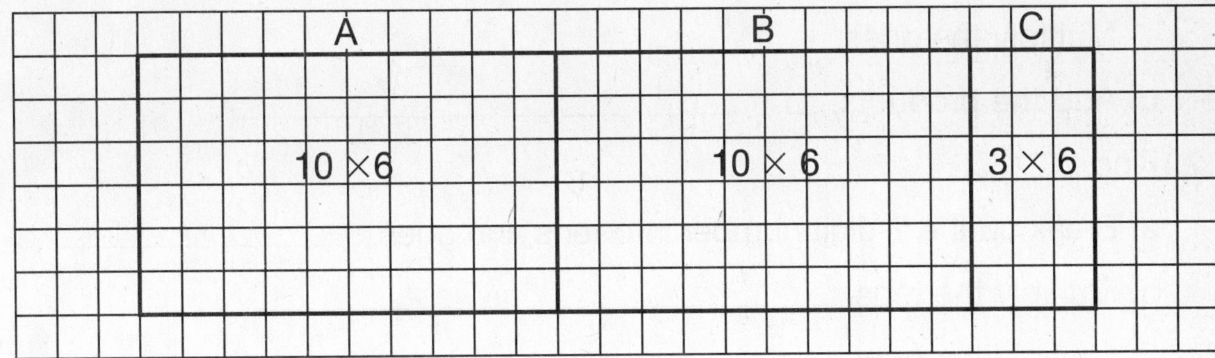

How many squares are in

a. Section A? ______ **b.** Section B? ______ **c.** Section C? ______

d. How many squares are there in all? ______

e. $6 \times 23 =$ ______

2. 15×3 ______ **3.** 72×2 ______ **4.** 23×7 ______

Name ______________________________

Multiplying 2-Digit Numbers

You can break up a 2-digit number to make it easier to multiply. You can multiply the tens, multiply the ones, and add these products together.

Find 4 × 18.

a. Break up the 2-digit number into tens and ones. 1 ten and 8 ones

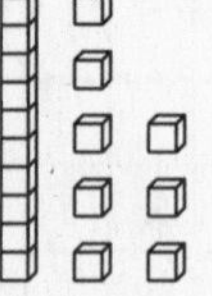

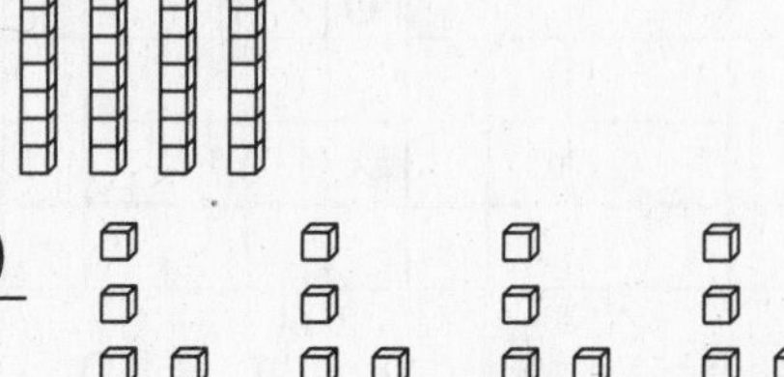

b. Multiply the tens. 1 ten × 4 = 4 tens (40)

Multiply the ones. 8 ones × 4 = 32 ones (32)

c. Add the products. 40 + 32 = 72

Find each product. Use place-value blocks to help.

1. Find 12 × 5.

a. Break up the 2-digit number into tens and ones. ____________

b. Multiply the tens. ____________

Multiply the ones. ____________

c. Add the products. ____________

2. Find 28 × 5.

a. Break up the 2-digit number into tens and ones. ____________

b. Multiply the tens. ____________

Multiply the ones. ____________

c. Add the products. ____________

3. Find 43 × 7.

a. Break up the 2-digit number into tens and ones. ____________

b. Multiply the tens. ____________

Multiply the ones. ____________

c. Add the products. ____________

Name ______________________

Another Look 9-7

Multiplying 3-Digit Numbers

Find 138 × 5.

Step 1 Multiply the ones. 8 × 5 = 40 ones

Write tens digit above the 3 in the tens place.

Write the ones digit in the ones place.

```
    4
  138
 ×  5
 ----
    0
```

Step 2 Multiply the tens. 3 × 5 = 15

Add the tens from Step 1. 15 + 4 = 19

Write the 1 above the 1 in the hundreds place.

Write the 9 in the tens place.

```
  [1]4
  138
 ×  5
 ----
  [9]0
```

Step 3 Multiply the hundreds. 1 × 5 = 5

Add the hundreds from Step 2. 5 + 1 = 6

Write the sum in the hundreds place.

```
  1 4
  138
 ×  5
 ----
 [6]90
```

138 × 5 = 690

Complete. Find each product.

1.
```
   1□
  236
 ×  3
 ----
  □□8
```

2.
```
   □4
   418
 ×   6
 -----
 □,□0□
```

3.
```
    □
   571
 ×   4
 -----
 2,□□4
```

4.
```
    □□
   329
 ×   8
 -----
 □,□□□
```

5.
```
     □
   607
 ×   9
 -----
 □,□□□
```

6.
```
   □□
   387
 ×   2
 -----
   □□□
```

Name ___________________________

Another Look
9-8

Multiplying Money

When you multiply dollars by a whole number, your answer will be in dollars. Is there a dollar sign and decimal point in the number you're multiplying? If there is, remember to put one in your answer!

Example 1 \$3.75 × 2

Does the answer to this problem need a dollar sign or a decimal point? It needs both.

\$3.75 × 2 = \$7.50

Example 2 \$375 × 2

Does the answer to this problem need a dollar sign or a decimal point? It needs a dollar sign.

\$375 × 2 = \$750

Multiply the same way you would with whole numbers. Use a dollar sign or a decimal point if needed.

1. \$1.15 × 2 = __________

Does the answer to this problem need a dollar sign or a decimal point? ____________________

2. \$2.56 × 3 = __________

Does the answer to this problem need a dollar sign or a decimal point? ____________________

3. \$491 × 5 = __________

Does the answer to this problem need a dollar sign or a decimal point? ____________________

4. \$3.75 × 4 = __________

Does the answer to this problem need a dollar sign or a decimal point? ____________________

Name ______________________________

Mental Math

When you multiply a 2-digit number, try this method for multiplying mentally:

Find the nearest multiple of 10 for the 2-digit number. Multiply the multiple by the other number and adjust.

Example Find 6×32.

a. What is the nearest multiple of 10 to 32? 30

b. Multiply with that number: $6 \times 30 = 180$

c. Is 32 greater than or less than 30? By how much? Greater; 2

d. Add 2 groups of 6 to your answer for **b.** $180 + 12 = 192$

Example Find 6×38.

a. What is the nearest multiple of 10 to 38? 40

b. Multiply with that number: $6 \times 40 = 240$

c. Is 38 greater or less than 40? By how much? Less; 2

d. Subtract 2 groups of 6 from your answer in **b.** $240 - 12 = 228$

---

1. Find 5×17.

a. What is the nearest multiple of 10 to 17? ________

b. Multiply with that number: ________________

c. Is 17 less than or greater than 20? By how much? ____________

d. Subtract 3 groups of 5 from your answer for **b.** ________________

Solve each problem mentally.

2. $3 \times 21 =$ ________

3. $42 \times 5 =$ ________

4. $2 \times 58 =$ ________

5. $26 \times 4 =$ ________

Name ______________________

Another Look 9-10

Analyze Strategies: Make a Table

Your family gets 3 magazines in January and your father puts them on the shelf. In February, there are 6 magazines on the shelf. In March, there are 9.

How many magazines will there be in June? One way to figure this out is to make a table. Fill in what you know.

Month	Jan.	Feb.	Mar.	Apr.	May	June
Magazines	3	6	9	12	15	18

Look for patterns in your table. The number of magazines is always 3 more than the previous month.

Continue the pattern. How many magazines will there be in June? 18

Complete the tables to solve each problem.

1. Marty washes the dishes 3 nights each week. How many times does he wash the dishes in one month (4 weeks)? ____________

Week	1	2	3	4
Dishes				

2. Carolyn mows the lawn twice a week. How many weeks will it take for Carolyn to mow the lawn 12 times? ____________

Week	1					
Mowing the Lawn	2					

Name ______________________________

Exploring Division Patterns

In your book, you used place-value patterns to divide numbers. Here is another way to explore division patterns.

Example 1

80 ÷ 2 =

8 tens ÷ 2 = 4 tens

4 tens is the same as __40__.

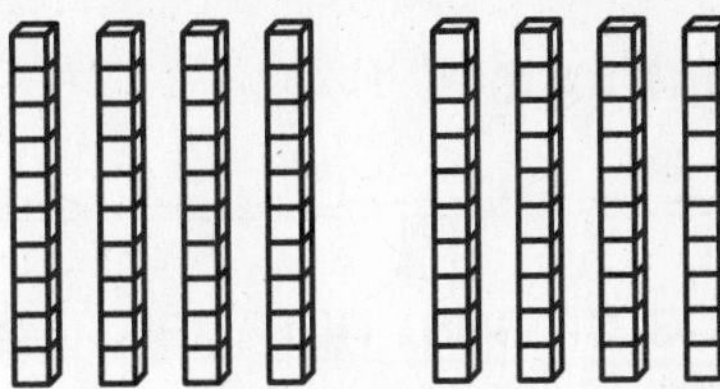

Example 2

800 ÷ 2 =

8 hundreds ÷ 2 = 4 hundreds

4 hundreds is the same as __400__.

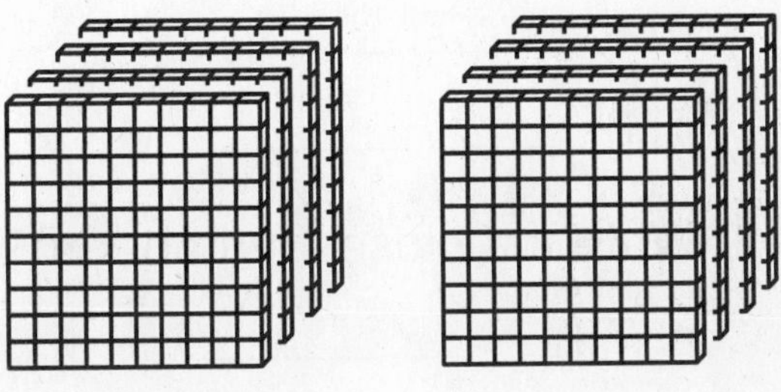

---

1. 40 ÷ 4

a. 4 ÷ 4 = ____

b. 4 tens ÷ 4 = ____ ten

c. 40 ÷ 4 = ____

2. 400 ÷ 4

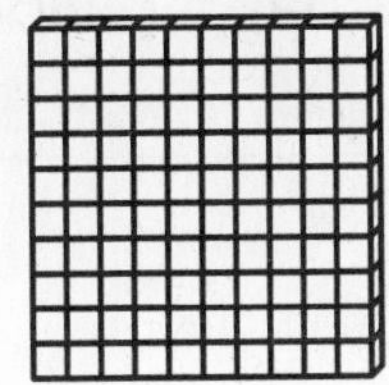
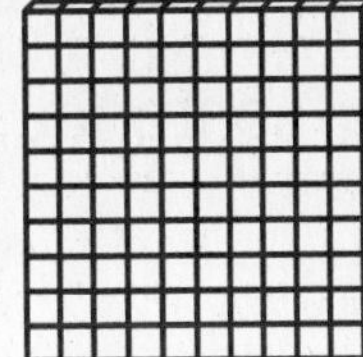

a. 4 ÷ 4 = ____

b. 4 hundreds ÷ 4
= ____ hundred

c. 400 ÷ 4 = ____

3. 240 ÷ 8

a. 24 tens ÷ ____ = ____ tens

b. 240 ÷ ____ = ____

4. 70 ÷ 1

a. 7 tens ÷ 1 = ____ tens

b. 70 ÷ 1 = ____

5. 600 ÷ 3

a. 6 hundreds ÷ 3 = ____ hundreds

b. 600 ÷ 3 = ____

Name ______________________________

Another Look
9-12

Estimating Quotients

Estimate 79 ÷ 9.

Step 1 Write the closest number to 79 that 9 divides evenly: 81

Step 2 81 ÷ 9 = 9

79 ÷ 9 is about 9.

---

1. Write the closest number to 38 that can be evenly divided by:

a. 4 ________ **b.** 5 ________

c. 6 ________ **d.** 7 ________

e. 8 ________ **f.** 9 ________

2. Write the closest number to 58 that can be evenly divided by:

a. 7 ________ **b.** 8 ________

c. 9 ________ **d.** 6 ________

e. 5 ________ **f.** 4 ________

Estimate each quotient.

3. 16 ÷ 5

a. Write the closest number to 16 that 5 divides evenly. ________

b. Write a new number sentence. ________

c. 16 ÷ 5 is about ________.

4. 64 ÷ 7

a. Write the closest number to 64 that 7 divides evenly: ________

b. Write a new number sentence. ________

c. 64 ÷ 7 is about ________.

5. 58 ÷ 8 ________ ÷ 8 = ________ **6.** 31 ÷ 4 ________ ÷ 4 = ________

7. 37 ÷ 5 ________ ÷ 5 = ________ **8.** 70 ÷ 9 ________ ÷ 9 = ________

9. 26 ÷ 7 ________ ÷ 7 = ________ **10.** 41 ÷ 6 ________ ÷ 6 = ________

Name ______________________________

Another Look 9-13

Exploring Division with Remainders

In your book you used counters to find quotients and remainders. Here is another way to find remainders.

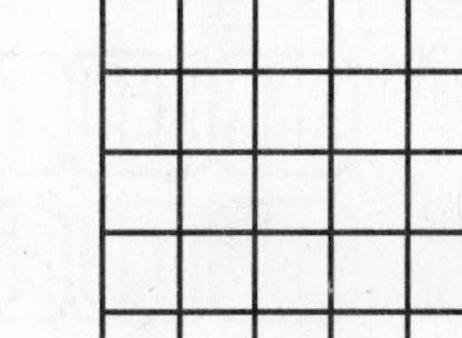

You can use grid paper to help you divide.

36 ÷ 7 = ________

Step 1 Outline 36 squares.

Step 2 Circle groups of 7 squares. Shade in any remaining squares.

Step 3 Count the number of groups you circled.

This is the quotient.

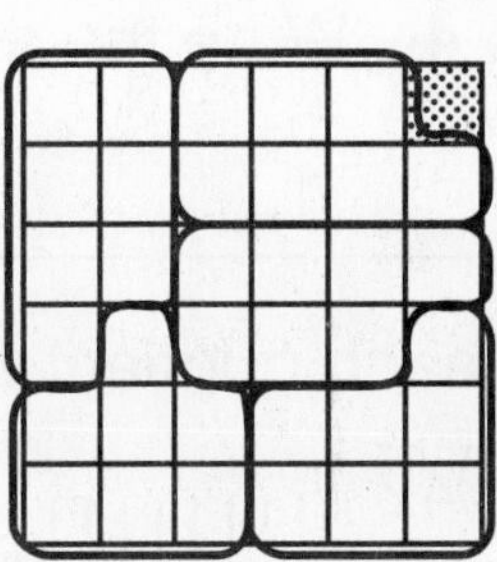

Step 4 Count the number of shaded squares.

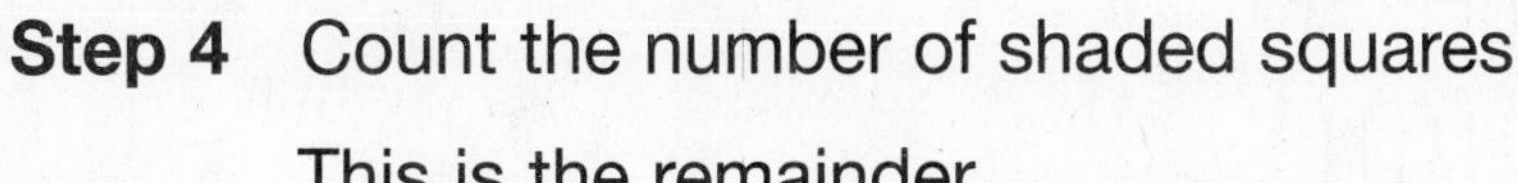

This is the remainder.

36 ÷ 7 = __5__ R __1__

Divide. You may use grid paper to help.

1. 26 ÷ 8

a. Outline 26 squares.

b. How many groups of 8 did you circle? ________

c. How many squares did you shade? ________

d. 26 ÷ 8 = ________ R ________

2. 37 ÷ 4

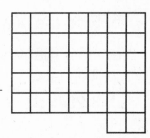

a. Outline 37 squares.

b. How many groups of 4 did you circle? ________

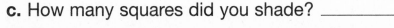

c. How many squares did you shade? ________

d. 37 ÷ 4 = ________ R ________

3. $8\overline{)42}$ **4.** $5\overline{)21}$ **5.** $7\overline{)57}$ **6.** $6\overline{)55}$

Name ______________________________

Another Look
9-14

Dividing

You can use tally marks to find quotients and remainders.

4)37

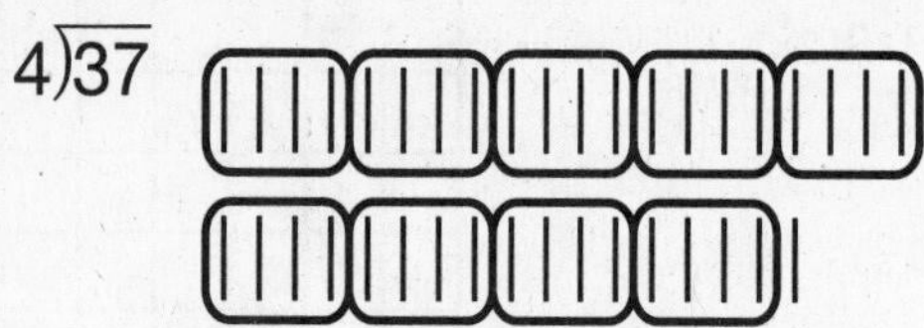

Step 1 Circle groups of 4.

Step 2 Find the number of groups. 9

Step 3 How many tallies are left over? 1

Step 4 Write the answer. 4)37 = 9 R1

Find each quotient and remainder.

1. 5)42

a. Circle groups of 5.

b. Find the number of groups. ________

c. How many are left over? ________

d. Write the answer. 5)42

2. 3)20

a. Circle groups of 3.

b. Find the number of groups. ________

c. How many are left over? ________

d. 3)20

3. 5)27 **4.** 4)31 **5.** 9)52

Name ______________________

Decision Making

You are planning a 13 mile race. You need to set up First Aid stations every 4 miles. How many stations do you need?

a. How many miles long is the race? 13
b. How many miles between First Aid stations? 4
c. Show the problem as a number sentence: 13 ÷ 4 = 3R
d. How many stations will there be? 3

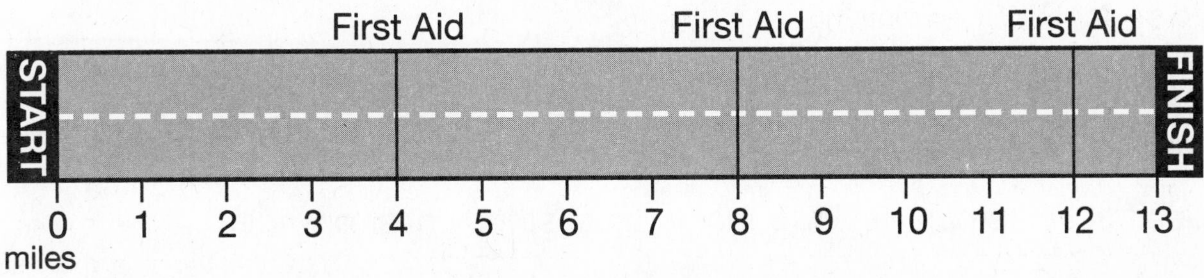

---

1. You need to set up check-in points every 3 miles for a 17-mile race. How many stations will there be?

a. How many miles long is the race? ______________

b. How many miles between check-in points? ______________

c. Show the problem as a number sentence: ______________

d. How many stations will there be? ______________

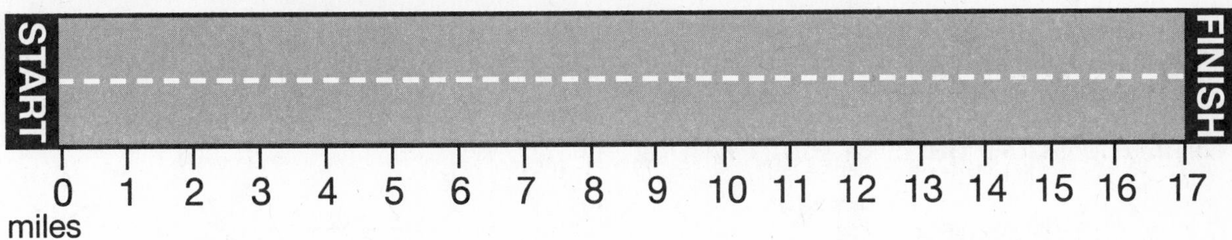

2. You need to set up water stations every 2 miles for a 10-mile race. How many stations will there be?

a. Show the problem as a number sentence: ______________

b. How many stations will there be? ______________

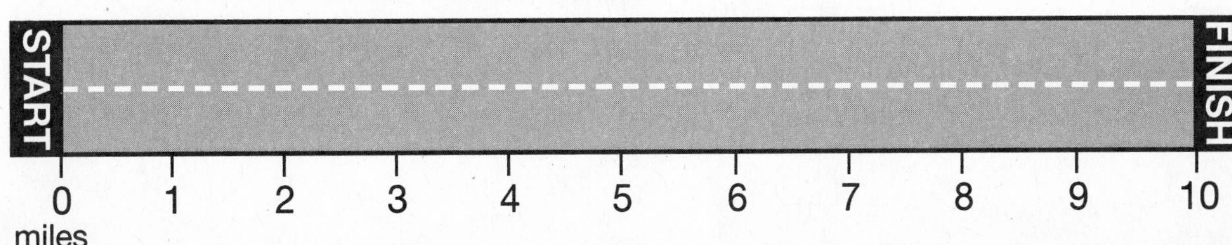

Name ______________________________

Exploring Equal Parts

In your book you found equal parts using geoboards. Here is another way to find equal parts.

Use fraction strips. Match or cover a whole with $\frac{1}{2}$ strips. How many strips do you need?

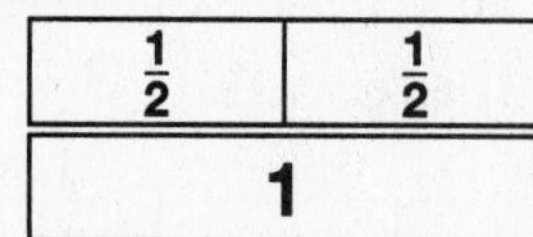

You need 2 strips.

Use fraction strips. Tell how many equal strips cover a whole.

1. $\frac{1}{3}$ strips ________ **2.** $\frac{1}{4}$ strips ________ **3.** $\frac{1}{5}$ strips ________

4. $\frac{1}{6}$ strips ________ **5.** $\frac{1}{8}$ strips ________ **6.** $\frac{1}{10}$ strips ________

7. What pattern do you see in the number of strips needed to cover a whole?

____

____

Name the equal parts of each whole.

8. ________ 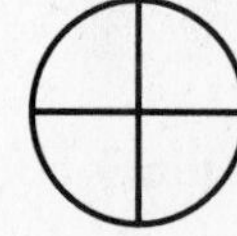

9. ________ 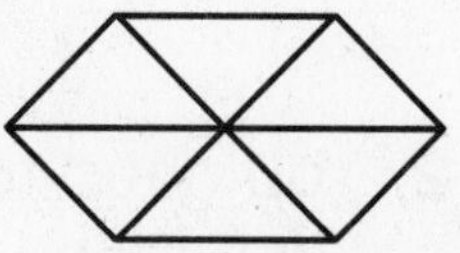

10. ________ 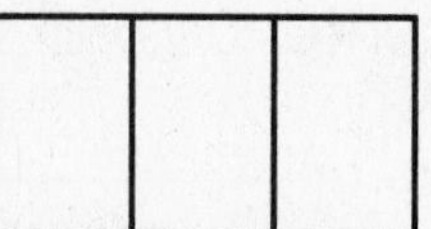

11. ________ 

12. ________ 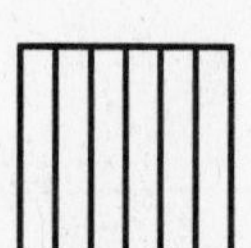

12. ________ 

Name ____________________

Naming and Writing Fractions

A **fraction** may name part of a whole.

The square is divided into 3 equal parts. 2 parts are shaded. The fraction $\frac{2}{3}$ (two thirds) names the shaded part of the square.

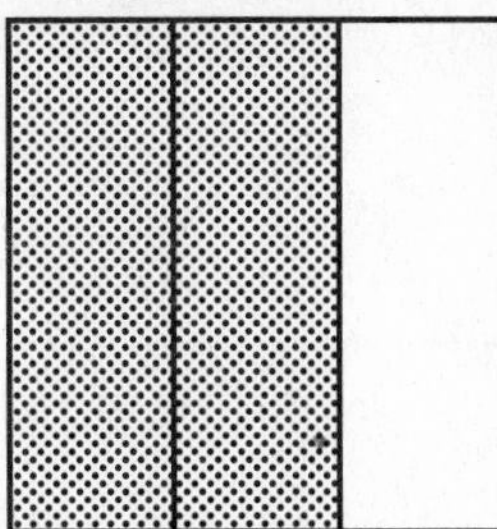

The **numerator** tells the number of shaded parts. → 2

3 ← The **denominator** tells the total number of equal parts.

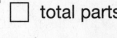

Write the fraction of each figure that is shaded.

1. $\frac{\square}{\square}$ shaded part / total parts

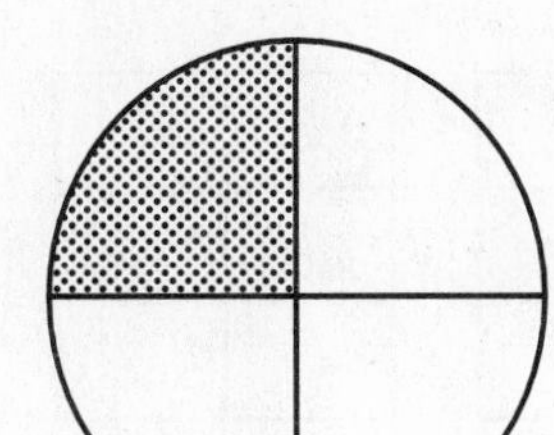

2. $\frac{\square}{\square}$ shaded part / total parts

3. ______

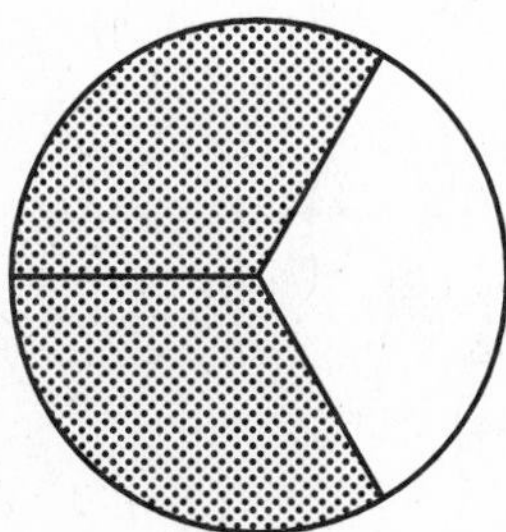

4. ______

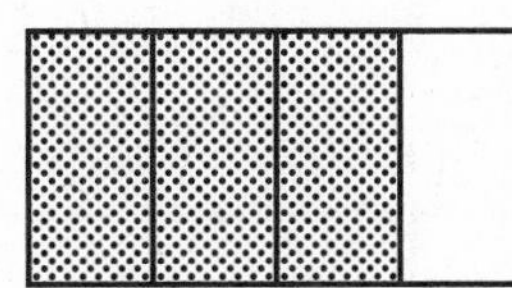

5. ______

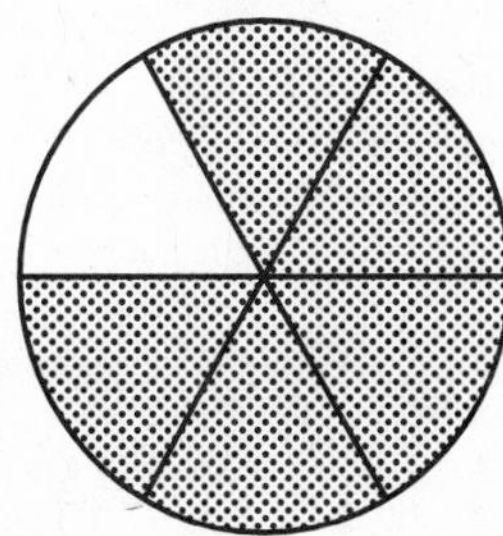

Name ______________________________

Another Look
10-3

Exploring Equivalent Fractions

In your book you found fractions that name the same amount using fraction strips. Here is another way to find equivalent fractions.

Look at the two rectangles.

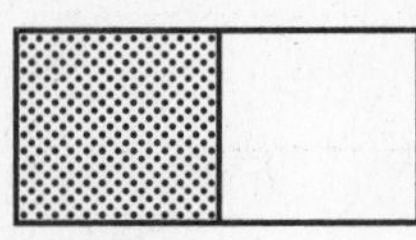

$\frac{1}{2}$ **is shaded.**

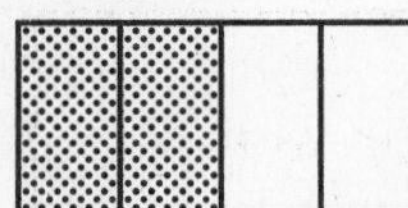

$\frac{2}{4}$ **is shaded.**

Think: Both rectangles are the same size.
The shaded parts on both are the same size.
$\frac{1}{2}$ and $\frac{2}{4}$ show the same amount.

Fractions that name the same amount are called **equivalent fractions**. $\frac{1}{2}$ and $\frac{2}{4}$ are equivalent fractions.

Complete to show equivalent fractions.

1.

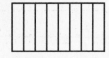

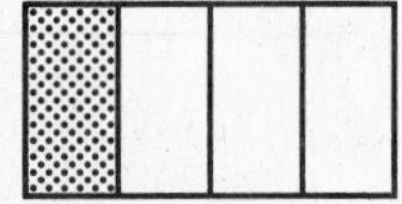

Think: 2 shaded parts, 8 parts in all

$\frac{1}{4} = \frac{\square}{8}$

2.

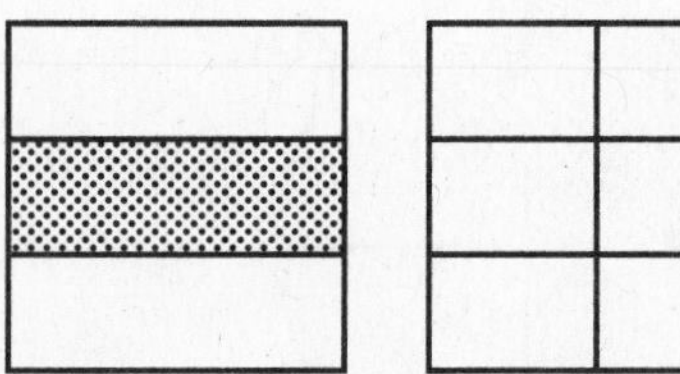

Think: 2 shaded parts, 6 parts in all

$\frac{1}{3} = \frac{\square}{6}$

3.

$\frac{3}{4} = \frac{\square}{8}$

4.

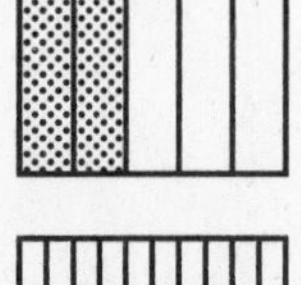

$\frac{2}{5} = \frac{\square}{10}$

5.

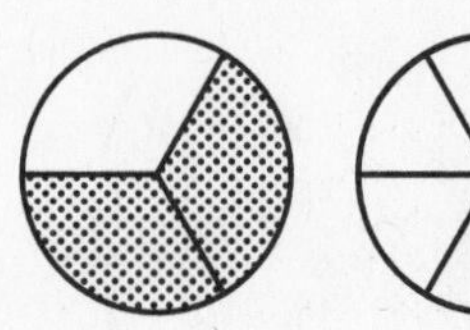

$\frac{2}{3} = \frac{\square}{6}$

Name ______________________________

Another Look
10-4

Exploring Comparing and Ordering Fractions

In your book you used fraction strips to write fractions. Here is another way to compare fractions.

Use the rectangles to compare fractions.

1							
$\frac{1}{2}$	$\frac{1}{2}$						
$\frac{1}{3}$	$\frac{1}{3}$	$\frac{1}{3}$					
$\frac{1}{4}$	$\frac{1}{4}$	$\frac{1}{4}$	$\frac{1}{4}$				
$\frac{1}{5}$	$\frac{1}{5}$	$\frac{1}{5}$	$\frac{1}{5}$	$\frac{1}{5}$			
$\frac{1}{6}$	$\frac{1}{6}$	$\frac{1}{6}$	$\frac{1}{6}$	$\frac{1}{6}$	$\frac{1}{6}$		
$\frac{1}{8}$	$\frac{1}{8}$	$\frac{1}{8}$	$\frac{1}{8}$	$\frac{1}{8}$	$\frac{1}{8}$	$\frac{1}{8}$	$\frac{1}{8}$

Compare $\frac{1}{3}$ and $\frac{1}{2}$.

Think: The rectangle that shows $\frac{1}{3}$ is smaller than the rectangle that shows $\frac{1}{2}$.

So, $\frac{1}{3} < \frac{1}{2}$.

Compare $\frac{2}{4}$ and $\frac{2}{6}$.

Think: The rectangles that show $\frac{2}{4}$ ($\frac{1}{4}$ and $\frac{1}{4}$) are larger in total than the rectangles that show $\frac{2}{6}$ ($\frac{1}{6}$ and $\frac{1}{6}$).

So, $\frac{2}{4} > \frac{2}{6}$.

Compare. Write $<$, $>$, or $=$. Use the rectangles or fraction strips to help.

1. $\frac{1}{2}$ ◯ $\frac{1}{8}$

2. $\frac{1}{3}$ ◯ $\frac{1}{5}$

3. $\frac{1}{8}$ ◯ $\frac{1}{4}$

4. $\frac{1}{4}$ ◯ $\frac{2}{8}$

5. $\frac{2}{4}$ ◯ $\frac{3}{6}$

6. $\frac{1}{3}$ ◯ $\frac{1}{6}$

7. $\frac{1}{3}$ ◯ $\frac{2}{6}$

8. $\frac{3}{8}$ ◯ $\frac{2}{4}$

9. $\frac{2}{8}$ ◯ $\frac{2}{6}$

10. $\frac{3}{4}$ ◯ $\frac{2}{3}$

11. $\frac{3}{5}$ ◯ $\frac{3}{6}$

12. $\frac{7}{8}$ ◯ $\frac{1}{2}$

13. $\frac{3}{6}$ ◯ $\frac{2}{5}$

14. $\frac{2}{4}$ ◯ $\frac{4}{8}$

15. $\frac{2}{3}$ ◯ $\frac{5}{6}$

Name ______________________________

Estimating Fractional Amounts

Use fractions you know to estimate the size of other fractions.

Step 1 Draw lines to show fractions you know.

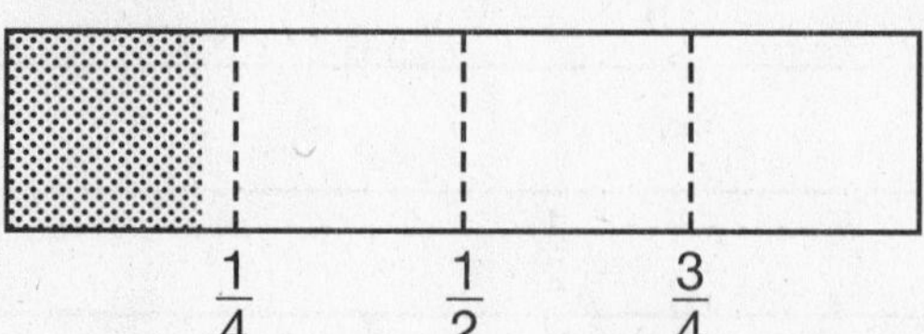

Step 2 Use the lines to estimate the fraction.

Think: The shaded part is a little less than $\frac{1}{4}$.

Here's another example.

Step 1 Draw lines to show fractions you know.

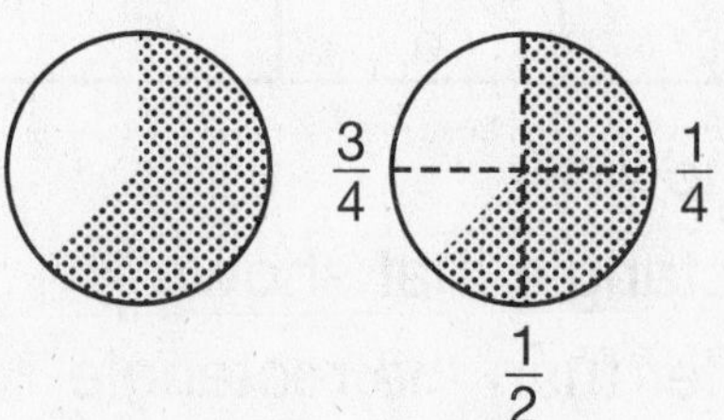

Step 2 Use the lines to estimate the fractions.

Think: The shaded part is more than $\frac{1}{2}$ and less than $\frac{3}{4}$.

Estimate each shaded amount.

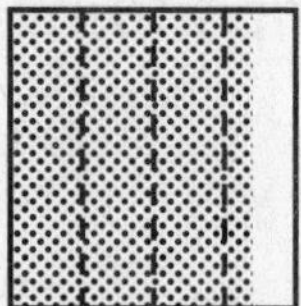

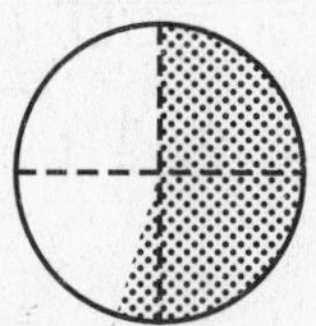

1. ______________________ 2. ______________________

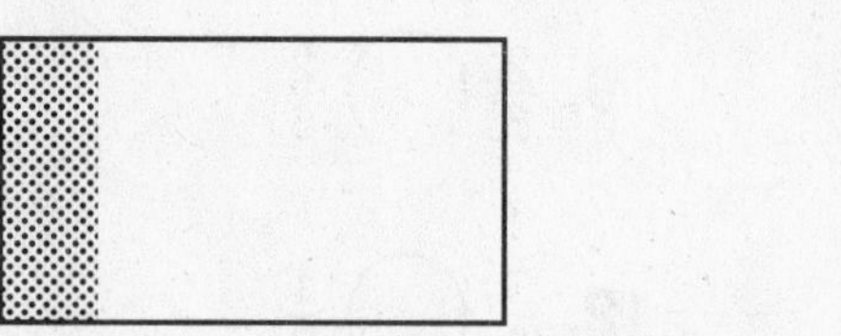

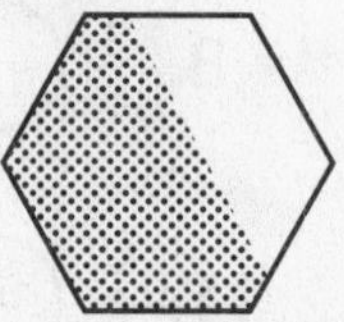

3. ______________________ 4. ______________________

Name ______________________________

Fractions and Sets

- A **set** is a group of things that can be counted.
- A **fraction** is a number that describes part of the set.

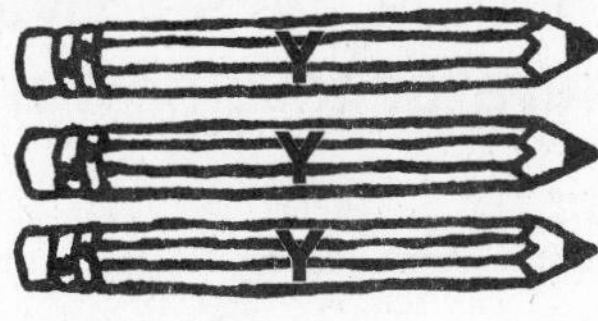

Suppose you have 10 pencils and 3 of them are yellow. What fraction of the pencils are yellow?

There are 10 pencils in all. 3 of the pencils are yellow. 3 out of 10 is written as $\frac{3}{10}$.

---

1. If you have 2 apples and 1 of them is green, what fraction of the apples are green?

____

2. If you have 3 hats and 2 of them have feathers, what fraction of the hats have feathers?

____

3. If you have 4 pets and 3 of them are dogs, what fraction of the pets are dogs?

____

Write a fraction to tell what part of the set is circled.

4. __________ **5.** __________ **6.** __________

Name ______________________________

Another Look 10-7

Exploring Finding a Fraction of a Number

In your book you found fractions of numbers using counters. You can think about sets to find fractional parts of numbers.

- The **denominator** tells how many equal groups to make. Divide the set by this number.
- The **numerator** tells how many of the groups to count.

$\frac{1}{5}$ ← numerator (1), ← denominator (5)

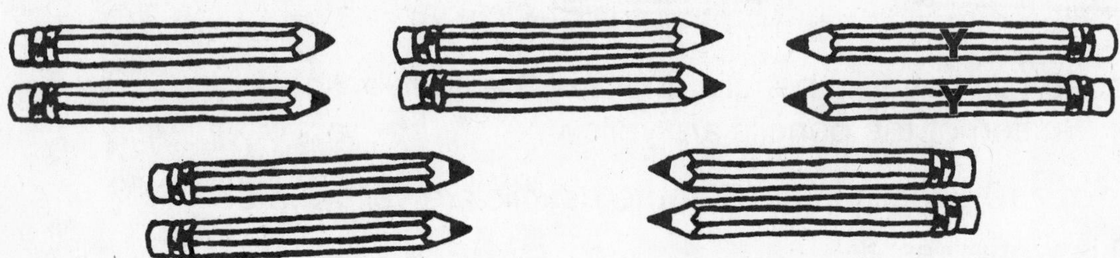

If you have 10 pencils and $\frac{1}{5}$ of them are yellow, how many pencils are yellow?

The denominator, 5, tells you to make 5 groups. The numerator 1 tells you to count 1 of the groups.

2 of the pencils are yellow.

---

1. $\frac{1}{2}$ of the apples are green.
   How many apples are green? ________

2. $\frac{2}{3}$ of the hats are blue.
   How many hats are blue? ________

3. $\frac{3}{4}$ of the cats like to play with yarn.
   How many like to play with yarn? ________

4. $\frac{1}{4}$ of 12 = ________

5. $\frac{1}{6}$ of 24 = ________

Name ______________________

Mixed Numbers

- A **whole number** can tell how many complete (or whole) things are in a set.
- A **fraction** can tell how much of an incomplete thing is in a set.
- A **mixed number** can describe a set that has one or more complete things and an incomplete thing in it.

Count the number of whole items. 5 full glasses

Write a fraction for the partial item. $\frac{3}{4}$ full glass

Combine the whole number and fraction to write a mixed number.

The picture shows $5\frac{3}{4}$ glasses of juice.

Write a mixed number for each.

1. 

______

2. 

______

3. 

______

4. 

______

Name ________________________________

Another Look
10-9

Exploring Adding and Subtracting Fractions

In your book you used fraction strips to add and subtract fractions. Here is another way to add and subtract fractions.

The denominator describes *the kind* of groups you're working with. The denominator stays the same when you add or subtract fractions with like denominators. The numerator tells *how many* of the groups you're working with. This is the number to add or subtract.	$\frac{1}{3}$ ← numerator, ← denominator

$\frac{1}{3} + \frac{1}{3} = \underline{\frac{2}{3}}$

The denominator stays the same.

Add the numerators.

$\frac{4}{5} - \frac{1}{5} = \underline{\frac{3}{5}}$

The denominator stays the same.

Subtract the numerators.

Find each sum or difference.

1. $\frac{1}{4} + \frac{1}{4} =$ ________
2. $\frac{5}{8} + \frac{3}{8} =$ ________
3. $\frac{3}{10} + \frac{4}{10} =$ ________
4. $\frac{6}{9} + \frac{2}{9} =$ ________
5. $\frac{1}{5} + \frac{3}{5} =$ ________
6. $\frac{2}{3} - \frac{1}{3} =$ ________
7. $\frac{2}{6} + \frac{3}{6} =$ ________
8. $\frac{8}{12} - \frac{4}{12} =$ ________

Name ___________________________

Decision Making

There are 8 people to feed. You want to give each person 2 slices of pizza. If each pizza is cut into 6 slices, how many pizzas will you need?

2 slices $\times$ 8 people = 16 slices

Each pizza has 6 slices.

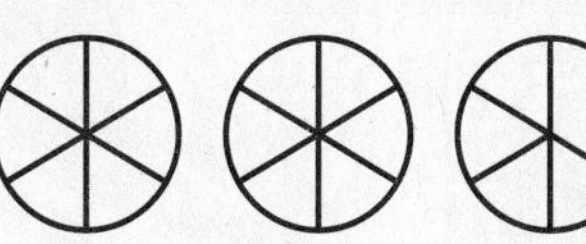

16 $\div$ 6 = 2 R4

You will need 3 pizzas.

---

1. There are 6 people to feed. You want to give each person 2 hot dogs. There are 10 hot dogs per package. How many packages will you need?

   ____

2. There are 10 people who are thirsty. You want to give each person 2 glasses of juice. If there are 8 glasses worth of juice per bottle, how many bottles will you need?

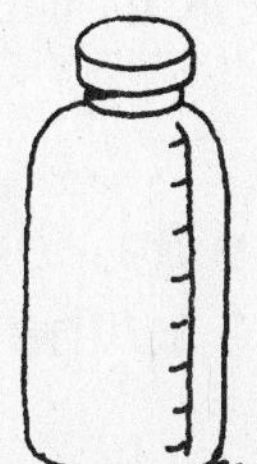

   ____

3. There are 12 people to feed. You want to give each person 3 crackers. There are 18 crackers in a box. How many boxes will you need?

   ____

Name ______________________

Exploring Length

In your book you explored length using paper clips and pencils. Here is another way to understand length.

You can measure the height of this chipmunk using a small object like a postage stamp. The length of a postage stamp is about one inch.

About how many postage stamps tall is this chipmunk? The chipmunk is about 3 postage stamps tall.

You can also use a ruler. Align one end of the ruler with the bottom of the chipmunk's feet. How tall is the chipmunk in inches? 3 inches

---

Estimate the length of each figure. Then use a ruler to measure to the nearest inch.

1. 

Estimate: ________

Actual: ________

2. 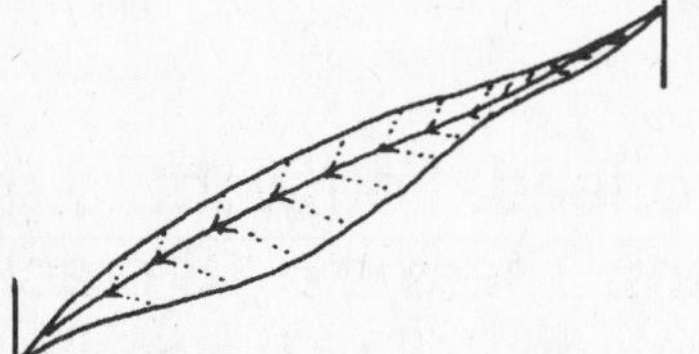

Estimate: ________

Actual: ________

3. 

Estimate: ________

Actual: ________

4. 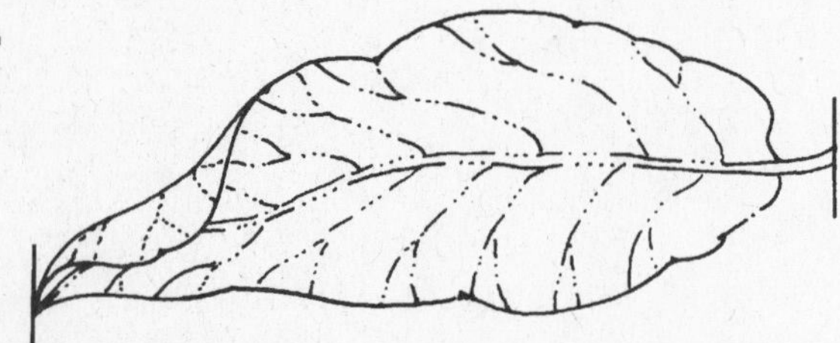

Estimate: ________

Actual: ________

5. 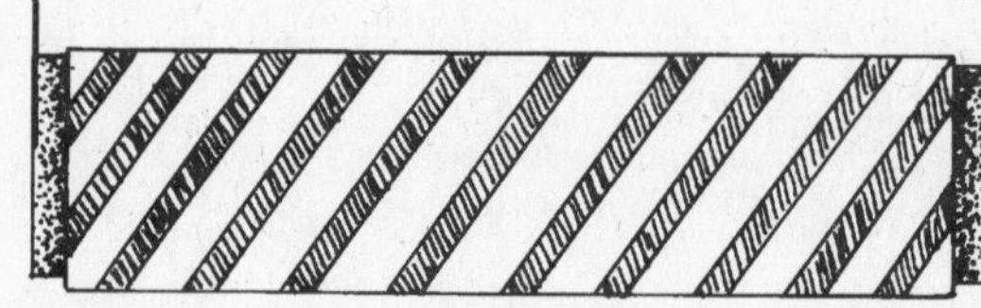

Estimate: ________

Actual: ________

Name ______________________________

Another Look 10-12

Measuring to the Nearest $\frac{1}{2}$ Inch and $\frac{1}{4}$ Inch

You can measure to the nearest inch. You can make a measurement closer to the actual length by measuring:

to the nearest $\frac{1}{2}$ inch.

The chain measures between 2 and $2\frac{1}{2}$ inches. Since it is closer to $2\frac{1}{2}$ inches, its measurement is $2\frac{1}{2}$ inches.

to the nearest $\frac{1}{4}$ inch.

For a closer measurement, you can measure to the nearest $\frac{1}{4}$ inch. This chain is between 2 and $2\frac{1}{4}$ inches long. Since it is closer to $2\frac{1}{4}$ inches, its measurement is $2\frac{1}{4}$ inches.

Measure the length of each object to the nearest $\frac{1}{2}$ inch.

1. ____________

2. ____________

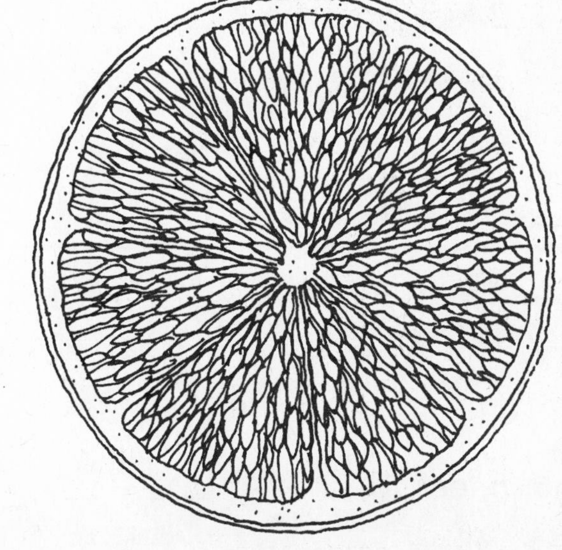

Measure the length of the object to the nearest $\frac{1}{4}$ inch.

3. ____________

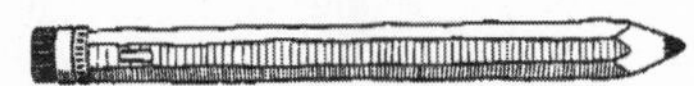

Name ______________________________

Another Look
10-13

Exploring Length in Feet and Inches

In your book you explored length by estimating distances. Here is another way to understand feet and inches.

You can use place-value blocks to write measurements in feet as measurements in inches.

How many inches are in 4 feet, 3 inches?

Step 1 Use place-value blocks to show 12. Since there are 12 inches in 1 foot, this represents 1 foot.

Step 2 Use the blocks to show 3 more groups of 12. These represent 3 more feet. Show 3 more ones blocks for the 3 more inches.

Step 3 How many ones are there? 11

Regroup. 11 ones = 1 ten 1 one

How many tens are there? 4

How many inches are in 4 feet, 3 inches? 51 inches

Use place-value blocks to write each measurement in inches.

1. 2 feet, 5 inches ________

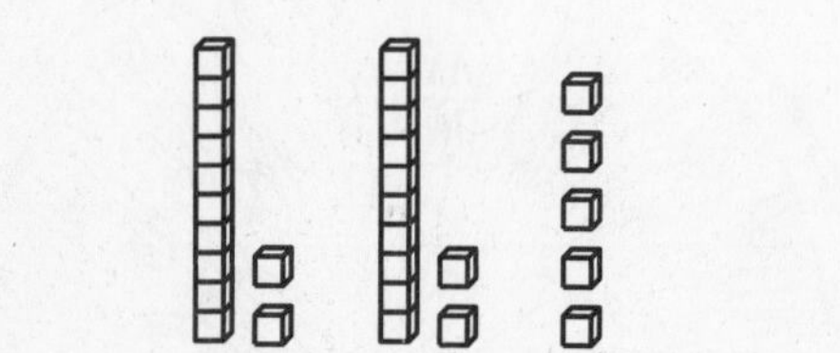

2. 1 foot, 10 inches ________

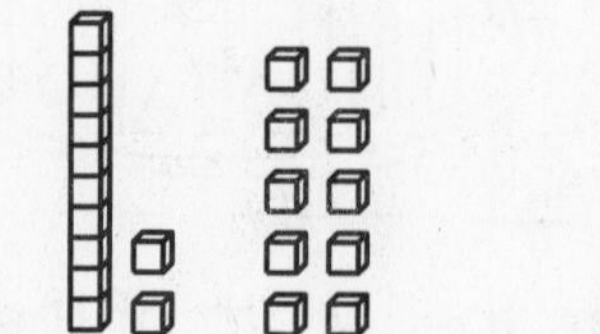

3. 3 feet, 1 inch ________

4. 2 feet, 9 inches ________

5. 5 feet ________

6. 3 feet, 3 inches ________

Name ______________________

Feet, Yards, and Miles

The standard units of measure for distance are inches, feet, yards, and miles. Inches are used to measure the length of very small objects such as bugs and leaves. Miles are used to measure distances you would travel in a car or plane.

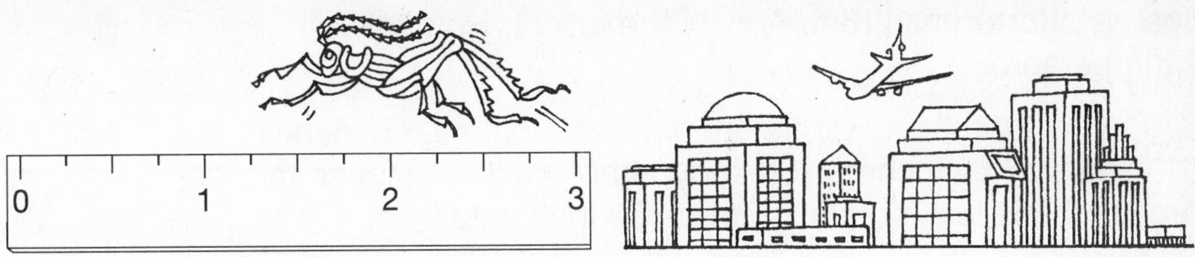

Which is the greater distance? 2 feet or 17 inches?

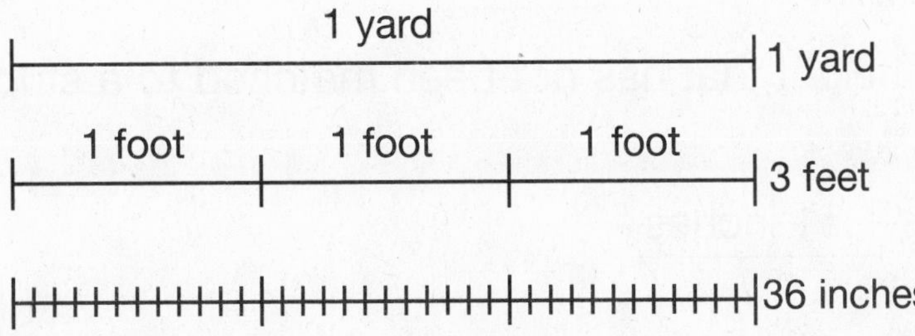

Look at the diagram. There are 12 inches in every foot. 17 inches is a little over 1 foot. So, 2 feet is the greater distance.

2 feet > 17 inches

Compare. Write <, >, or =. Use the diagram to help.

1. 1 yard ◯ 2 feet

2. 5 feet ◯ 27 inches

3. 21 feet ◯ 16 yards

4. 1 yard ◯ 3 feet

5. 36 inches ◯ 3 yards

6. 6 feet ◯ 60 inches

Choose an estimate for each.

_____ **7.** an adult's height

_____ **8.** the height of a skyscraper

_____ **9.** the length of a butterfly

a. 2 inches

b. 5 feet

c. 250 yards

Name ______________________________

Analyze Strategies: Use Logical Reasoning

Josh, Seth, Amy, and Kim measured their heights. Their measurements are 47 inches, 49 inches, 51 inches, and 52 inches. Kim is 49 inches tall. Seth is taller than Kim. Josh is shorter than Kim. Amy is the tallest. How tall is each person?

You know that the students are either 47 inches, 49 inches, 51 inches or 52 inches. You know that Kim is 49 inches tall. Amy is the tallest, so she must be 52 inches tall.

Look at what you know. Who is taller, Kim or Josh? Kim

What is Josh's height? 47 inches

What is the only height that has not been matched to a student?

51 inches

How tall is Seth? 51 inches

Liang, Steve, Marcie, and Bob are trying to figure out the order in which they were born. Marcie is older than Bob. Liang and Steve are younger than Bob. Bob is 11 years old. Liang is younger than the other students. If the students are either 9, 10, 11, or 12 years old, what are their ages?

1. Whose age is given in the problem? ____________
2. Who is older than Bob? ____________
3. Who is the youngest? ____________
4. Write each person's name and age.

____

____

Name ______________________

Exploring Tenths

In your book you explored tenths with grids. Here is another way to understand tenths.

1 dime is one-tenth of a dollar.
0.10 is one tenth.

10 dimes are the same as 1 whole dollar.
10 tenths are the same as 1 whole.

7 dimes are seven-tenths of a dollar.

$0.70 = $\frac{7}{10}$ = 0.7

2 dimes are two-tenths of a dollar.
1 dollar 2 dimes can be shown as $1.20.

$1.20 = $1\frac{2}{10}$ = 1.2

1.2 is read "one and two tenths."

Use what you know about decimals and fractions to complete the table.

	Money	Money Amount	Fraction	Decimal	Word Name
1.					four tenths
2.			$\frac{9}{10}$		
3.		$1.60			
4.				3.1	

Name ______________________________

Hundredths

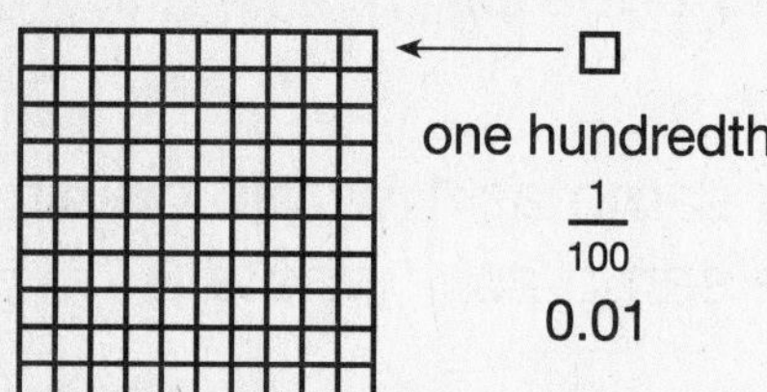

Each block in a hundredth grid equals one hundredth.

An entire hundredths grid equals one whole.

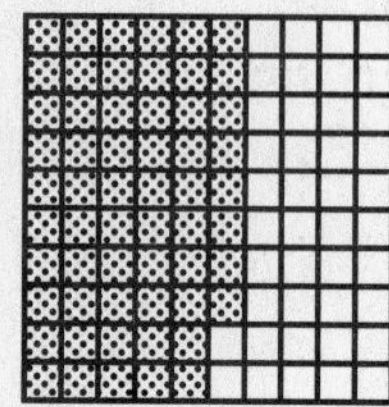

58 out of 100 boxes are shaded.

So, $\frac{58}{100}$ of the grid is shaded.

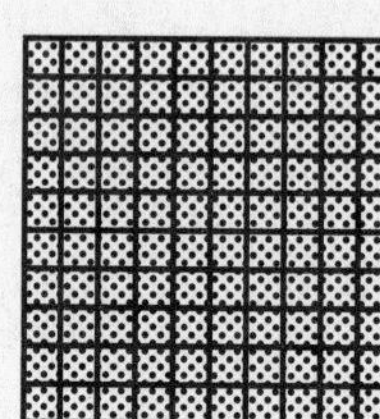 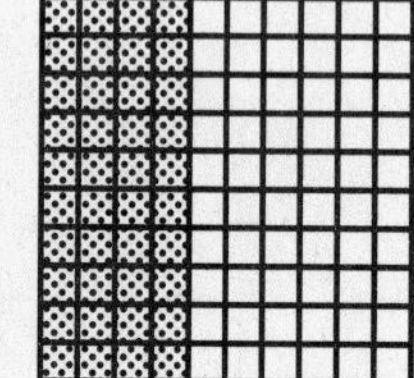

1 whole square and 40 out of 100 boxes of the second square are shaded. $1\frac{40}{100}$ of the grids are shaded.

You can name the same number in different ways.

word name	fraction	decimal
fifty-eight hundredths	$\frac{58}{100}$	0.58
one and forty hundredths	$1\frac{40}{100}$	1.40

Write the word name, fraction, and decimal to name the shaded part.

	Grids	Word Name	Fraction	Decimal
1.		seventy-five hundredths		
2.		one and ____________		

Name ______________________

Exploring Adding and Subtracting Decimals

In your book you added and subtracted decimals using grids. Here is another way to add and subtract decimals.

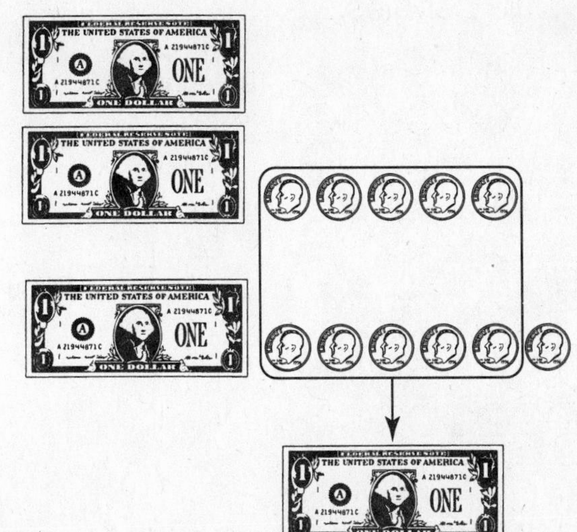

Add 2.5 and 1.6.

Show 2.5 using dollars and dimes.

Show 1.6 using dollars and dimes.

Combine the dimes. Can you exchange some for a dollar? Yes

How many dollars are there all together? 2 + 1 + 1 = 4

Write the sum as a decimal. 4.1

---

1. Add 0.6 and 0.8.

a. Combine the dimes. Can you exchange some for a dollar? ______

b. Write the sum. ______

2. Subtract 2.2 and 1.7.

a. Exchange 1 dollar for 10 dimes.
Take away 7 dimes.
How many dimes remain? ______

b. Take away 1 dollar.
How many dollars remain? ______

c. Write the difference. ______

Name ________________________

Connecting Decimals and Money

Money amounts are written as decimals. You can think of cents as fractional parts of whole dollars.

This square shows 100 pennies. Each column in the square shows 10 pennies.

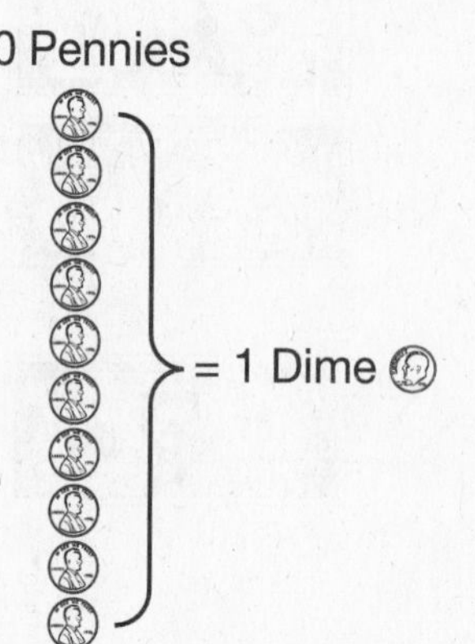

$\frac{1}{100}$ of the pennies is 1 penny or 1¢. $\frac{10}{100}$ of the pennies is 1 dime or 10¢.

$\frac{36}{100}$ of the pennies is 36¢.

Three dollars and forty-five cents is $3.45.

Write each as a money amount. Draw pictures to help.

1. $\frac{32}{100}$ ____________
2. $\frac{7}{100}$ ____________
3. $\frac{80}{100}$ ____________
4. four dollars and 30 cents ____________
5. two dollars and 20 cents ____________
6. six dollars and forty-five cents ____________

Name ______________________

Decision Making

It's June 24, and you and your family are visiting Mt. Washington in New Hampshire. It is 1:30 P.M. Do you have enough time to visit the top?

The mountain road closes at 6:00 P.M.

The one-way driving time is about 1 hour.

The guidebooks suggest a one-hour stay at the top in order to have enough time to visit the Summit Museum, which remains open until 8:00 P.M.

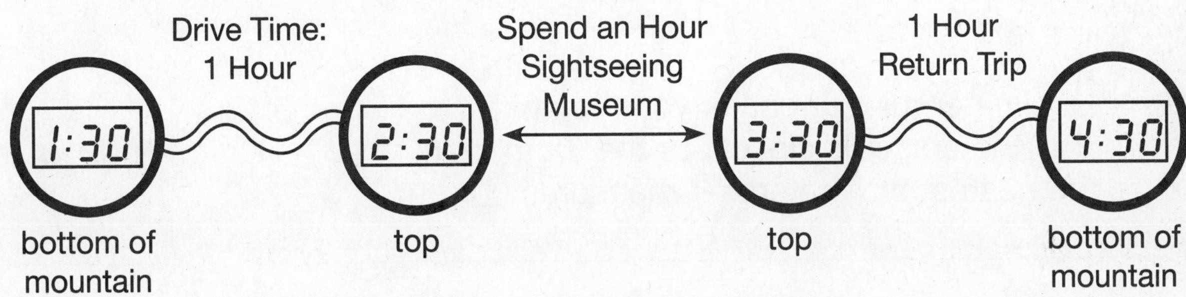

Yes, you have enough time to make the trip by car.

____

1. The cost to drive the mountain road is $14.00 for the driver and $5.00 for each additional adult. Children between the ages of 5 and 12 cost $3.00 each. Children under 5 are admitted for free. You are eight and your sister is four. How much will it cost for you, your sister, and your mom and dad? ________

2. The cog railroad to the top of Mt. Washington is a three-hour round trip. The train departs every hour on the hour until 4:00 P.M. The cost is $35.00 for adults and $24.00 for children ages 6–12. How much will it cost for you, your sister, and your mom and dad to take the cog railroad? ________

Name ______________________________

Exploring Centimeters and Decimeters

In your book you estimated distance. Here is another way to estimate length in centimeters.

The width of your index finger is about 1 centimeter.

Use your index finger to estimate the length of the eraser.
The eraser is about 3 finger widths long, so it's about 3 cm long.

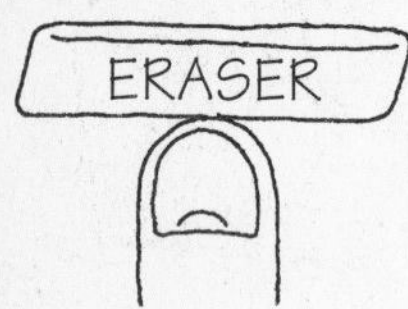

Use a centimeter ruler to check your estimate.
The end of the eraser is closest to the 3 cm mark.
So, to the nearest cm the eraser measures <u>3 cm</u>.

Estimate the length of each object shown. Then find the actual length to the nearest centimeter.

1.

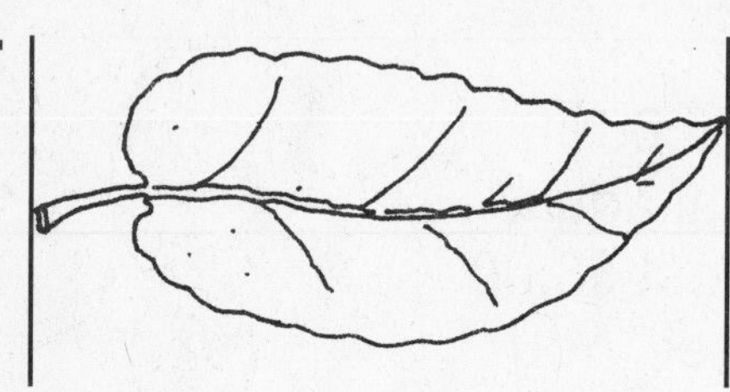

estimate ______

actual ______

2.

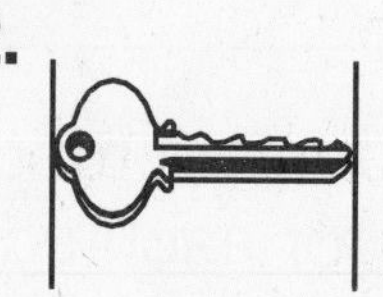

estimate ______

actual ______

3.

estimate ______

actual ______

4.

estimate ______

actual ______

Name ______________________

Meters and Kilometers

Meters and kilometers are used to measure large objects or great distances.

The cat measures less than a meter. Use centimeters to measure.

Meters are used to measure distances you could walk in a few minutes or less.

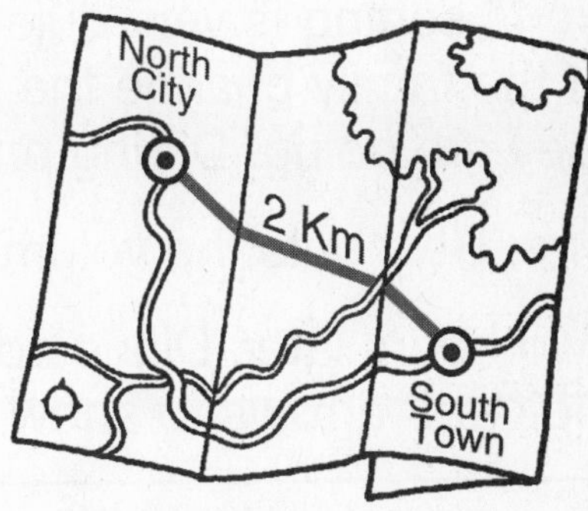

Long distances you would travel by car or plane are measured in kilometers.

Write whether you would measure each in cm, m, or km.

1.  ________

2.  ________

3.  ________

4. the height of a mountain ________

5. the length of a chalkboard ________

6. a chalkboard eraser ________

7. the distance from your house to the other side of the street ________

Name ______________________

Another Look
11-8

Compare Strategies: Use Objects and Draw a Picture

The volume control for the CD-player in the Best family has 10 settings. A "1" setting is very quiet while a "10" setting is very loud. The members of the family change the settings according to where they are and what they are doing. During one day, the volume was changed four times.

Mrs. Best sets the volume at "3."

Two hours later, Diane adjusts the volume up 6 settings. Draw volume indicator arrows to show the new setting. What is the new setting? 9

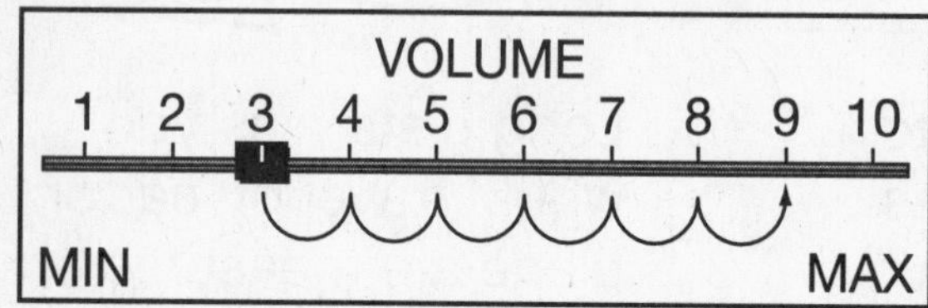

Mr. Best lowers the volume 4 settings.

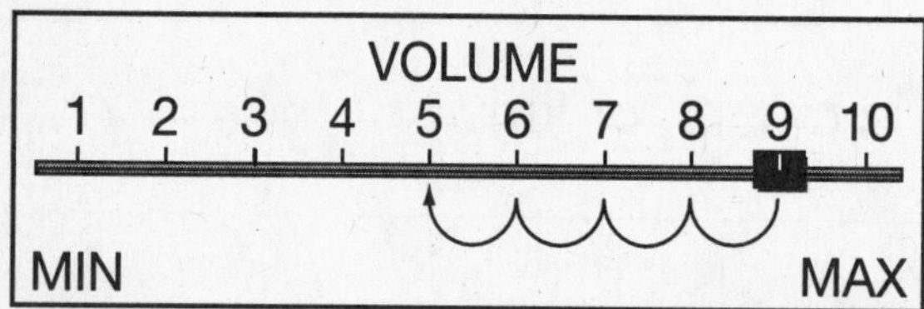

But when Jerry arrives home for lunch he turns up the volume by 5 settings. Use the drawing to show the volume change. Where is the volume set now? 10

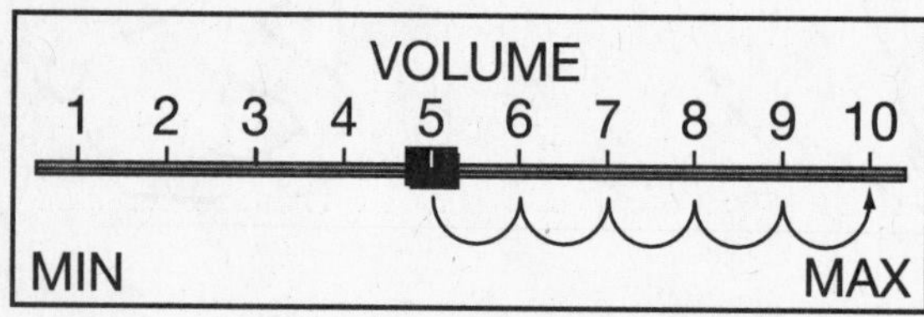

Draw a picture or use objects to solve.

1. An elevator starts at the first floor and goes up to the fifth floor. Then it goes down 2 floors and up 6 floors. It goes down 3 floors to pick up Mr. Wayt. At what floor did Mr. Wayt get on the elevator? ______

2. Suppose you are decorating a square cake. You have 12 flowers made of icing. You want to put the same number of flowers on each of the cake's 4 sides. How many flowers can you put on each side? ______

Name ______________________________

Exploring Capacity: Customary Units

In your book you explored capacity by finding containers that hold 1 cup, 1 pint, 1 quart, and 1 gallon. Here is another way to understand capacity.

Capacity is the amount a container will hold.

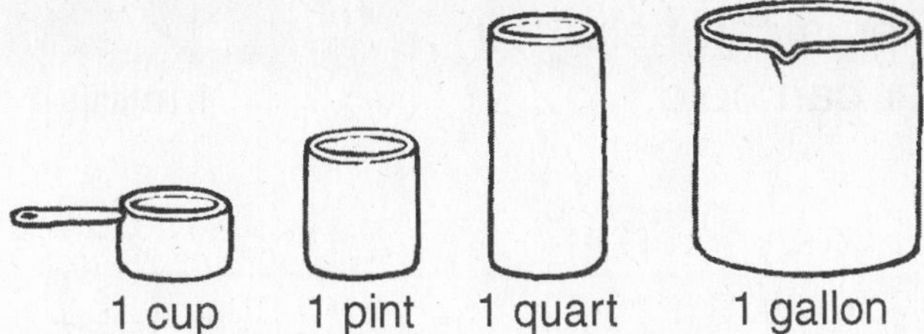

The units of capacity are related.		
2 cups = 1 pint	2 pints = 1 quart	4 quarts = 1 gallon

How many quarts are in 3 gallons?
There are 4 quarts in 1 gallon.

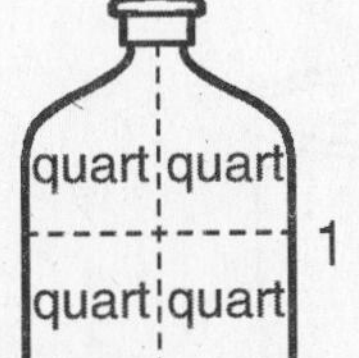

1 gallon

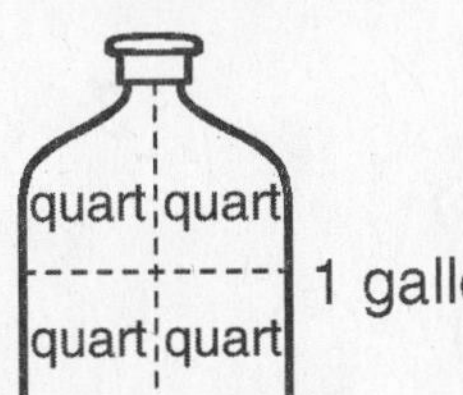

1 gallon

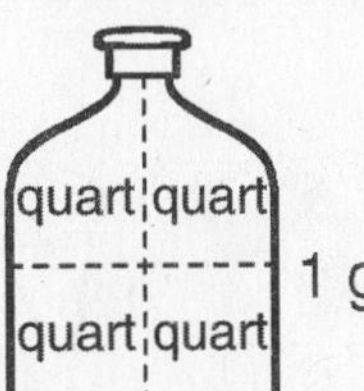

1 gallon

3 gallons = 12 quarts
Compare 3 gallons and 10 quarts.
12 quarts $>$ 10 quarts
3 gallons $>$ 10 quarts

Complete.

1. 1 pint = ________ cups

2. 1 gallon = ________ quarts

3. 1 quart = ________ pints

4. ________ quarts = 4 pints

5. 1 gallon = ________ cups

6. 1 gallon = ________ pints

Compare. Write $<$, $>$, or $=$.

7. 1 quart ◯ 1 pint

8. 1 gallon ◯ 4 quarts

9. 2 pints ◯ 3 cups

10. 3 quarts ◯ 1 gallon

11. 4 cups ◯ 1 pint

12. 5 quarts ◯ 1 gallon

Name ______________________________

Another Look
12-2

Measuring Capacity: Metric Units

A **milliliter** (mL) and a **liter** (L) are units of capacity in the metric system. They are used to measure liquids.

1 milliliter

Milli- means "thousand." So 1 liter is 1,000 milliliters.

Thinking how much 1 milliliter or 1 liter is can help you estimate how much liquid a container can hold.

About how much water will this glass hold: 250 mL or 250 L?

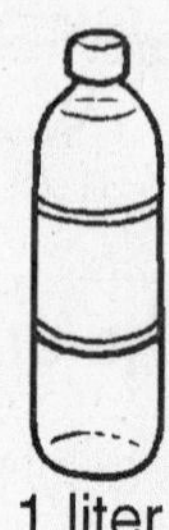
1 liter

Think: A 1-liter bottle of juice can fill more than one glass.

250 mL is the better estimate.

Circle the better estimate for each.

1.

2 mL 2 L

2.

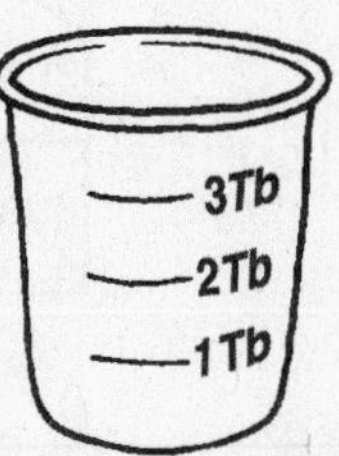

30 mL 30 L

3.

20 mL 20 L

4.

90 mL 90 L

5.

250 mL 250 L

6.

4 mL 4 L

Name ____________________

Exploring Weight: Customary Units

In your book you explored weight by using a balance scale. Here is another way to understand weight.

Think about how much 1 ounce or 1 pound weighs to estimate other weights.

Example

About how much does a child's T-shirt weigh: 6 oz or 6 lb?

?

1 ounce

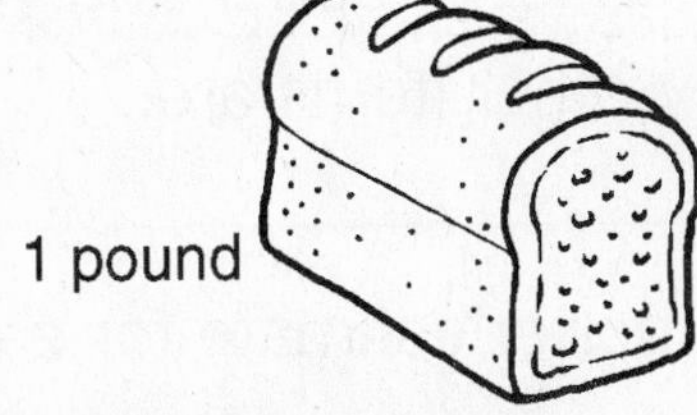
1 pound

Think: A child's T-shirt weighs more than a key but less than a loaf of bread. So 6 pounds is much greater than the weight of a child's T-shirt.

6 oz is the better estimate.

Circle the better estimate for each.

1. 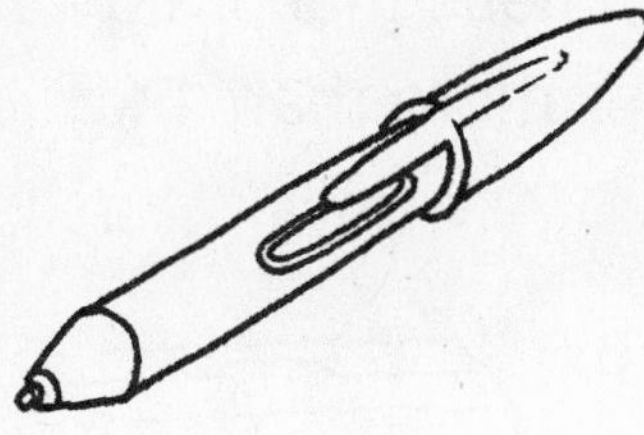

   1 oz 1 lb

2. 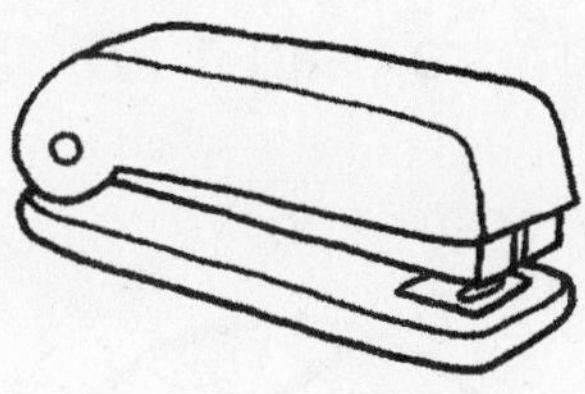

   1 oz 1 lb

3. 

   5 oz 5 lb

4. 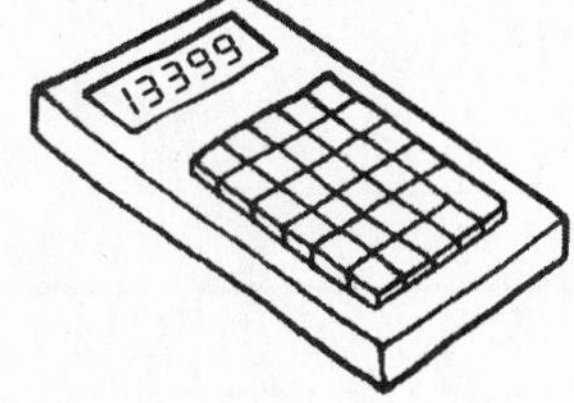

   less than 1 lb
   more than 1 lb

5. 

   less than 1 lb
   more than 1 lb

6. 

   less than 1 lb
   more than 1 lb

Name ______________________________

Grams and Kilograms

How much is a gram? How much is a kilogram? Find out.

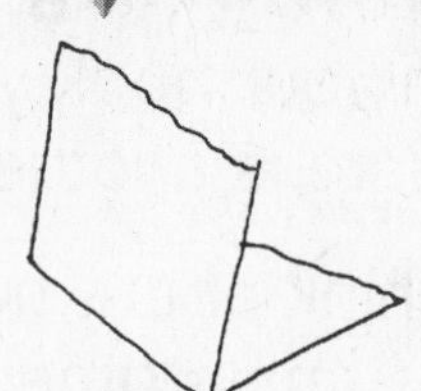

Take a sheet of paper. Fold it in half. Then fold it in half again. Unfold the page and cut out one of the 4 sections. Hold this one section in your hand. This is about 1 gram.

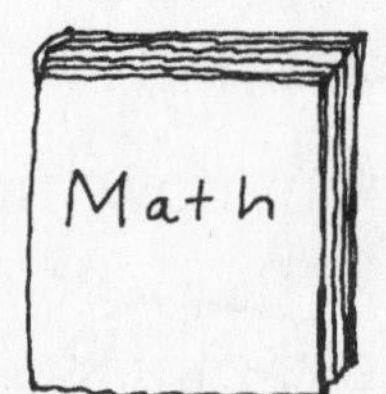

Now hold your math book in your other hand. This is about 1 kilogram (kg).

Use the $\frac{1}{4}$ sheet of paper and your math book to estimate how heavy other items are.

Circle the better estimate for each.

1.

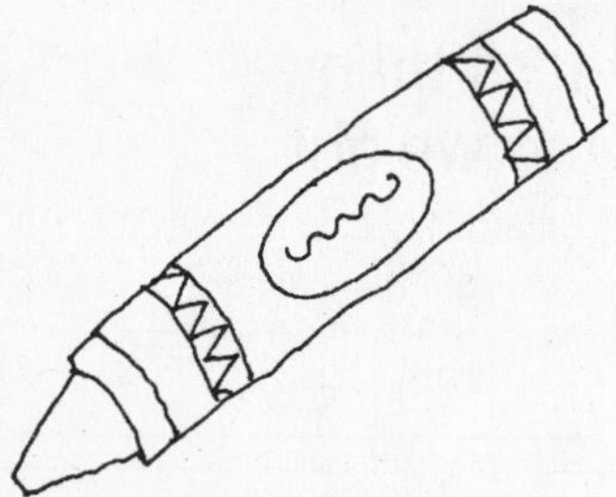

less than 1 kg
more than 1 kg

2.

less than 1 kg
more than 1 kg

3.

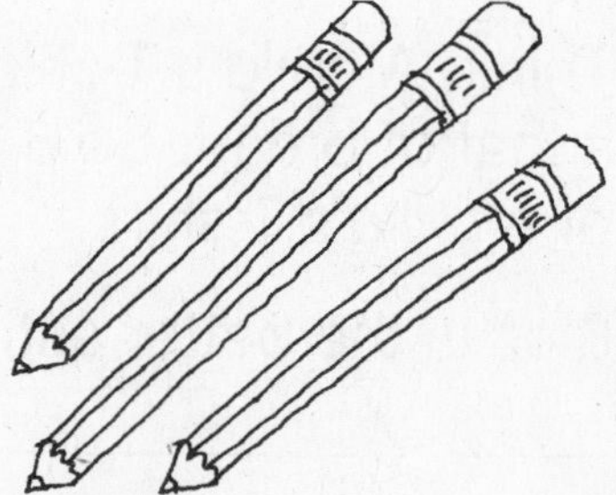

less than 1 kg
more than 1 kg

4.

2 g　　2 kg

5.

180 g　　180 kg

6.

1 g　　1 kg

 Use with pages 492–493.

Name ______________________________

Another Look 12-5

Temperature

We use Celsius and Fahrenheit thermometers.

Find the temperature on the thermometer.

First find the closest number to the temperature. 20°C is closest. Each small mark on the thermometer shows 2°, so count up by 2s from 20° to the temperature.

The temperature shown on this thermometer is 26°C.

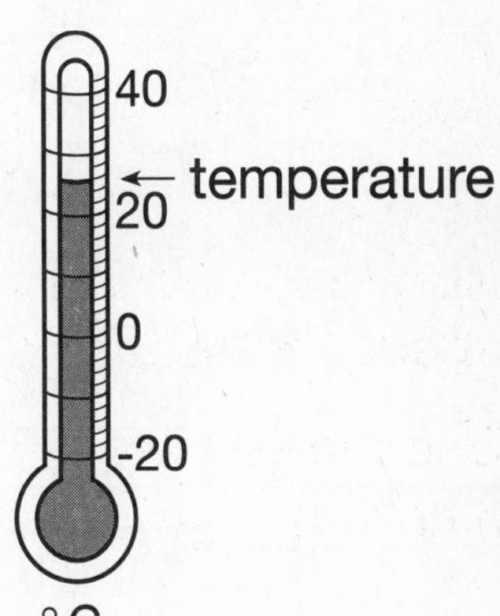

Write each temperature using °C or °F.

1. 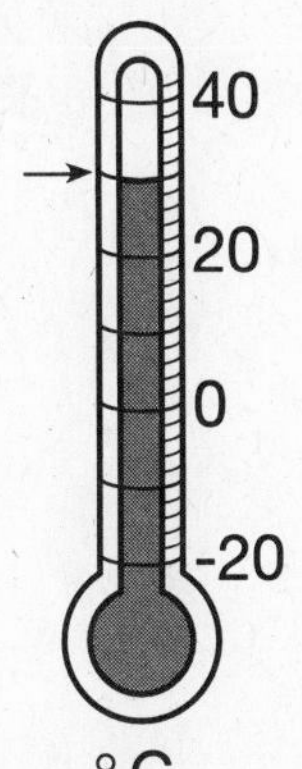

____

2. 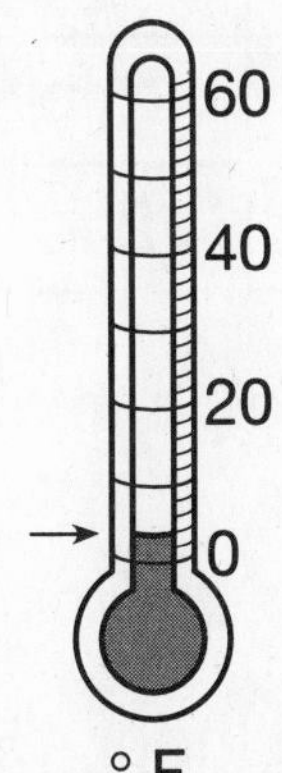

____

3. 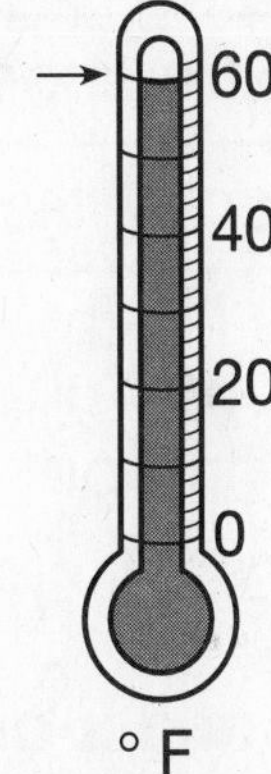

____

Count backward to find negative temperatures. Write each temperature, using – and °C. The first one has been done for you.

4. 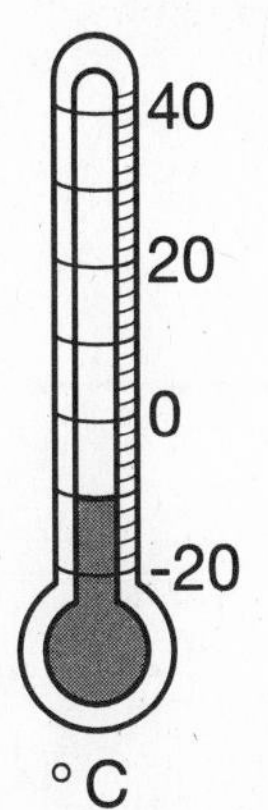

–10°C

5. 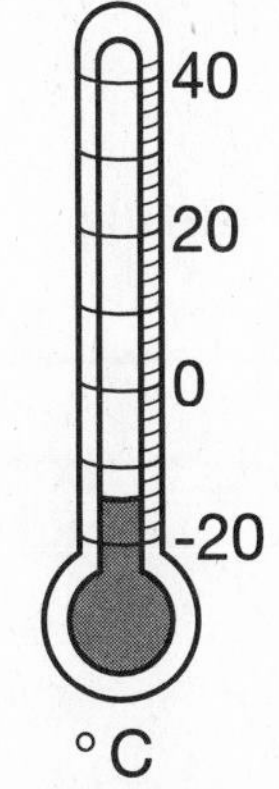

____

6. 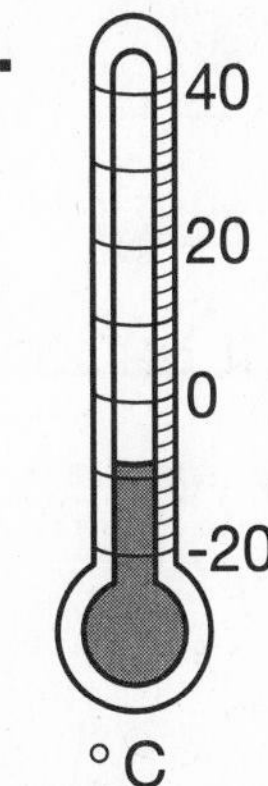

____

Name ____________________

Another Look
12-6

Decision Making

Suppose you're packing for a visit to a friend's house. You will be staying 7 days. You are going to carry your things in a backpack. You don't want to carry more than 15 pounds. Here's what you're taking so far.

Item	Weight
backpack	3 lb
2 pairs of pants	1 lb
3 shirts	1 lb
4 books	3 lb
1 tape player	1 lb
8 cassette tapes	1 lb
extra shoes	2 lb
socks, t-shirts, and so on	2 lb

How much do the items on your list weigh in all? Add all the weights to find out.

3 + 1 + 1 + 3 + 1 + 1 + 2 + 2 = 14 lb

Do they weigh under or over 15 lb? Under 15 lb

____

What if you decide to take 2 more pairs of pants (4 pairs in all) and 3 more shirts (6 shirts in all)?

1. How much extra weight is 2 pairs of pants? ____________

   3 shirts? ____________

2. How much weight would you carry in all? ____________

3. Is the weight under or over 15 lb? ____________

4. What could you do to make the weight exactly 15 lb?

   ____

   ____

Name ______________________________

Exploring Likely and Unlikely

In your book you made a table to decide whether statements were impossible, possible, or certain. Here is another way to explore likely and unlikely.

The pictures show things that are impossible, possible, and certain.

Impossible	**Possible**	**Certain**
something that would never happen	something that could happen	something that will definitely happen

Look at each picture. Decide whether it is impossible, possible, or certain. Write the answer on the line.

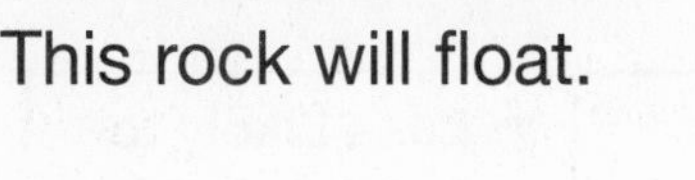

This rock will float.

1. ______________

You may already have won a prize.

2. ______________

The 3 P.M. train will be late.

3. ______________

The sun's heat will melt the snow.

4. ______________

Name ______________________________

Another Look
12-8

Exploring Predictions

In your book you tested predictions by recording data in a table. Here is another way to explore predictions.

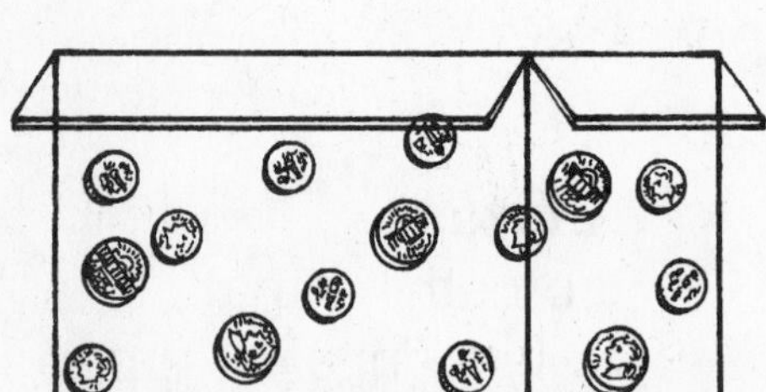

	More Likely to Pull out of Box	Less Likely to Pull out of Box
	✔	
		✔

Think: There are more dimes in the box than nickels. Since there are more dimes to choose from, you are more likely to pull a dime out of the box.

Look at each box. Predict what you are more likely and less likely to pull out of it. Complete each table.

1.

	More Likely to Pull out of Box	Less Likely to Pull out of Box

2.

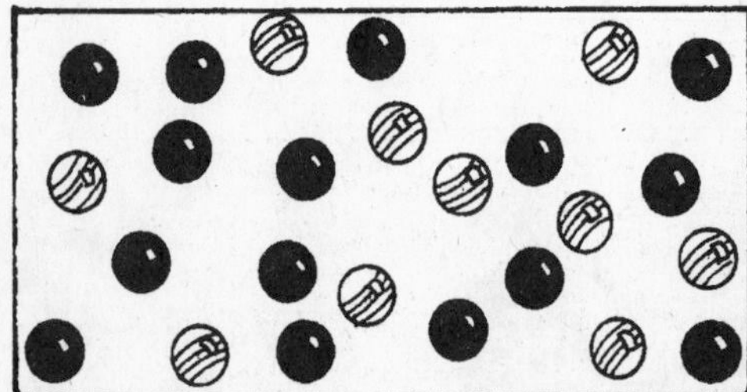

	More Likely to Pull out of Box	Less Likely to Pull out of Box

3.

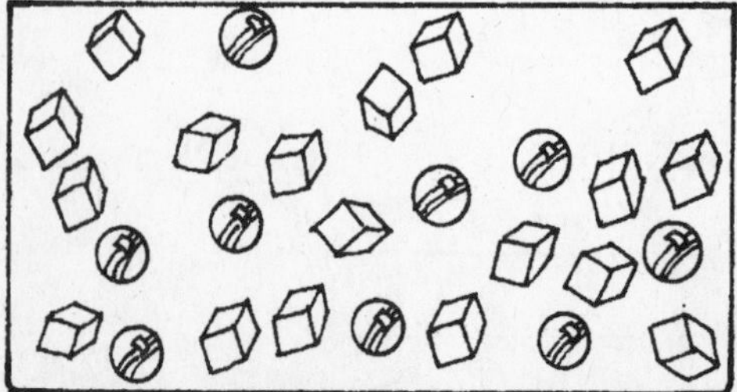

	More Likely to Pull out of Box	Less Likely to Pull out of Box

Name ______________________________

Another Look
12-9

Exploring Probability

In your book you explored probability with spinners to predict outcomes in the form of fractions. Here is another way to understand probability.

Count the flowers.

There are 8 flowers all together.

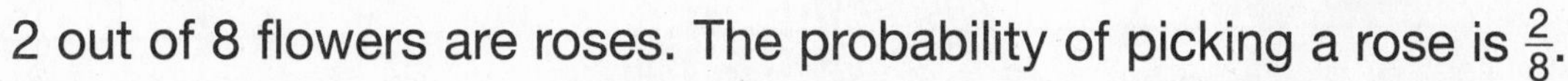

2 out of 8 flowers are roses. The probability of picking a rose is $\frac{2}{8}$.

3 out of 8 flowers are daisies. The probability of picking a daisy is $\frac{3}{8}$.

1 out of 8 flowers is a tulip. The probability of picking a tulip is $\frac{1}{8}$.

2 out of 8 flowers are daffodils. The probability of picking a daffodil is $\frac{2}{8}$.

Look at each picture. Imagine picking one item with your eyes closed. Complete a fraction to show the probability of getting each thing listed.

1. A striped card $\frac{\quad}{20}$

2. A spotted card $\frac{\quad}{20}$

3. A plain card $\frac{\quad}{20}$

4. A black card $\frac{\quad}{20}$

5. A spotted fish $\frac{\quad}{13}$

6. A white fish $\frac{\quad}{13}$

7. A striped fish $\frac{\quad}{13}$

8. A black fish $\frac{\quad}{13}$

Name ______________________________

Exploring Fair and Unfair

In your book you used fractions to determine if spinners were fair. Here is another way to explore fairness. Sometimes a visual check is all you need to determine fairness.

Look at these spinners. Without counting sections or writing fractions, decide which one is fair.

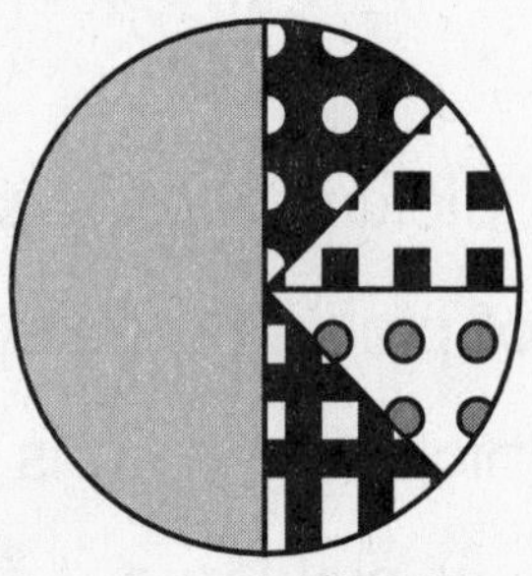

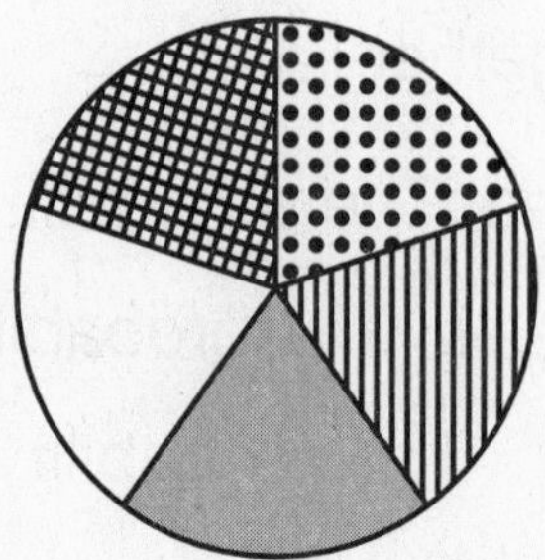

The spinner on the right is fair if you are playing a game, and each of 5 players is assigned a section. There are 5 equal sections, so there are __5__ equally likely outcomes.

The spinner on the left has 5 sections of unequal size. So, if you are playing a game where each person is assigned a section for the same number of points, the 5 outcomes are not equally likely. The game is __unfair__.

Look at these spinners. Are the outcomes equally likely? If game players were each assigned a different possible outcome, would the game be fair? Write *fair* or *unfair* on the line.

1. 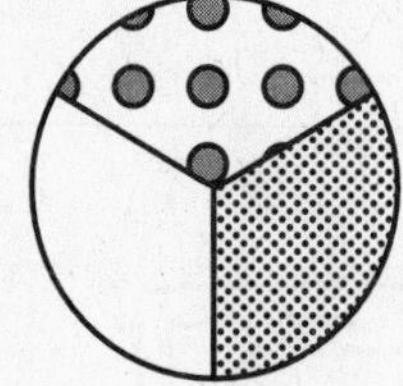 ______________

2. 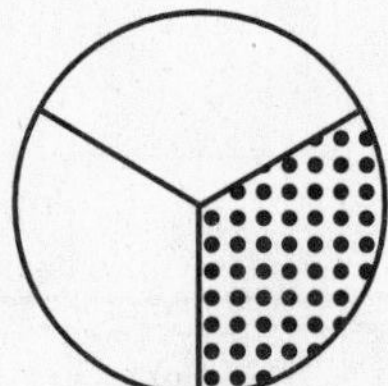 ______________

3.  ______________

4.  ______________

5.  ______________

6.  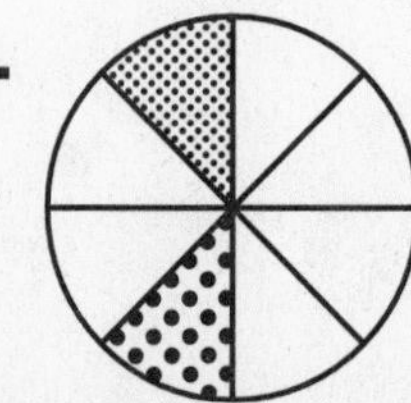 ______________

Name ______________________________

Analyze Strategies: Work Backward

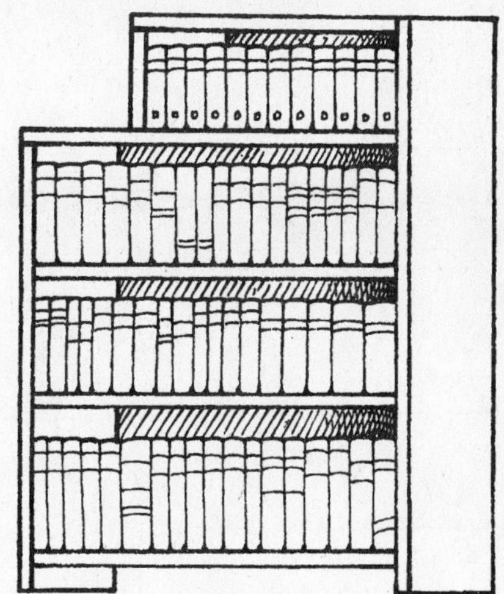

Alison puts half of her book collection on 4 shelves. She puts 12 books on 1 short shelf. Then she puts 18 books on each of 3 long shelves. How many books does Alison have?

Figure out how many books in all went on the long shelves. $18 \times 3 =$ 54

Add that number to the number of books that went on the short shelf. 54 + 12 = 66

Since this is only half of Alison's collection, double the result.

66 × 2 = 132

Work backward to solve these problems.

1. Carly read her book in 4 days. She read 36 pages on Monday, 24 pages on Tuesday, and 48 pages on Wednesday. On Thursday, she read twice as many pages as on Wednesday. How many pages did the book have?
   a. How many pages in all did Carly read on Monday, Tuesday, and Wednesday? ________
   b. How many pages did Carly read on Thursday? ________
   c. How many pages are there in Carly's book? ________
2. Linda picked a number. She added 43, subtracted 9, and multiplied the result by 4. If Linda ended up with 164, what number did she start with?
   a. Fill in the diagram to show what Linda did.

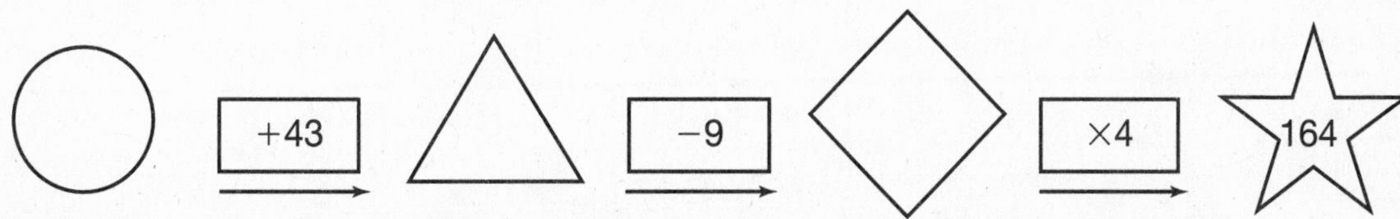

   Work backwards to complete the diagram.

   b. What number did Linda start with? ________

Name ______________________

Another Look 1-1

Reading Pictographs

The pictograph shows that ☺ = 5 people.

There are 3 faces next to face painting.

Face Painting	☺☺☺

People at Carnival Events

Face Painting	☺☺☺
Relay Races	☺☺☺☺☺
Pie Eating	☺☺☺☺
Ball Toss	☺

☺ = 5 people

How many people were at the face painting? 15

How do you know? There are 3 symbols, so count 5, 10, 15.

1.

Relay Races	☺☺☺☺☺

How many people were at the Relay Races? 25

How do you know? There are 5 symbols, so count 5, 10, 15, 20, 25.

2.

Pie Eating	☺☺☺☺

How many people were at the Pie Eating? 20

How do you know? There are 4 symbols, so count 5, 10, 15, 20.

3.

Ball Toss	☺

How many people were at the Ball Toss? 5

How do you know? There is one symbol, so count 5.

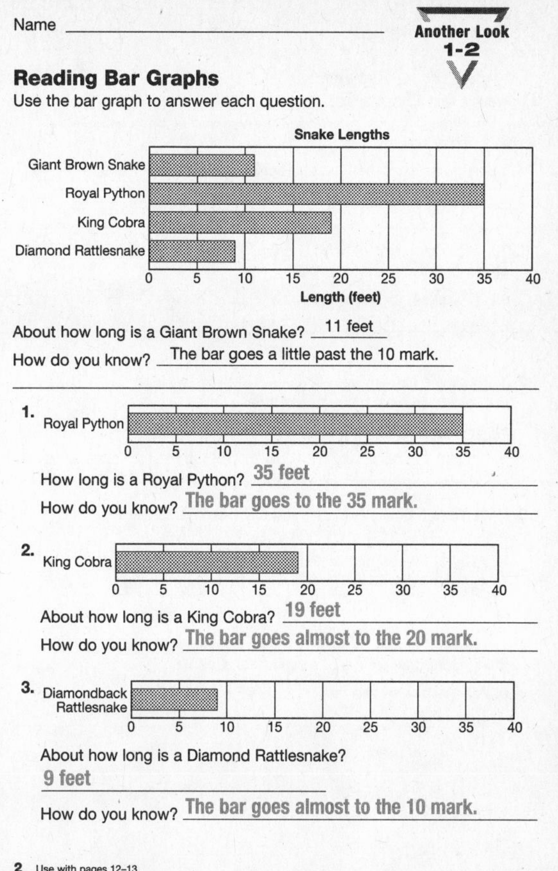

Name ______________________

Another Look 1-2

Reading Bar Graphs

Use the bar graph to answer each question.

About how long is a Giant Brown Snake? 11 feet

How do you know? The bar goes a little past the 10 mark.

1.

How long is a Royal Python? 35 feet

How do you know? The bar goes to the 35 mark.

2.

About how long is a King Cobra? 19 feet

How do you know? The bar goes almost to the 20 mark.

3.

About how long is a Diamond Rattlesnake? 9 feet

How do you know? The bar goes almost to the 10 mark.

Name ______________________

Another Look 1-3

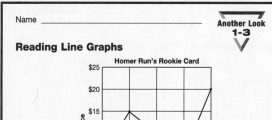

Reading Line Graphs

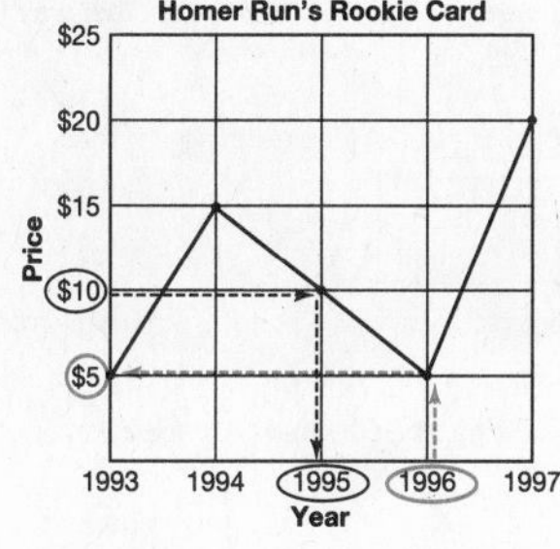

In what year was Homer Run's card worth $10.00?

Circle $10 on the graph. Draw a straight line from $10 across the graph until you reach a point. Draw a line straight from the point until you reach a year. Circle the year.

Homer Run's card was worth $10 in 1995.

Use the line graph to answer each question.

1. How much was Homer Run's card worth in 1996?
   - **a.** Circle 1996 on the graph.
   - **b.** Draw a straight line up from 1996 until you reach a point.
   - **c.** Draw a line to the left of the point until you reach a money amount.
   - **d.** Circle the money amount.
   - **e.** Homer Run's card was worth $5 in 1996.
2. In what year was Homer Run's card worth $15? 1994
3. How much was Homer Run's card worth in 1997? $20

Name ______________________

Another Look 1-4

Analyze Word Problems: Introduction to Problem Solving

Look how many shooting stars the campers saw on their trip!

Shooting Stars

Night	Number Seen
Friday	☆☆
Saturday	☆☆☆
Sunday	☆
Monday	☆☆☆☆

☆ = 5 shooting stars

How many shooting stars did the campers see on Friday and Saturday?

You want to know the total number of stars seen on 2 days.

Friday ☆☆ Saturday ☆☆☆

2 + 3 = 5

5 stars in the pictograph show 25 shooting stars. So, they saw 25 shooting stars on Friday and Saturday.

Use the pictograph to answer each question.

1. How many more shooting stars did they see on Monday than on Sunday?
   - **a.** I need to compare, so I will subtract.
   - **b.** Write the operation and the answer.

     ☆☆☆☆ ☆

     4 − 1 = 3
   - **c.** 3 stars on the pictograph show 15 shooting stars.
2. How many shooting stars did they see on Saturday and Sunday? 20
3. How many more stars did they see on Monday than on Saturday? 5

Name ______________________

Analyze Word Problems: Choose an Operation

Add or subtract? Juan's family owns 7 cows and 6 sheep. How many animals do they own?

The question asks for the total number of animals. I will add.

Solve: 7 + 6 = 13. Juan's family owns 13 animals.

1. The first grade has 10 boys and 9 girls. How many students are in the first grade?
   a. Will you add or subtract? Add
   b. Solve: 10 + 9 = 19; There are 19 students in the first grade.

2. Jacob has 6 videotapes. He gives 3 of them to his school library. How many does he have left?
   a. Will you add or subtract? Subtract
   b. Solve: 6 − 3 = 3; Jacob has 3 videotapes left.

3. Beth reads 5 books in March and 6 books in April. How many books does she read in March and April?
   a. Will you add or subtract? Add
   b. Solve: 5 + 6 = 11; Beth reads 11 books in March and April.

4. Amir has 6 drawers to clean out. He cleans out 4. How many more drawers does he have to clean?
   a. Will you add or subtract? Subtract
   b. Solve: 6 − 4 = 2; Amir has 2 drawers to clean.

Name ______________________

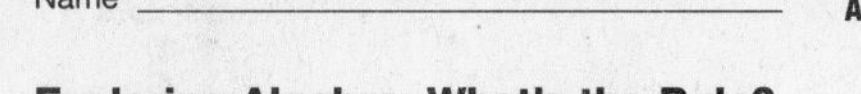

Exploring Algebra: What's the Rule?

In your book you explored algebra using tables. Here is another way to complete tables and find the rule.

You can use counters to help you find rules in a table.

In	1	2	4	7	8	10
Out	4	5	7	10	11	13

The first In number is 1. Place 1 counter on your desk.

The first Out number is 4. Place more counters so that you have 4 in all.

Write the step you took to change 1 counter into 4 counters. Added 3

The next In number is 2. Place 2 counters on your desk.

The next Out number is 5. Place more counters so that you have 5 in all.

Write the step you took to change 2 counters into 5 counters. Added 3

Check your rule on the third pair of numbers in the table.

In	Rule	Out
4	+ 3	= 7

If your rule works, it is correct. Use the rule to complete the table.

Complete each table. Write the rule for each. Use counters to help.

1.

In	1	3	4	6	10	12
Out	6	8	9	11	15	17

Rule: Add 5.

2.

In	2	3	5	8	9	12
Out	1	2	4	7	8	11

Rule: Subtract 1.

Name ______________________

Exploring Organizing Data

In your book you used tally tables to organize data. Here is another way to organize data.

Favorite Vegetables

Squash	Peas	Carrots
Jenny Michael Taylor Sara Maggie	Sue Maria	Jordan Mark Milo

Sue took a survey to find her friends' favorite vegetables. She has decided to organize the data in a bar graph.

Sue colored in one square for each of her friends who like squash. Color in squares to show how many of Sue's friends like peas and carrots.

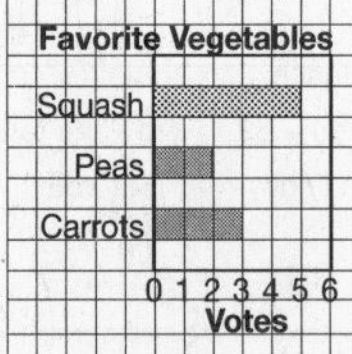

Favorite Fruit

Apples	Oranges	Grapes
Margo Thomas	Elaine Agatha Kelly Max	Matt Mary Ann Martin Vi

Matt took a survey of his friends' favorite fruits. Complete the bar graph shown to organize the data.

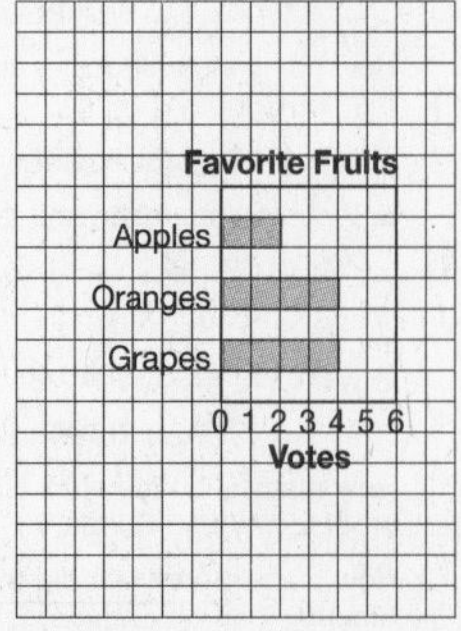

Name ______________________

Another Look
1-8

Exploring Making Pictographs

In your book you made pictographs. Here is another way to make pictographs. You can use counters to help you make a pictograph.

This tally table shows students' favorite things to read.

Books	卌 卌 ǁ
Magazines	ǁǁ

Each symbol in your pictograph will equal 2 students' votes.

Use counters to figure out how many symbols to draw.

Use counters to count by 2s until you reach the number of tallies in the table.

For books, count 2, 4, 6, 8, 10, 12. How many counters do you have out? 6

Draw the same number of symbols in the pictograph.

For magazines, count 2, 4. How many counters do you have out? 2

Complete the pictograph.

Favorite Things to Read

Books	■ ■ ■ ■ ■ ■
Magazines	■ ■

■ = 2 votes

This tally table shows how many students ride their bikes and how many take the bus to school.

Use the tally table to complete the pictograph.

Ride Bike	卌 卌
Bus	卌 卌 ǁ

Ways to Get to School

Ride Bike	● ● ● ● ●
Bus	● ● ● ● ● ●

● = 2 votes

Name ______________________

Another Look 1-9

Exploring Making Bar Graphs

In your book you made bar graphs using data from a tally table. Here is another way to make bar graphs.

You can make a bar graph of the data in the table. This table shows students' favorite seasons.

Favorite Seasons	
Season	**Number**
Winter	4
Spring	12
Summer	10
Fall	8

Use a scale of 1. Start with 0 at the bottom of the scale in the graph. Number each mark by 1s.

Draw bars on the graph by coloring 1 square for each vote. Four squares have been colored in for winter since there are 4 votes for winter.

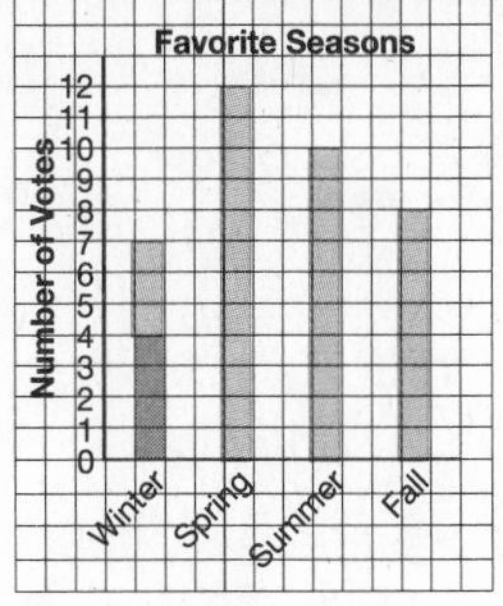

1. Complete the bar graph. Draw bars for spring, summer, and fall.
2. Which number on the scale matches the height of the bar for Summer? 10
3. Which number on the scale matches the height of the bar for Fall? 8
4. Suppose the next 3 people surveyed said that winter is their favorite season. Add this data to the bar graph.
   Check students' graphs.

Name ______________________

Another Look 1-10

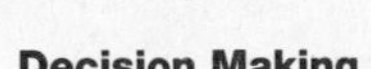

Decision Making

Your class has decided to adopt a wild animal through an environmental charity. To the right is a tally table showing the votes for which animal to adopt.

Whale	𝍸 𝍸
Dolphin	||||
Elephant	𝍸 |||

Complete the pictograph to organize the data.

Have each symbol = 2 votes.

Whale	♥♥♥♥♥♥♥♥
Dolphin	♥♥
Elephant	♥♥♥♥

Based on the graph, which animal do you think your class should adopt? Explain.
Whale; because it received the most votes

After deciding on an animal, your class must decide which chores they will perform to earn money for their adopted animal. The tally table shows the number of students willing to do each chore.

Chores	Tally
Garden Work	𝍸 𝍸 ||||
Baby Sit	𝍸 |
School Fundraising Fair	𝍸 𝍸 ||
Deliver Papers	𝍸 |||

1. Make a pictograph. Let each symbol show 2 votes.

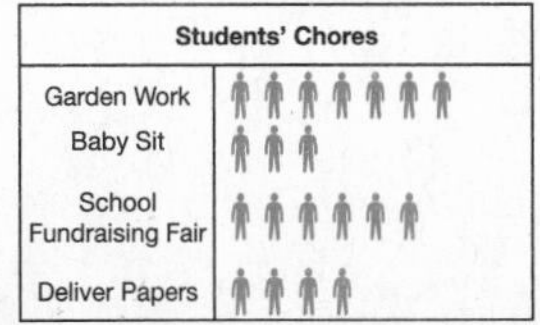

2. Which chore are most students willing to do? Garden Work
3. How many students are willing to deliver papers? 8 students

Name ______________________

Another Look 1-11

Analyze Strategies: Look for a Pattern

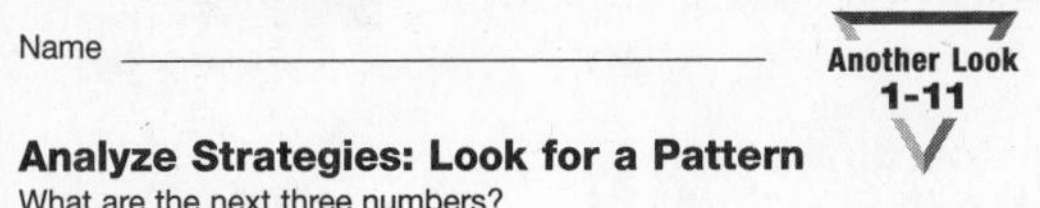

What are the next three numbers?

3, 6, 9, 12, ▩, ▩, ▩

Start comparing between numbers in the pattern.

3 + [3] = 6

6 + [3] = 9

9 + [3] = 12

What is the pattern? Add 3

Add 3 to get the next three numbers.

12 + 3 = 15

[15] + 3 = 18

[18] + 3 = 21

1. 37, 31, 25, 19
   a. What is the difference of each pair of numbers? 6
   b. What is the pattern? Subtract 6
   c. What are the next three numbers? 13, 7, 1
2. a. What are the next three numbers?
   4, 8, 12, 16, 20, 24, 28
   b. What is the pattern?
   Add 4
3. a. What are the next three numbers?
   35, 30, 25, 20, 15, 10, 5
   b. What is the pattern?
   Subtract 5

Name ______________________

Another Look 2-1

Place Value Through Hundreds

The place-value chart shows how many.

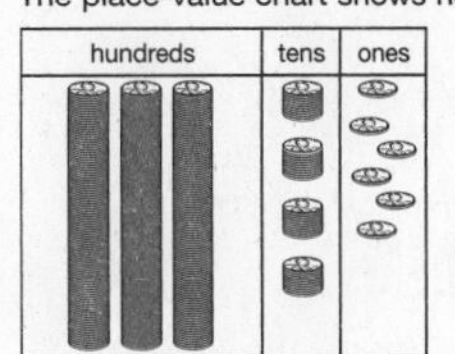

300 + 40 + 6 = 346

Write how many in standard form. Then write the word name.

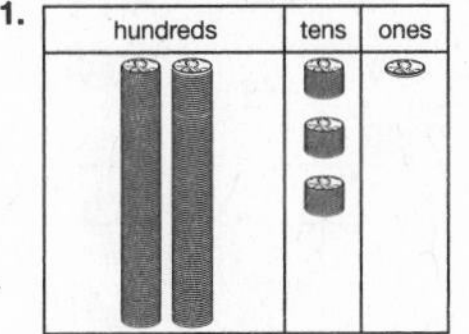

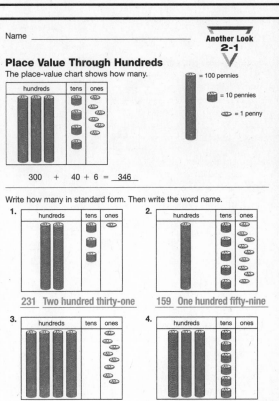

1. 231 Two hundred thirty-one
2. 159 One hundred fifty-nine

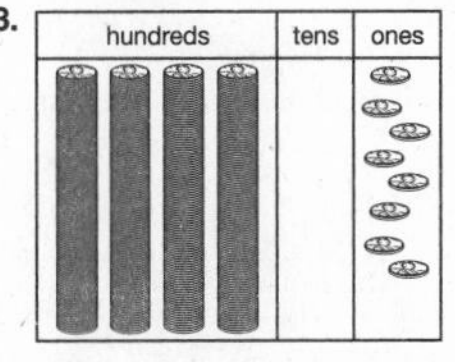

3. 408 Four hundred eight
4. 360 Three hundred sixty

Name ______________________

Another Look 2-2

Exploring Place-Value Relationships

In your book, you played a game using place-value blocks. Here is another way to use place-value blocks to explore number patterns.

10 tens = 1 hundred

Use place value blocks. Write how many.

1. 10 ones = 1 ten

2. 10 hundreds = 1 thousand

3. 30 ones = 3 tens

Use with pages 54–55. 13

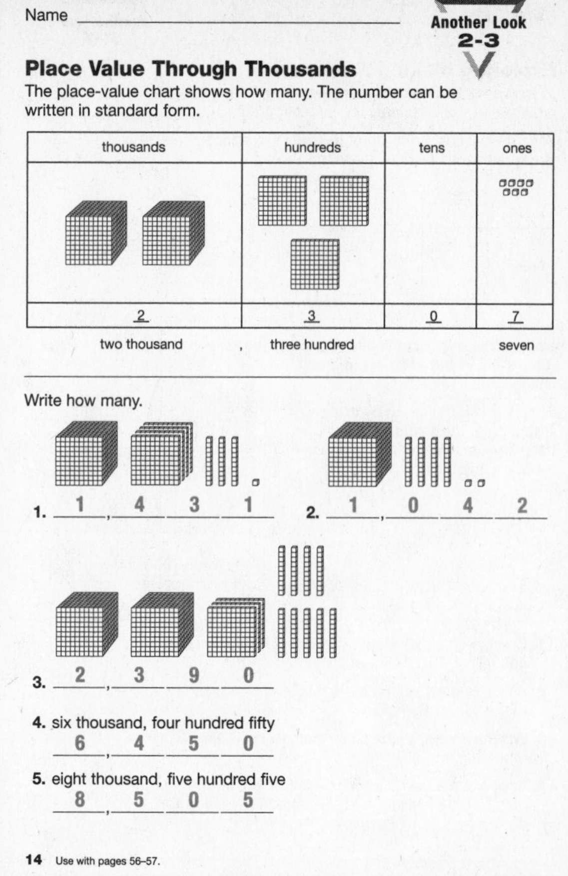

Name ______________________

Another Look 2-3

Place Value Through Thousands

The place-value chart shows how many. The number can be written in standard form.

thousands	hundreds	tens	ones
2	3	0	7
two thousand,	three hundred		seven

Write how many.

1. 1, 4 3 1

2. 1, 0 4 2

3. 2, 3 9 0

4. six thousand, four hundred fifty
6, 4 5 0

5. eight thousand, five hundred five
8, 5 0 5

14 Use with pages 56–57.

Name ______________________

Another Look 2-4

Place Value Through Hundred Thousands

The place-value chart shows the value of each digit.

Thousands			Ones		
hundred thousands	ten thousands	thousands	hundreds	tens	ones
4	2	7	8	9	1

Read: 427 thousand, 891

1. Complete the table.

hundred thousands	ten thousands	thousands	hundreds	tens	ones	read
1	6	2	3	7	5	162 thousand, 375
3	0	9	2	6	0	309 thousand, 260
8	4	9	7	5	5	849 thousand, 755
5	7	0	2	9	1	570 thousand, 291
1	2	2	5	6	7	122 thousand, 567
6	9	4	3	2	1	694 thousand, 321

Write each number in standard form.

2. five hundred thousand 500,000
3. forty-five thousand 45,000
4. six hundred sixty-four thousand, five hundred seventy-three 664,573
5. 30,000 + 4,000 + 500 + 60 + 1 34,561
6. 10,000 + 3,000 + 600 + 80 + 9 13,689
7. 600,000 + 40,000 + 7,000 + 300 + 2 647,302
8. 200,000 + 60,000 + 5,000 + 200 + 10 + 8 265,218

Use with pages 58–59. 15

Name ______________________

Another Look 2-5

Analyze Strategies: Make an Organized List

Make a list or use any strategy to help solve each problem. You can use place-value blocks to help.

Suppose Marilee packed 35 venus fly traps in boxes that hold 10 plants or 1 plant. How many ways could she pack the boxes?

How many plants can she pack in 3 tens boxes? 30

List all possible ways Marilee could pack the plants.

tens boxes	3	2	1	0
ones boxes	5	15	25	35

How many ways are there? 4 ways

1. Suppose you are choosing pots for Marilee. You can pick 2 pots. There are 2 yellow pots, 2 red pots, and 2 blue pots. How many different combinations could you choose?

a. List all the possible combinations. Use Y to stand for yellow. Use R to stand for red. Use B to stand for blue.
YY, YR, YB, RR, RB, BB

b. How many combinations are there? 6 combinations

2. Suppose Peter wants to order 52 pounds of soil. He can buy the soil in ten-pound bags or 1-pound bags. How many ways could he order the soil?

a. List all possible ways Peter could order the soil.

ten-pound bags	5	4	3	2	1	0
one-pound bags	2	12	22	32	42	52

b. How many ways are there? 6 ways

16 Use with pages 60–61.

Name ______________________

Comparing Numbers

Place-value blocks can help you compare numbers.

Compare 1,440 and 1,550. Circle the greater number.

thousands	hundreds	tens	ones
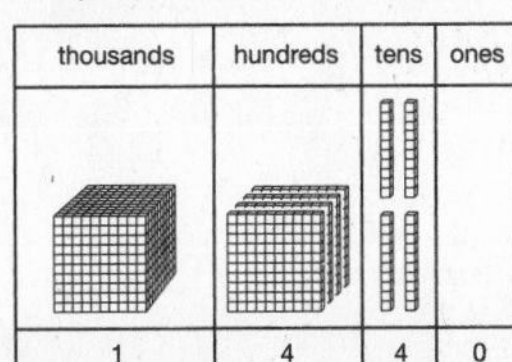			
1	4	4	0

thousands	hundreds	tens	ones
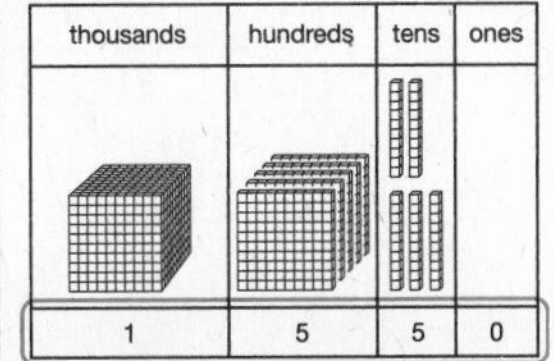			
1	5	5	0

Circle 1,550 because there are more hundreds in 1,550 than 1,440.

1. Compare 146 and 126. Circle the greater number.

thousands	hundreds	tens	ones
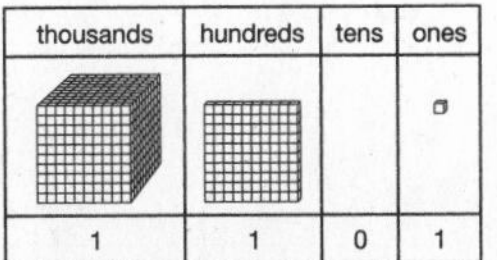			
0	1	4	6

thousands	hundreds	tens	ones
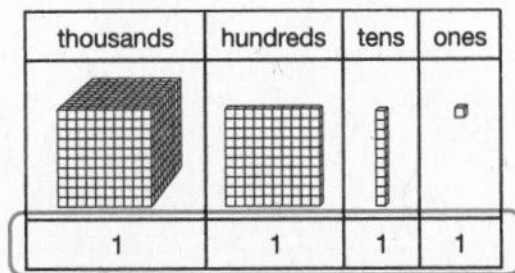			
0	1	2	6

2. Compare 1,101 and 1,111. Circle the greater number.

thousands	hundreds	tens	ones
1	1	0	1

thousands	hundreds	tens	ones
1	1	1	1

Name ______________________

Another Look
2-7

Ordering Numbers

You can use a number line to help you order numbers.

Order 100, 200 and 150. First, show each number on a number line.

50 75 **100** 125 **150** 175 **200** 225 250

Look at the number line.

Which of the three numbers is farthest to the right? 200

Which number is greatest? 200

Which of the three numbers is farthest to the left? 100

Which number is least? 100

Order the numbers from greatest to least. 200, 150, 100

Show each number on the number line. Then list them in order.

1. Order 50, 70, and 30 from greatest to least.

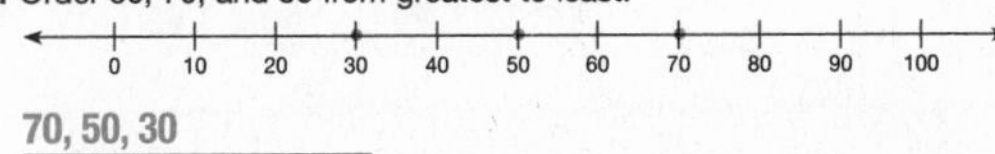

70, 50, 30

2. Order 3,000; 1,500, and 4,500 from least to greatest.

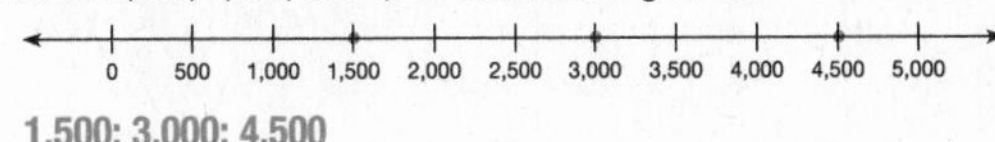

1,500; 3,000; 4,500

3. Order 45, 90, and 60 from least to greatest.

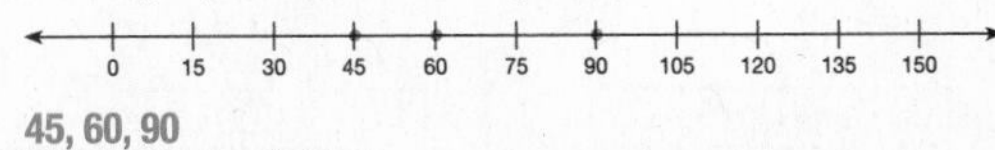

45, 60, 90

Name ______________________

Rounding to Tens

You can use place value to round to the nearest ten.

If the digit in the ones place is 5, 6, 7, 8, or 9, then round to the next greater ten. If the digit is less than 5, do not change the digit in the tens place.

Round 17 to the nearest ten: 20

Explain. 7 is in the ones place. Round to the next greater ten.

Round 53 to the nearest ten: 50

Explain. Because 3 is in the ones place and 3 is less than 5, the digit in the tens place doesn't change.

Round 75 to the nearest ten: 80

Explain. Because the 5 in the ones place is 5 or greater, round to the next greater ten.

1. Round 12 to the nearest ten: 10

Explain. Because 2 is in the ones place, and 2 < 5

2. Round 236 to the nearest ten: 240

Explain. Because 6 is in the ones place, and 6 > 5

Look carefully at the following numbers. You are going to round to the nearest ten.

127 22 351 918 892

84 75 9 41 103

3. In which numbers should you *not* change the digits in the tens place?

22, 351, 892, 84, 41, 103

Explain. The digit in the ones place is less than 5.

4. Which numbers should you round to the next greater ten?

127, 918, 75, 9

Explain. The digit in the ones place is 5 or greater.

Name ______________________

Another Look
2-9

Rounding to Hundreds

You can use place value to round to the nearest hundred.

If the digit in the tens place is 5, 6, 7, 8, or 9, round to the next greater hundred. If the digit in the tens place is less than 5, do not change the digit in the hundreds place.

Round 117 to the nearest hundred: 100

Explain. Because the digit in the tens place is 1, do not change the digit in the hundreds place.

Round 152 to the nearest hundred: 200

Explain.

Since the digit in the tens place is 5, round to the next greater hundred.

1. Round 186 to the nearest hundred: 200

Explain. The digit in the tens place is greater than 5.

2. Round 236 to the nearest hundred: 200

Explain. The digit in the tens place is less than 5.

3. Round 9,124 to the nearest hundred: 9,100

Explain. The digit in the tens place is less than 5.

1,207 220 351 918 892

840 175 199 410 103

4. When rounding to the nearest hundred, in which of the numbers given above will you *not* change the digit in the hundreds place?

1,207; 220; 918; 840; 410; 103

5. When rounded to the nearest hundred, which numbers will round to greater hundreds?

351; 892; 175; 199

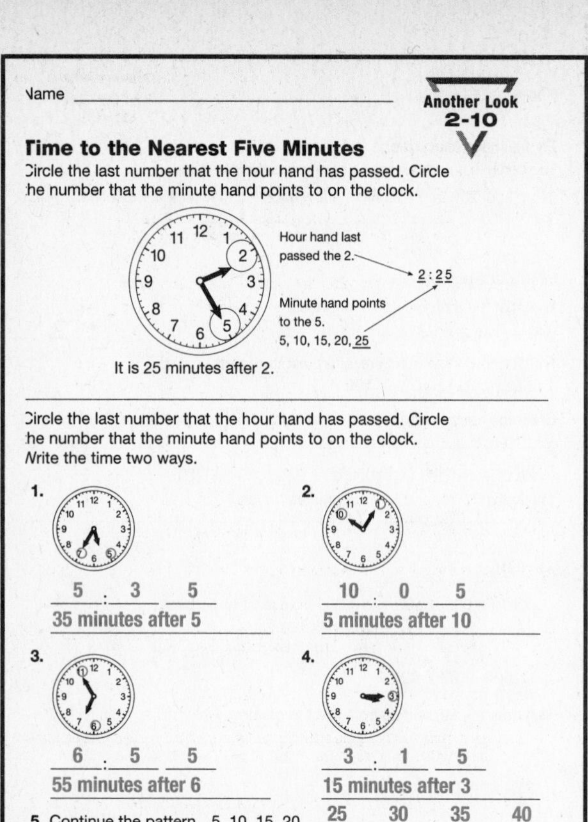

Name ______________________

Another Look 2-10

Time to the Nearest Five Minutes

Circle the last number that the hour hand has passed. Circle the number that the minute hand points to on the clock.

It is 25 minutes after 2.

Circle the last number that the hour hand has passed. Circle the number that the minute hand points to on the clock. Write the time two ways.

1. 5 : 3 5
35 minutes after 5

2. 10 : 0 5
5 minutes after 10

3. 6 : 5 5
55 minutes after 6

4. 3 : 1 5
15 minutes after 3

5. Continue the pattern. 5, 10, 15, 20, 25, 30, 35, 40

6. How many minutes are in one hour? 60

7. What is another way to write 20 minutes before 8? 7:40

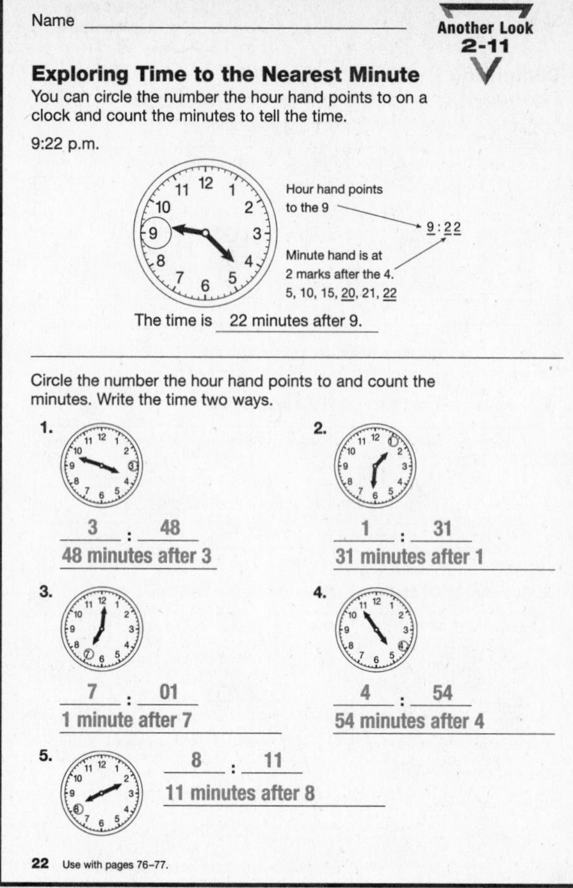

Name ______________________

Another Look 2-11

Exploring Time to the Nearest Minute

You can circle the number the hour hand points to on a clock and count the minutes to tell the time.

9:22 p.m.

The time is 22 minutes after 9.

Circle the number the hour hand points to and count the minutes. Write the time two ways.

1. 3 : 48
48 minutes after 3

2. 1 : 31
31 minutes after 1

3. 7 : 01
1 minute after 7

4. 4 : 54
54 minutes after 4

5. 8 : 11
11 minutes after 8

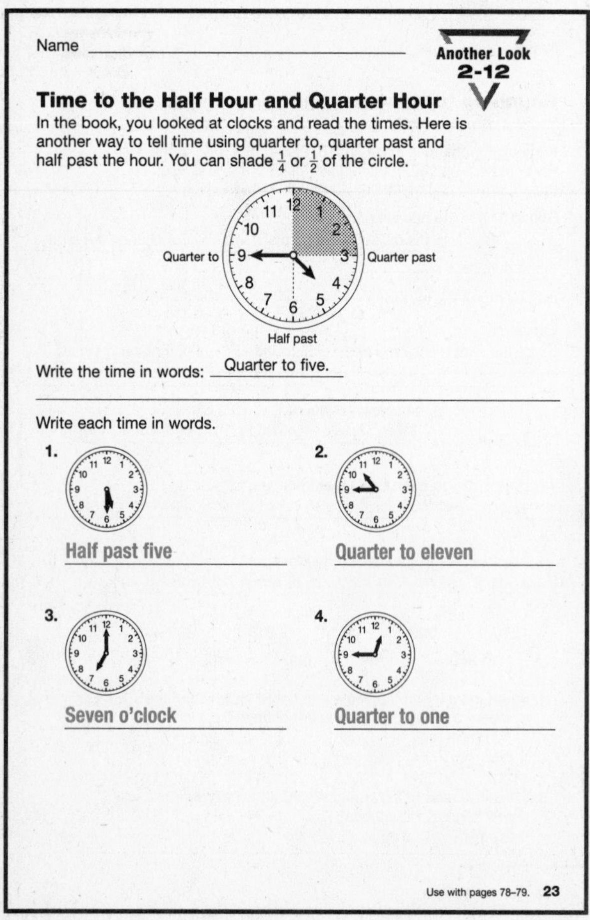

Name ______________________

Another Look 2-12

Time to the Half Hour and Quarter Hour

In the book, you looked at clocks and read the times. Here is another way to tell time using quarter to, quarter past and half past the hour. You can shade $\frac{1}{4}$ or $\frac{1}{2}$ of the circle.

Write the time in words: Quarter to five.

Write each time in words.

1. Half past five

2. Quarter to eleven

3. Seven o'clock

4. Quarter to one

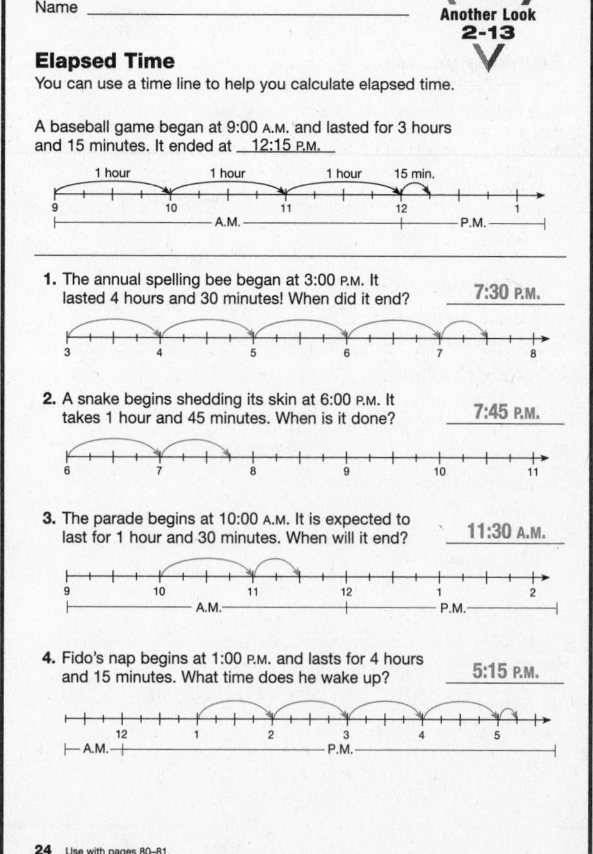

Name ______________________

Another Look 2-13

Elapsed Time

You can use a time line to help you calculate elapsed time.

A baseball game began at 9:00 A.M. and lasted for 3 hours and 15 minutes. It ended at 12:15 P.M.

1. The annual spelling bee began at 3:00 P.M. It lasted 4 hours and 30 minutes! When did it end? 7:30 P.M.

2. A snake begins shedding its skin at 6:00 P.M. It takes 1 hour and 45 minutes. When is it done? 7:45 P.M.

3. The parade begins at 10:00 A.M. It is expected to last for 1 hour and 30 minutes. When will it end? 11:30 A.M.

4. Fido's nap begins at 1:00 P.M. and lasts for 4 hours and 15 minutes. What time does he wake up? 5:15 P.M.

Name ______________________

Another Look 2-14

Ordinal Numbers and the Calendar

In your book you used ordinal numbers to name dates on a calendar. Here, you will use ordinal numbers to complete some sentences. Watch for the clue in each sentence.

Julia is sitting at a desk that is (four) rows from the front of the room. Her desk is in the fourth row.

1. Kevin is sitting at a desk that is three rows from the front of the room. His desk is in the third row.
2. There are five students in line ahead of Luke. He's in the number 6 spot. Luke is the sixth student in line.
3. There are ten students in line ahead of Kim. She is the eleventh student in line.
4. No one is in line ahead of Dillon. He is the first student in line.
5. Rosa hung her coat on a hook between the first and third hooks on the wall. Her coat is on the second hook.
6. Write the missing information in the chart below. Use numbers in the first column; use words in the second column.

Ordinal Numbers	
Number	**Word**
9th	ninth
11th	eleventh
14th	fourteenth

7. Circle the third Wednesday of the month.

S	M	T	W	T	F	S
					1	2
3	4	5	6	7	8	9
10	11	12	13	14	15	16
17	18	19	(20)	21	22	23
24	25	26	27	28	29	30

Name ______________________

Another Look 2-15

Decision Making

When you know how much time in all you have to get all your activities done, you can make a schedule.

Your karate class lasts for one hour and has four activities: (1) warm-ups, (2) punches and kicks, (3) karate forms, and (4) cool-down.

If each activity lasts the same amount of time, then each activity will last for 15 minutes.

If the class starts at 2:30, then:

the first activity should start at 2:30,

the second activity should start at 2:45,

the third activity should start at 3:00,

and the last activity should start at 3:15.

Complete.

1. You have four activities to fit into a two-hour class.
   a. If each activity takes the same amount of time, how long will each one last? 30 minutes
   b. If the class begins at 5:00 P.M., when will the second activity begin and end? begin: 5:30 P.M. end: 6:00 P.M.
2. You have six activities to fit into a one-hour class.
   a. If each activity takes the same amount of time, how long will each one last? 10 minutes
   b. If the class begins at 2:00 P.M., when will the third activity begin and end? begin: 2:20 P.M. end: 2:30 P.M.
   c. If the class begins at 2:00 P.M., when will the last activity begin and end? begin: 2:50 P.M. end: 3:00 P.M.

Name ______________________

Another Look 3-1

Exploring Addition Patterns

In your book you used basic facts to add greater numbers. Here is another way to add.

2 ones + 3 ones = 5 ones

2 + 3 = 5

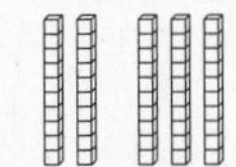

2 tens + 3 tens = 5 tens

20 + 30 = 50

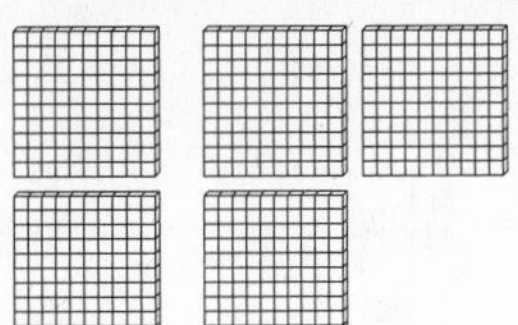

2 hundreds + 3 hundreds = 5 hundreds

200 + 300 = 500

Find each sum. Draw place value blocks to help you.

1. 4 + 5 = 9 Students should draw 4 ones blocks and 5 ones blocks.
2. 40 + 50 = 90 Students should draw 4 tens blocks and 5 tens blocks.
3. 400 + 500 = 900 Students should draw 4 hundreds blocks and 5 hundreds blocks.
4. 600 + 700 = 1,300 Students should draw 6 hundreds blocks and 7 hundreds blocks.

Name ______________________

Another Look 3-2

Exploring Adding on a Hundred Chart

1	2	3	4	5	6	7	8	9	10
11	12	13	14	15	16	17	18	19	20
21	22	23	24	25	26	27	28	29	30
31	32	33	34	35	36	37	38	39	40
41	42	43	44	45	46	47	48	49	50
51	52	53	54	55	56	57	58	59	60
61	62	63	64	65	66	67	68	69	70
71	72	73	74	75	76	77	78	79	80
81	82	83	84	85	86	87	88	89	90
91	92	93	94	95	96	97	98	99	100

You can use a hundred chart to help you find 44 + 37.

Put your finger on 44. Move forward (down) 3 tens, then to the right 7 ones. When you reach the end of the row, go to the first number in the next row.

Your finger is now on the number 81.

44 + 37 = 81

Use a hundred chart to find each sum.

1. 23 + 5 = 28
2. 50 + 8 = 58
3. 30 + 18 = 48
4. 49 + 22 = 71
5. 36 + 19 = 55
6. 27 + 35 = 62
7. 42 + 27 = 69
8. 56 + 29 = 85
9. 73 + 24 = 97
10. 33 + 48 = 81
11. 35 + 52 = 87
12. 64 + 22 = 86
13. 45 + 39 = 84
14. 56 + 22 = 78

Name ______________________

Another Look 3-3

Exploring Algebra: Missing Numbers

In your book, you found missing numbers using color cubes and workmats. Here is another way to find missing numbers.

1	2	3	4	5	6	7	8	9	10
11	12	13	14	15	16	17	18	19	20
21	22	23	24	25	26	27	28	29	30
31	32	33	34	35	36	37	38	39	40
41	42	43	44	45	46	47	48	49	50
51	52	53	54	55	56	57	58	59	60
61	62	63	64	65	66	67	68	69	70
71	72	73	74	75	76	77	78	79	80
81	82	83	84	85	86	87	88	89	90
91	92	93	94	95	96	97	98	99	100

☐ + 3 = 10

Find the missing number using a hundred chart.

Put your finger on the 3. Move it forward to the 10.

How many spaces did you move to get from the 3 to the 10?

4, 5, 6, 7, 8, 9, 10

You moved 7 spaces from 3 to get to 10.

__7__ + 3 = 10

Use a hundred chart to find the missing numbers.

1. [7] + 5 = 12
   a. Where do you put your finger first? __on the 5__
   b. How many spaces do you move to get to 12? __7__
   c. What is the missing number? __7__
   d. Write it in the number sentence above.
2. 6 + __12__ = 18
3. __9__ + 13 = 22

Name ______________________

Another Look 3-4

Estimating Sums

Estimate the sum of 424 and 175.

Which hundred is closer to 424?

Is 424 closer to 400 or 500? __400__

Which hundred is closer to 175?

Is 175 closer to 100 or 200? __200__

424 → 400
+ 175 → + 200
600

The sum of 424 and 175 is about __600__.

---

1. 327 + 159
   a. Is 327 closer to 300 or 400? __300__
   b. Is 159 closer to 100 or 200? __200__
   c. __300__ + __200__ = __500__
2. 498 + 111
   a. 498 is closer to __500__ than 400.
   b. 111 is closer to __100__ than __200__.
   c. __500__ + __100__ = __600__

Estimate each sum.

3. 112 + 790 __900__
4. 27 + 31 __60__
5. 546 + 329 __800__
6. 702 + 566 __1,300__
7. 33 + 84 __110__
8. 49 + 32 __80__
9. 622 + 131 __700__
10. 515 + 572 __1,100__
11. 331 + 609 __900__
12. 890 + 622 __1,500__

Name ______________________

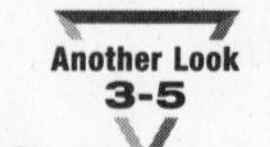

Another Look 3-5

Exploring Adding with Regrouping

In your book you added using place-value blocks. Here is another way to add.

Add 26 + 17. Use grid paper.

Show 26 and 17 by shading 26 squares and 17 squares. You can put the two groups together.

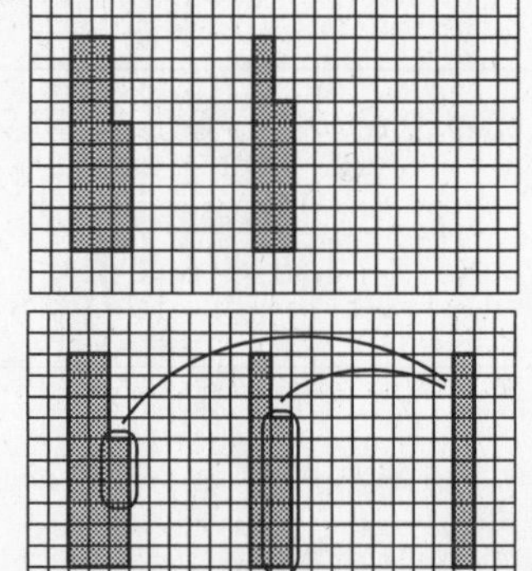

How many ones are there? __13__

Regroup 10 ones for 1 ten.

How many tens are there? __4 tens__

26 + 17 = __43__

---

1. Use place-value blocks or grid paper to find the sum of 23 + 28.
   a. How many ones are there? __11 ones = 1 ten 1 one__
   b. How many tens are there? __5 tens__
   c. What is the sum of 23 + 28? __51__
2. Use place-value blocks or grid paper to find the sum of 35 + 57.
   a. How many ones are there? __12 ones = 1 ten, 2 ones__
   b. How many tens are there? __9__
   c. What is the sum of 35 + 57? __92__

Find each sum.

3. 49 + 28 = __77__
4. 21 + 32 = __53__
5. 56 + 18 = __74__
6. 47 + 13 = __60__

Name ______________________

Another Look 3-6

Adding 2-Digit Numbers

Add 14 + 27.

Use place-value blocks to help you add.

Add the ones.

4 ones + 7 ones = __11 ones__

You need to regroup.

11 ones = 1 ten, 1 one

You write:

  1
  14
+ 27
   1

Add the tens.

1 ten + 1 ten + 2 tens = 4 tens

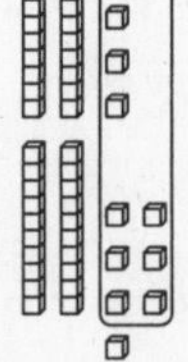

You write:

  1
  14
+ 27
  41

14 + 27 = __41__

Add. Estimate to check.

1. 23 + 39
   a. 3 ones + 9 ones = __12__ ones = __1__ ten, __2__ ones
   b. __1__ ten + 2 tens + __3__ tens = __6__ tens
   c. 23 + 39 = __62__
2. 35 + 18 = __53__
3. 52 + 38 = __90__
4. 44 + 27 = __71__
5. 36 + 42 = __78__
6. 78 + 19 = __97__
7. 51 + 47 = __98__

Name ____________________

Another Look 3-7

Adding 3-Digit Numbers

Place-value blocks can help you find the sum of 274 and 342.

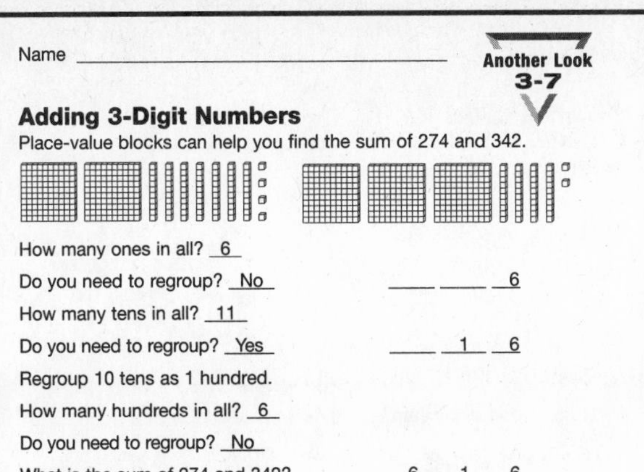

How many ones in all? 6

Do you need to regroup? No ___ ___ 6

How many tens in all? 11

Do you need to regroup? Yes ___ 1 6

Regroup 10 tens as 1 hundred.

How many hundreds in all? 6

Do you need to regroup? No

What is the sum of 274 and 342? 6 1 6

Use the place-value blocks to find each sum. Regroup as needed.

1. 472 + 319 = 791

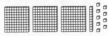

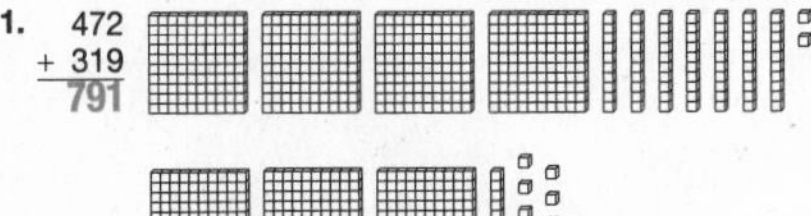

2. 568 + 174 = 742
3. $709 + 253 = $962
4. $386 + 525 = $911
5. 364 + 871 = 1,235
6. 494 + 325 = 819
7. 688 + 392 = 1,080
8. 434 + 725 = 1,159
9. 207 + 495 = 702

Name ____________________

Another Look 3-8

Adding 4-Digit Numbers: Choose a Calculation Method

You can use place-value blocks to find the sum of 1,537 and 2,148.

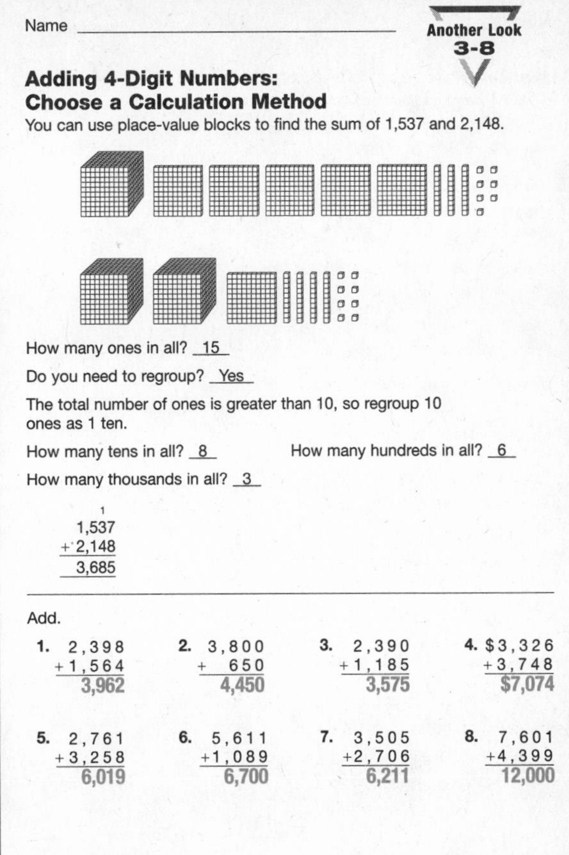

How many ones in all? 15

Do you need to regroup? Yes

The total number of ones is greater than 10, so regroup 10 ones as 1 ten.

How many tens in all? 8 How many hundreds in all? 6

How many thousands in all? 3

$$\begin{array}{r} {}^{1} \\ 1{,}537 \\ +\,2{,}148 \\ \hline 3{,}685 \end{array}$$

Add.

1. 2,398 + 1,564 = 3,962
2. 3,800 + 650 = 4,450
3. 2,390 + 1,185 = 3,575
4. $3,326 + 3,748 = $7,074
5. 2,761 + 3,258 = 6,019
6. 5,611 + 1,089 = 6,700
7. 3,505 + 2,706 = 6,211
8. 7,601 + 4,399 = 12,000

Name ____________________

Another Look 3-9

Column Addition

Number sentences can help you find the sum of three addends.

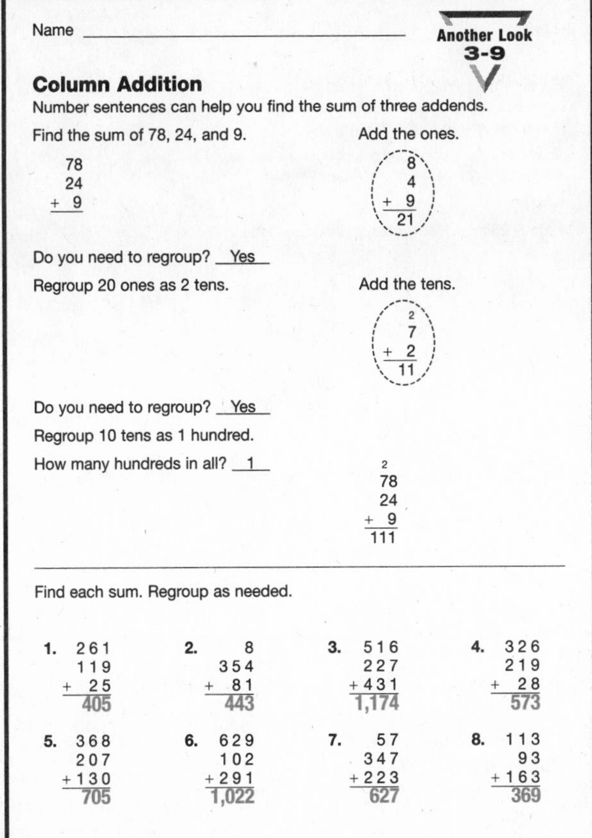

Find the sum of 78, 24, and 9.

$$\begin{array}{r} 78 \\ 24 \\ +\;9 \\ \hline \end{array}$$

Add the ones.

$$\begin{array}{r} 8 \\ 4 \\ +\;9 \\ \hline 21 \end{array}$$

Do you need to regroup? Yes

Regroup 20 ones as 2 tens.

Add the tens.

$$\begin{array}{r} {}^{2} \\ 7 \\ +\;2 \\ \hline 11 \end{array}$$

Do you need to regroup? Yes

Regroup 10 tens as 1 hundred.

How many hundreds in all? 1

$$\begin{array}{r} {}^{2} \\ 78 \\ 24 \\ +\;9 \\ \hline 111 \end{array}$$

Find each sum. Regroup as needed.

1. 261 + 119 + 25 = 405
2. 8 + 354 + 81 = 443
3. 516 + 227 + 431 = 1,174
4. 326 + 219 + 28 = 573
5. 368 + 207 + 130 = 705
6. 629 + 102 + 291 = 1,022
7. 57 + 347 + 223 = 627
8. 113 + 93 + 163 = 369

Name ____________________

Another Look 3-10

Analyze Strategies: Guess and Check

Josh needs to record the score of a school baseball game. He knows that the Cubs beat the Hawks by 6 runs and that a total of 24 runs were scored, but he doesn't remember the score!

Josh made a list of what he knows about the game.

The scores are 6 runs apart.
The Cubs won the game.
A total of 24 runs were scored.

Josh picked 2 numbers, 22 and 2, whose sum is 24.

22 + 2 = 24 12 + 12 = 24

Then he checked to see if the difference of the pair was 6. No

Josh guessed again, picking 12 and 12.

22 − 2 = 20 too large ↗ 12 − 12 = 0 too small ↗

Josh knew that the number of runs for one team was between 22 and 12. He tried a few more guesses until he found numbers that worked.

18 + 6 = 24 18 − 6 = 12

16 + 8 = 24 16 − 8 = 8

15 + 9 = 24 15 − 9 = 6

The Cubs scored 15 runs and the Hawks scored 9 runs.

Follow the same steps to answer these questions.

1. The Hawks lost to the Eagles by 7 runs. A total of 19 runs were scored. How many runs did each team score?
   Eagles scored 13 runs. Hawks scored 6 runs.
2. The Eagles beat the Cubs by 4 runs. A total of 28 runs were scored. How many runs did each team score?
   Eagles scored 16 runs. Cubs scored 12 runs.
3. The Panthers beat the Jaguars by 13 runs. A total of 17 runs were scored. How many runs did each team score?
   Panthers scored 15 runs. Jaguars scored 2 runs.

Name ______________________

Mental Math

Knowing basic addition facts can help you add mentally.

Sam has $38 saved. He earns $6 raking leaves. How much money does Sam have now?

$38 + $6

Step 1
Rewrite 38. 38 = 30 + 8

Step 2
Add the ones $8 + $6 = $14

Step 3
Add the tens. $10 + $30 = $40

How much money does Sam have? $44

Use mental math to find each sum.

1. 26 + 5
   6 + 5 = 11
   10 + 20 = 30
   26 + 5 = 31

2. 36 + 21
   6 + 1 = 7
   30 + 20 = 50
   36 + 21 = 57

3. 49 + 8 = 57 4. 52 + 11 = 63 5. 28 + 41 = 69

6. 84 + 9 = 93 7. 47 + 32 = 79 8. 64 + 19 = 83

9. 17 + 52 = 69 10. 37 + 44 = 81 11. 27 + 74 = 101

12. 23 + 57 = 80 13. 45 + 27 = 72 14. 16 + 79 = 95

15. 49 + 22 = 71 16. 34 + 17 = 51 17. 36 + 38 = 74

Name ______________________

Another Look
3-12

Counting Coins

You can find the total value of coins by adding their values mentally.

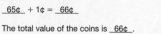

25¢ + 25¢ = 50¢
50¢ + 10¢ = 60¢
60¢ + 5¢ = 65¢
65¢ + 1¢ = 66¢

The total value of the coins is 66¢.

Write the total value in cents.

1.  

25¢ + 10¢ = 35¢
35¢ + 10¢ = 45¢
45¢ + 10¢ = 55¢
55¢ + 5¢ = 60¢

2.   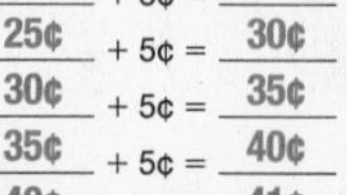 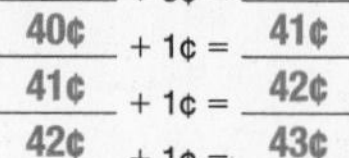

10¢ + 10¢ = 20¢
20¢ + 5¢ = 25¢
25¢ + 5¢ = 30¢
30¢ + 5¢ = 35¢
35¢ + 5¢ = 40¢
40¢ + 1¢ = 41¢
41¢ + 1¢ = 42¢
42¢ + 1¢ = 43¢

3. 

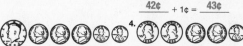

50¢ + 5¢ = 55¢
55¢ + 5¢ = 60¢
60¢ + 5¢ = 65¢
65¢ + 1¢ = 66¢
66¢ + 1¢ = 67¢

4.

25¢ + 25¢ = 50¢
50¢ + 5¢ = 55¢
55¢ + 5¢ = 60¢
60¢ + 1¢ = 61¢

Name ______________________

Another Look
3-13

Using Dollars and Cents

Write the value of the coins in dollars and cents.

You can write the value of coins by counting on. Start with the coin having the greatest value. Find the value of the quarters by counting by 25s.

$0.25. . . $0.50
$0.50 in quarters

Count on the dimes by counting by 10s.
. . . $0.60 . . . $0.70 . . .$0.80 $0.80 in quarters and dimes

Count on the nickels by counting by 5s.
. . . $0.85 . . . $0.90 . . . $0.95 . . . $1.00 . . . $1.05 $1.05 in quarters, dimes and nickels.

Count on the pennies by counting by 1s.
. . . $1.06 . . . $1.07 . . . $1.08 $1.08 in all.

Write the value of the coins in dollars and cents.

1.      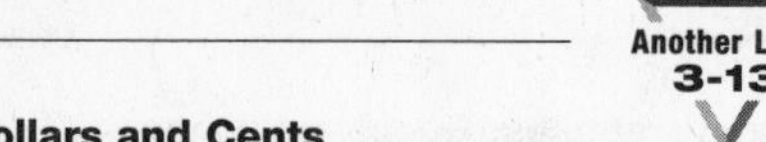

$0.25 . . . $0.50 . . . $0.60 . . . $0.70 . . . $0.80 . . . $0.90 . . . $0.95 . . . $1.00 . . . $1.05

2.     

$0.25 . . . $0.50 . . . $0.75 . . . $0.85 . . . $0.95 . . . $1.00 . . . $1.05 . . . $1.06 . . . $1.07

Name ______________________

Exploring Making Change

In your book, you made change using coins and bills. Here is another way to make change.

At an art sale, Robert gives $2.00 for a clay mug that costs $0.28. How much change will he receive?

$2.00 = 200¢ $0.28 = 28¢

200¢ − 28¢ = change owed to Robert

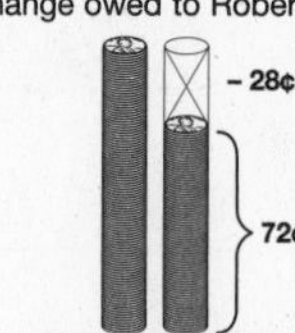

172¢ = $1.72

Follow the steps above to make change. Think of pennies to help you.

1. Keisha gives you $3.00 for a painting that costs $1.54.
   $3.00 = 300¢ $1.54 = 154¢
   300¢ − 154¢ = 146¢ = $1.46

2. Kelly gives you $5.00 for a clay pot that costs $2.31.
   500¢ − 231¢ = 269¢; 269¢ = $2.69

You can use other coins to make change.

3. What other coins and bills could you use for Keisha's change in **1**?
   Possible answer: 1 penny, 2 dimes, 1 quarter, 1 dollar bill

4. What other coins could you use for Kelly's change in **2**?
   Possible answer: 4 pennies, 1 nickel, 1 dime, 2 quarters, 2 dollar bills

Name ______________________

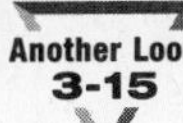

Adding Money

You go to the market. You decide to buy milk and bread. Milk costs $2.09. Bread costs $1.78. How much will both items cost?

Since you want to find the total cost, you add $2.09 + $1.78.

Step 1
Change the amounts to cents
$2.09 = 209¢
$1.78 = 178¢

Step 2
Add.
209¢
+ 178¢
387¢

Step 3
Change the sum to dollars and cents.
387¢ = $3.87

209¢ + 178¢ = 387¢

$2.09 + $1.78 = $3.87

Use the steps above to add.

1. $4.33 + 0.75 = $5.08
2. $1.45 + 1.96 = $3.41
3. $0.37 + 3.41 = $3.78
4. $0.99 + 3.33 = $4.32
5. $5.59 + 9.23 = $14.82
6. $2.42 + 3.98 = $6.40
7. $1.16 + 2.93 = $4.09
8. $5.63 + 2.28 = $7.91
9. $6.78 + 3.64 = $10.42

10. Find the sum of $2.59 and $1.17. $3.76

11. Add $3.42 and $7.21. $10.63

Name ______________________

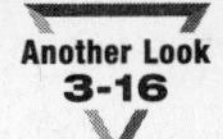

Front-End Estimation

Front-end estimation can help you estimate sums.

Example 1
Make the other digits 0.
Add the front digits.

10 → 10
22 → 20
+ 17 → + 10
40

The sum of 10 + 22 + 17 is about 40.

Example 2
Make the other digits 0.
Add the front digits.

$2.40 → $2.00
4.68 → $4.00
+ 1.76 → $1.00
$7.00

The sum of $2.40 + $4.68 + $1.76 is about $7.00.

Use front-end estimation to estimate each sum.

1. 29 + 42 → 20 + 40 = 60
2. 408 + 263 + 211 → 400 + 200 + 200 = 800
3. $9.43 + 5.38 + 1.82 → $9.00 + 5.00 + 1.00 = $15.00
4. $3.09 + 4.24 + 2.49 → $3.00 + 4.00 + 2.00 = $9.00
5. 88 + 92 + 21 → 80 + 90 + 20 = 190
6. 775 + 619 → 700 + 600 = 1,300
7. $6.51 + 8.27 + 3.39 → $6.00 + 8.00 + 3.00 = $17.00
8. 336 + 120 + 291 → 300 + 100 + 200 = 600
9. 891 + 117 → 800 + 100 = 900

10. 445 + 286 + 535 400 + 200 + 500 = 1,100

11. $3.01 + $9.12 + $1.46 $3.00 + $9.00 + $1.00 = $13.00

Name ______________________

Another Look 3-17

Analyze Word Problems: Exact Answer or Estimate?

The entire grade is taking a field trip to the county museum. Each bus has 40 seats. Will Ms. D'Angelo's class and Mrs. Smith-Francis' class be able to travel together on one bus?

Teacher	Students
Ms. D'Angelo	23
Mr. Fernandez	21
Mrs. Smith-Francis	14
Mr. Jones	18

You know that there are 40 seats on a bus. Ms. D'Angelo has 23 students. Mrs. Smith-Francis has 14 students.

You can estimate the sum of 23 + 14.

Estimate. 23 is close to 20.
14 is close to 10
20 + 10 = 30

Ms. D'Angelo's and Mrs. Smith-Francis' classes can all ride on the same bus.

Follow the model above to solve the problem.

1. Can Mr. Jones' class and Mr. Fernandez's class fit together on one bus?
Yes

2. How many 40-seat buses will be needed for the entire grade?
2

3. All the students want to ride on one larger bus.
a. About how many seats should the bus have?
About 70 seats
b. Find the exact number for all the students. How many seats will be needed?
76 seats

Name ______________________

Another Look 4-1

Reviewing the Meaning of Subtraction

For taking away, comparing, and finding the missing part, clue words are often used. When you see these clue words, you know you have to subtract:

how many more
how many less
how much more
how much of an -*er* word (such as *larger, smaller, taller, shorter*)
difference
remain
left
fewer
greater

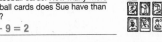

How many more balloons are there in the first group than in the second?

Subtract. 5 − 3 = 2

There are 2 more balloons in the first group.

Read each problem. Underline the clue words. Then write a number sentence for each and solve.

1. Jack has 9 baseball cards. Sue has 11 baseball cards. How many more baseball cards does Sue have than Jack?
11 − 9 = 2

2. How much longer is the first truck?
12 inches − 6 inches = 6 inches

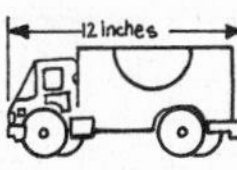

3. Marianne has six stamps. She uses two to mail two letters. How many stamps does Marianne have left?
6 − 2 = 4

4. Four people are in a tent. Two leave the tent. How many people remain in the tent?
4 − 2 = 2

Name ______________________

Another Look 4-2

Exploring Subtraction Patterns

In your book you used patterns to subtract larger numbers. Here is another way to subtract larger numbers.

Find 900 − 500.

Use a number line.

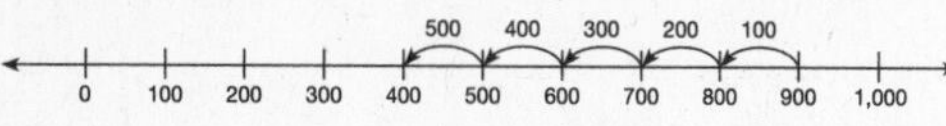

900 − 500 = 400

Find each difference using the number lines.

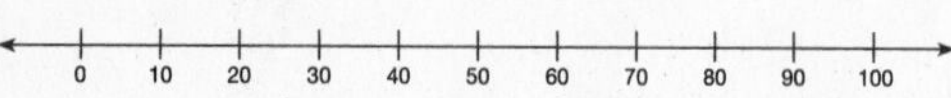

1. 60 − 40 = 20
2. 80 − 40 = 40
3. 70 − 10 = 60
4. 40 − 20 = 20
5. 100 − 30 = 70
6. 90 − 60 = 30
7. 20 − 10 = 10
8. 50 − 30 = 20

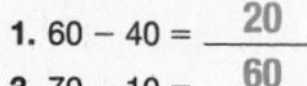

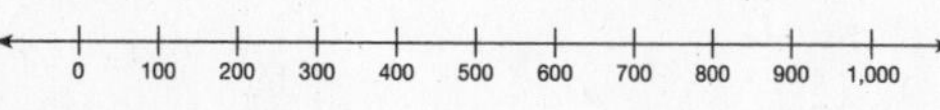

9. 600 − 200 = 400
10. 800 − 600 = 200
11. 700 − 500 = 200
12. 1,000 − 600 = 400
13. 1,000 − 400 = 600
14. 500 − 200 = 300
15. 900 − 300 = 600
16. 700 − 400 = 300

Name ______________________

Another Look 4-3

Exploring Subtracting On a Hundred Chart

In your book you used a hundred chart to explore subtraction. Here is another way to use the hundred chart.

You can use this partial hundred chart to subtract smaller numbers.

1	2	3	4	5	6	7	8	9	10
11	12	13	14	15	16	17	18	19	20
21	22	23	24	25	26	27	28	29	30
31	32	33	34	35	36	37	38	39	40
41	42	43	44	45	46	47	48	49	50

45 − 27

Put your pencil on 45.

Count back 27 squares.

What number is your pencil on? 18

45 − 27 = 18

1	2	3	4	5	6	7	8	9	10
11	12	13	14	15	16	17	18	19	20
21	22	23	24	25	26	27	28	29	30
31	32	33	34	35	36	37	38	39	40
41	42	43	44	45	46	47	48	49	50

You can find the difference without counting all the ones.

Put your pencil on 45 and just count back 7 ones. Then move your pencil up 2 rows to count back 2 tens. Your pencil should be on 18.

Complete.

1. If you subtract by counting back by ones, how many squares will you count back to subtract 36? 36
2. a. How many squares (ones) would you count back to subtract 56? 6
   b. How many rows (tens) would you move up to subtract 56? 5
3. a. How many ones would you count back to subtract 41? 1
   b. How many tens would you count back to subtract 41? 4

Find each difference using a hundred chart.

4. 42 − 21 = 21
5. 34 − 19 = 15
6. 22 − 7 = 15
7. 49 − 15 = 34
8. 37 − 28 = 9
9. 46 − 28 = 18

Name ______________________

Another Look 4-4

Estimating Differences

To estimate, you need to know how to round numbers. The chart lists steps for rounding numbers.

Rounding to the Nearest Tens or Hundreds		
Steps	**Tens**	**Hundreds**
Draw a box around the place to which you will round.	[5]2	[3]71
Is the digit to the right 5 or more? If it is not, make no change. Otherwise, add 1 to the digit in the box.	[5]2 The digit to the right is less than 5, so make no change.	[4]71 The digit to the right is more than 5, so add 1. Change 3 to 4.
Change all the digits to the right to zeros.	50	400

Round each 2-digit number to the nearest 10. Round each 3-digit number to the nearest 100.

1. 28 30
2. 394 400
3. 67 70
4. 683 700
5. 881 900
6. 737 700
7. 42 40
8. 649 600
9. 11 10
10. 74 70

Round to the nearest ten. Then estimate the difference.

11. 48 − 36 50 − 40 = 10
12. 83 − 27 80 − 30 = 50
13. 38 − 14 40 − 10 = 30
14. 68 − 26 70 − 30 = 40
15. 51 − 39 50 − 40 = 10

Name ______________________

Another Look 4-5

Exploring Regrouping

In your book you used place-value blocks to explore regrouping. Here is another way to explore regrouping.

1 dime is the same as 10 pennies.
1 ten is the same as 10 ones.

100 pennies or 1 dollar is the same as 10 dimes.
1 hundred is the same as 10 tens.

23¢ is the same as 1 dime and 13 pennies.
So, 23 is the same as 1 ten and 13 ones.

Regroup 1 ten for 10 ones. Use the pictures of coins to help.

1.

86¢ is the same as 7 dimes and 16 pennies.
So, 86 is the same as 7 tens and 16 ones.

2.

47¢ is the same as 3 dimes and 17 pennies.
So, 47 is the same as 3 tens and 17 ones.

Name ______________________

Exploring Subtracting 2-Digit Numbers

In your book you used place-value blocks to subtract 2-digit numbers. Here is another way to subtract 2-digit numbers.

27 – 14

You can draw a picture to subtract. Draw a number of objects equal to the first number in the subtraction problem (27). Cross off a number of objects equal to the second number in the subtraction problem (14). Count the remaining objects.

 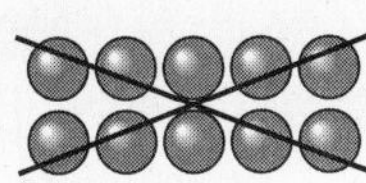 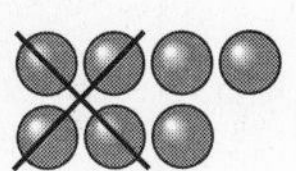

27 – 14 = 13

Find each difference. Draw pictures to help.

1. 18 – 12 = 6
2. 24 – 21 = 3
3. 31 – 15 = 16
4. 48 – 31 = 17
5. 57 – 19 = 38
6. 41 – 18 = 23
7. 64 – 21 = 43
8. 37 – 29 = 8

Name ______________________

Another Look
4-7

Subtracting 2-Digit Numbers

To find the difference between 86 and 29, you cannot take 9 ones from 6 ones. So, you have to regroup. Follow these steps to regroup tens as ones:

Steps	Example
Draw a box around the number in the tens place.	[8]6
Take 1 ten from the boxed number.	7 [8̶]6
Underline the number in the ones place.	7 [8̶]<u>6</u>
Add 10 ones to the underlined number.	7 16 [8̶]6̶

$$\begin{array}{r} \overset{7\,16}{\not8\not6} \\ -\ 29 \\ \hline 57 \end{array}$$

Now you can subtract ones and tens.

Read each problem. Do you need to regroup 1 ten as 10 ones? Answer yes or no.

1. 48 – 73 No
2. 94 – 36 Yes
3. 31 – 41 No
4. 62 – 27 Yes
5. 46 – 67 Yes
6. 24 – 12 No

Read each problem. Do you need to regroup 1 ten as 10 ones? If so, show how you would regroup.

For example: 86 – 68 $\overset{7\,16}{\not8\not6}$

7. 58 – 54 No
8. 73 – 15 $\overset{6\,13}{\not7\not3}$
9. 41 – 26 $\overset{3\,11}{\not4\not1}$
10. 93 – 52 No

Subtract. Regroup if necessary.

11. 28 – 17 = 11
12. 52 – 36 = 16
13. 44 – 28 = 16
14. 67 – 45 = 22
15. 82 – 76 = 6
16. 35 – 17 = 18

Name ______________________

Exploring Subtracting 3-Digit Numbers

In your book you used place-value blocks to subtract 3-digit numbers. Here is another way to subtract 3-digit numbers.

Find 143 – 67.

You can use money to show subtraction.

Show 143 using dollars, dimes, and pennies. You can think of one dollar as one hundred cents.

You can't take away 7 pennies, so exchange 1 dime for 10 pennies.

Cross off 7 pennies.

You can't take away 6 dimes from 3 dimes, so exchange the dollar for 10 dimes.

Cross off 6 dimes.

Count the amount of change that remains.

143¢ – 67¢ = 76¢

So, 143 – 67 = 76

Find each difference. Use money to help.

1. 261 – 49 = 212
2. 324 – 187 = 137

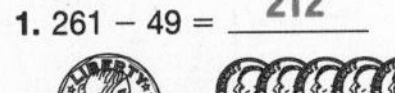 

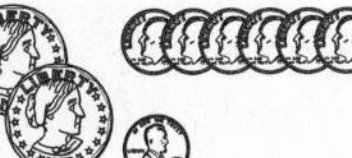 

3. 129 – 37 = 92
4. 382 – 157 = 225

Name ______________________

Another Look
4-9

Subtracting 3-Digit Numbers

You can use place-value blocks to help you subtract 3-digit numbers.

Subtract 341 – 126.

Show 341 with place-value blocks.

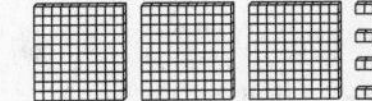

Step 1 First subtract the ones. Do you need to regroup 1 ten for 10 ones? Yes.

Step 2 Regroup 1 tens block for 10 ones blocks.

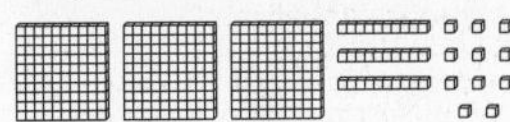

Step 3 Subtract the ones. Cross off 6 ones blocks.

Step 4 Subtract the tens. Cross off 2 tens blocks.

Step 5 Subtract the hundreds. Cross off 1 hundreds block.

Count the remaining blocks.

341 – 126 = 215.

Subtract. You may use place-value blocks to help.

1. Subtract 459 – 185.

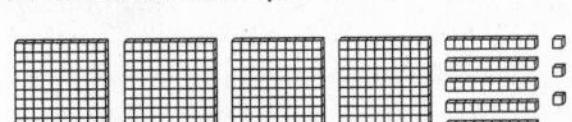

a. Do you need to regroup 1 ten for 10 ones? No

b. Do you need to regroup 1 hundred for 10 tens? Yes

c. 459 – 185 = 274

2. 322 – 217 = 105
3. 548 – 364 = 184
4. 619 – 221 = 398
5. 351 – 191 = 160

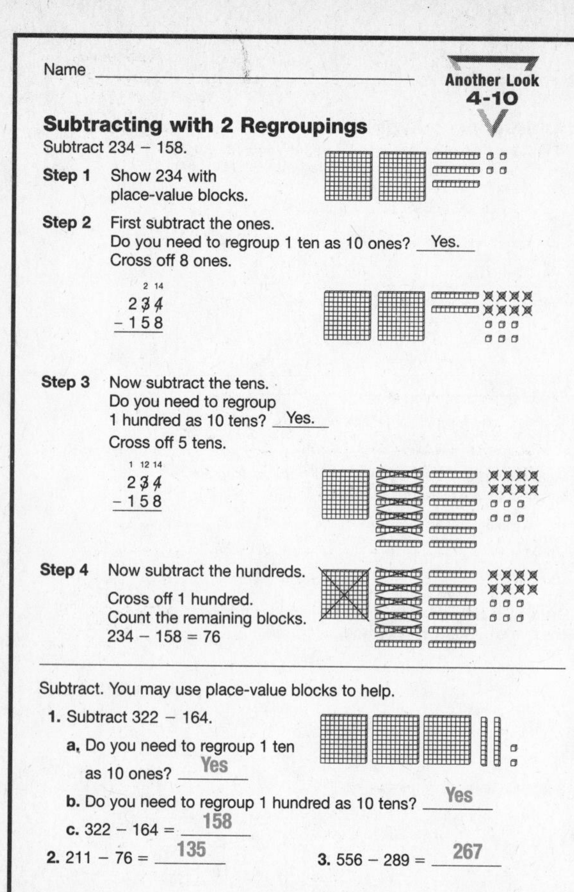

Name ______________________

Another Look 4-10

Subtracting with 2 Regroupings

Subtract 234 − 158.

Step 1 Show 234 with place-value blocks.

Step 2 First subtract the ones.
Do you need to regroup 1 ten as 10 ones? Yes.
Cross off 8 ones.

```
   2 14
   2 3 4
 − 1 5 8
```

Step 3 Now subtract the tens.
Do you need to regroup 1 hundred as 10 tens? Yes.
Cross off 5 tens.

```
 1 12 14
   2 3 4
 − 1 5 8
```

Step 4 Now subtract the hundreds.
Cross off 1 hundred.
Count the remaining blocks.
234 − 158 = 76

Subtract. You may use place-value blocks to help.

1. Subtract 322 − 164.
   a. Do you need to regroup 1 ten as 10 ones? Yes
   b. Do you need to regroup 1 hundred as 10 tens? Yes
   c. 322 − 164 = 158
2. 211 − 76 = 135
3. 556 − 289 = 267

Name ______________________

Another Look 4-11

Subtracting Across 0

Subtract 203 − 147.

Step 1 Since you can't take 7 ones from 3 ones, you need to regroup. There is a zero in the tens place.

Think: 2 hundreds 3 ones is the same as 20 tens 3 ones.

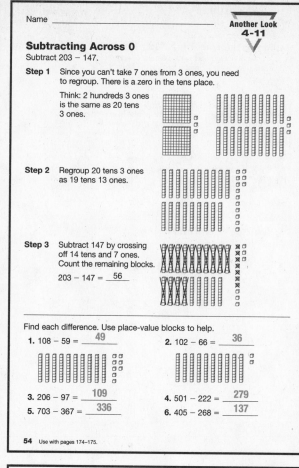

Step 2 Regroup 20 tens 3 ones as 19 tens 13 ones.

Step 3 Subtract 147 by crossing off 14 tens and 7 ones. Count the remaining blocks.
203 − 147 = 56

Find each difference. Use place-value blocks to help.

1. 108 − 59 = 49
2. 102 − 66 = 36
3. 206 − 97 = 109
4. 501 − 222 = 279
5. 703 − 367 = 336
6. 405 − 268 = 137

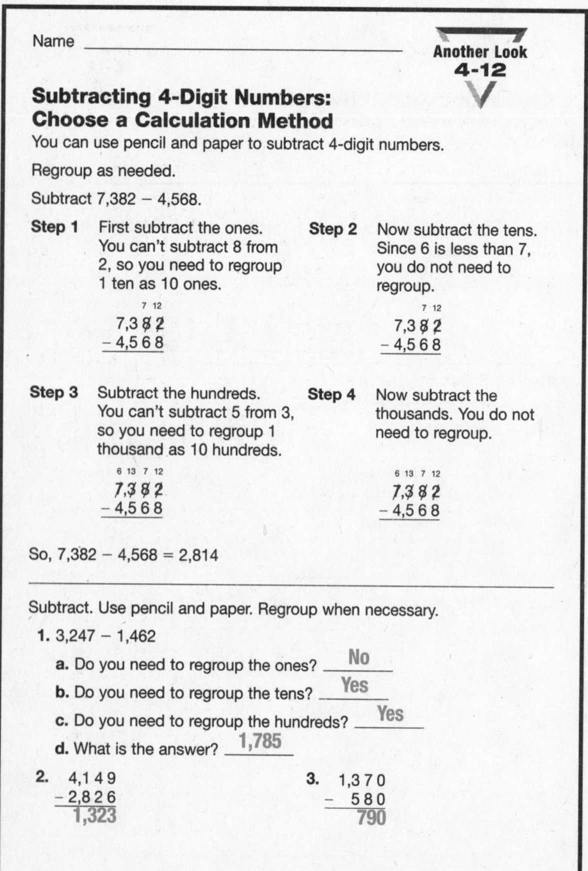

Name ______________________

Another Look 4-12

Subtracting 4-Digit Numbers: Choose a Calculation Method

You can use pencil and paper to subtract 4-digit numbers.

Regroup as needed.

Subtract 7,382 − 4,568.

Step 1 First subtract the ones. You can't subtract 8 from 2, so you need to regroup 1 ten as 10 ones.

```
      7 12
   7,3 8 2
 − 4,5 6 8
```

Step 2 Now subtract the tens. Since 6 is less than 7, you do not need to regroup.

```
      7 12
   7,3 8 2
 − 4,5 6 8
```

Step 3 Subtract the hundreds. You can't subtract 5 from 3, so you need to regroup 1 thousand as 10 hundreds.

```
 6 13 7 12
   7,3 8 2
 − 4,5 6 8
```

Step 4 Now subtract the thousands. You do not need to regroup.

```
 6 13 7 12
   7,3 8 2
 − 4,5 6 8
```

So, 7,382 − 4,568 = 2,814

Subtract. Use pencil and paper. Regroup when necessary.

1. 3,247 − 1,462
   a. Do you need to regroup the ones? No
   b. Do you need to regroup the tens? Yes
   c. Do you need to regroup the hundreds? Yes
   d. What is the answer? 1,785

2.
```
   4,1 4 9
 − 2,8 2 6
   1,323
```

3.
```
   1,3 7 0
 −   5 8 0
     790
```


Name ______________________

Another Look 4-13

Analyze Word Problems: Multiple-Step Problems

Sometimes you need more than one step to solve a problem. Make a plan. Then follow the plan to solve the problem.

Ray has $6. He will get $5 more today. How much more will he need to buy a Fun Park All-Day Ride Pass for $18?

Plan Add to find out how much money Ray has today. Subtract to find out how much more money he needs to buy the pass.

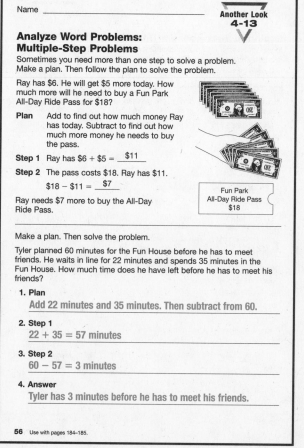

Step 1 Ray has $6 + $5 = $11

Step 2 The pass costs $18. Ray has $11.
$18 − $11 = $7

Ray needs $7 more to buy the All-Day Ride Pass.

Fun Park
All-Day Ride Pass
$18

Make a plan. Then solve the problem.

Tyler planned 60 minutes for the Fun House before he has to meet friends. He waits in line for 22 minutes and spends 35 minutes in the Fun House. How much time does he have left before he has to meet his friends?

1. **Plan**
   Add 22 minutes and 35 minutes. Then subtract from 60.
2. **Step 1**
   22 + 35 = 57 minutes
3. **Step 2**
   60 − 57 = 3 minutes
4. **Answer**
   Tyler has 3 minutes before he has to meet his friends.

Name ______________________________

Another Look 4-14

Mental Math

It is easier to add or subtract a multiple of 10. Numbers in problems can be adjusted so you can solve them mentally.

Example 1

34 − 26

Think: What number can I add to 26 to make it a multiple of 10? 4

But, to keep the problem accurate, add 4 to 34, too.

Think: Add 4. 34 → 38
Think: Add 4. − 26 → − 30
8

So, 34 − 26 = 8.

Example 2

85 − 47

Think: What number can I add to 47 to make it a multiple of 10? 3

But, to keep the problem accurate, add 3 to 85, too.

Think: Add 3. 85 → 88
Think: Add 3. − 47 → − 50
38

So, 85 − 47 = 38.

What number would you add to each in order to subtract mentally?

1. 24 − 7 3

2. 33 − 18 2

3. 43 − 36 4

4. 97 − 49 1

Add 1, 2, 3, or 4 to each number to make it easier to subtract mentally. Then subtract.

5. 46 → 48
− 28 → − 30
18

So, 46 − 28 = 18

6. 93 → 94
− 79 → − 80
14

So, 93 − 79 = 14

7. 82 → 86
− 56 → − 60
26

So, 82 − 56 = 26

8. 71 → 74
− 47 → − 50
24

So, 71 − 47 = 24

Name ______________________________

Another Look 4-15

Subtracting Money

You can use play money to help you subtract money.

Subtract: $2.75 − $1.13

Show $2.75 using dollars, dimes, and pennies.

To subtract, $1.13, cross off 1 dollar, 1 dime, and 3 pennies.

$2.75 − $1.13 = $1.62

Subtract.

1. $0.57 − 0.33 = $0.24

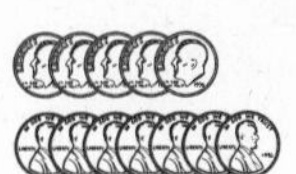

2. $5.48 − 0.54 = $4.94

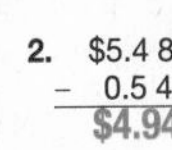

3. $1.87 − 0.59 = $1.28

4. $0.53 − 0.17 = $0.36

5. $3.60 − 1.24 = $2.36

6. $5.00 − 1.37 = $3.63

7. $6.31 − 2.72 = $3.59

8. $8.09 − 0.94 = $7.15

Name ______________________________

Another Look 4-16

Analyze Strategies: Use Objects

Jessie counted 7 cycle riders and 19 wheels go past her in the park. How many bicycles and how many tricycles passed her?

What do you know? There are 7 cycle riders.

There are 19 wheels.

Use two-color counters to show what Jessie saw.

Use 7 red counters to show the cycle riders.

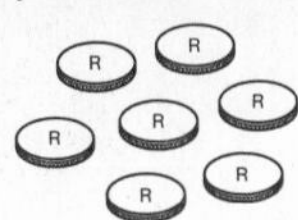

Use 19 yellow counters to show the wheels.

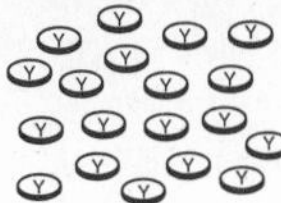

Match each rider with either 2 or 3 wheels until you run out of counters.

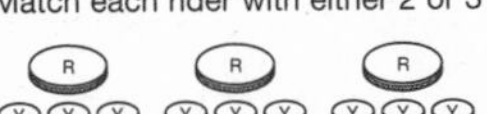

Two bicycles and 5 tricycles passed Jessie.

Solve. Use objects to help.

1. Antonio has 7 coins in his pocket. He has $1.00 in all. What coins does he have in his pocket?
Possible answer: 2 quarters, 5 dimes

2. You are riding on an elevator. You get on at the main level. You go up 5 floors, down 3 floors, up 8 floors, and then down 4 floors. Then you get off the elevator. What floor are you on? The sixth floor

3. You are making lunch. You have a choice of tuna or turkey sandwiches. You have a choice of pea, tomato, or chicken soup. How many different ways can you make lunch? 6

Name ______________________________

Another Look 5-1

Exploring Equal Groups

In your book you explored multiplication using counters or pictures. Here is another way to multiply equal groups.

Suppose Carl has 4 rows of 3 stickers. How many stickers does he have in all?

You can use grid paper to find how many stickers. Shade one row for each row of stickers.

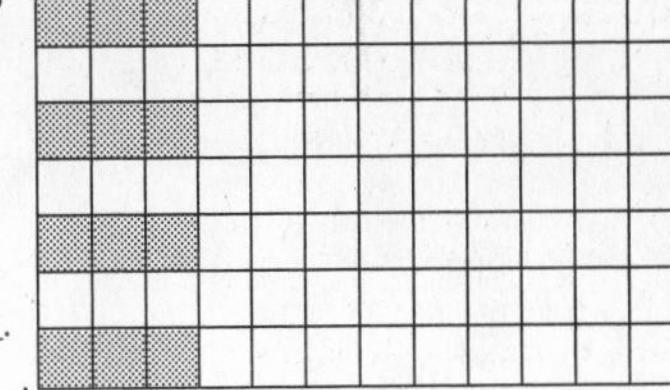

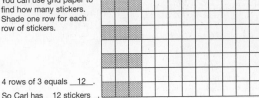

4 rows of 3 equals 12.

So Carl has 12 stickers.

Possible answers shown.

Use grid paper. Shade equal groups. Then write how many.

1. 3 rows of 3 equals 9.

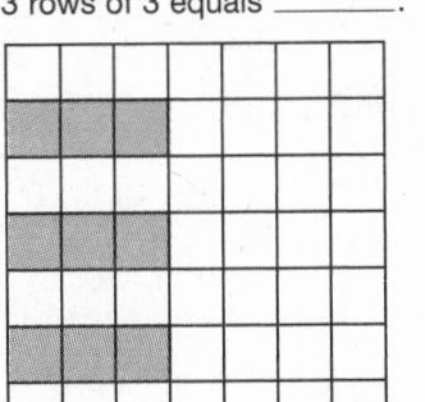

2. 2 rows of 5 equals 10.

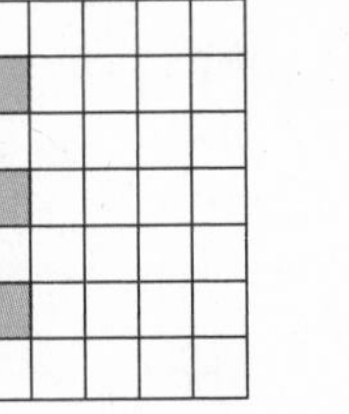

3. 4 rows of 4 equals 16.

4. 6 rows of 2 equals 12.

5. 3 rows of 7 equals 21.

6. 5 rows of 4 equals 20.

7. 4 rows of 6 equals 24.

8. 2 rows of 9 equals 18.

Name ______________________

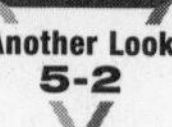

Another Look 5-2

Writing Multiplication Sentences

You can use counters to multiply equal groups.

3 groups of 5

3 × 5 = 15

↑ factor ↑ factor ↑ product

Use counters to complete.

1. 

a. 3 groups of 4

b. 4 + 4 + 4 = 12

c. 3 × 4 = 12

2. 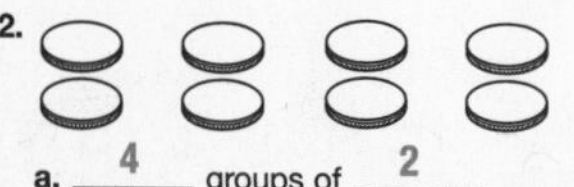

a. 4 groups of 2

b. 2 + 2 + 2 + 2 = 8

c. 4 × 2 = 8

3. 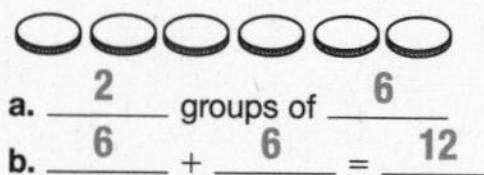

a. 2 groups of 6

b. 6 + 6 = 12

c. 2 × 6 = 12

Name ______________________

Another Look 5-3

Exploring Multiplication Stories

Story: Colleen gives each of her aunts 2 bracelets. She has 3 aunts.

Question: How many bracelets does she give? You can draw a picture to solve.

3 aunts
2 bracelets for each aunt

3 × 2 = 6

She gave 6 bracelets in all.

Write a multiplication story for each. You may use a picture to solve.

1. 3 × 5 = 15

Story: Look for 3 groups of 5.

Question: ______________________

2. 4 × 2 = 8

 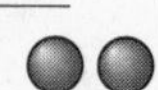  

Story: Look for 4 groups of 2.

Question: ______________________

Name ______________________

Another Look 5-4

2 as a Factor

You can use a hundreds chart to find products.

The numbers you multiply are **factors**.

The answer is the **product**.

Skip-count by 2s on the chart when 2 is a factor.

To find 7 × 2, start at 2 and shade 7 boxes. You will land on 14. You can shade each box you land on to see patterns.

The product of 7 and 2 is 14.

7 × 2 = 14

↑ factor ↑ factor ↑ product

1	2	3	4	5	6	7	8	9	10
11	12	13	14	15	16	17	18	19	20
21	22	23	24	25	26	27	28	29	30
31	32	33	34	35	36	37	38	39	40
41	42	43	44	45	46	47	48	49	50
51	52	53	54	55	56	57	58	59	60
61	62	63	64	65	66	67	68	69	70
71	72	73	74	75	76	77	78	79	80
81	82	83	84	85	86	87	88	89	90
91	92	93	94	95	96	97	98	99	100

Use the chart. Find each product.

1. 2 × 4 = 8
2. 1 × 2 = 2
3. 9 × 2 = 18
4. 2 × 5 = 10
5. 2 × 3 = 6
6. 8 × 2 = 16

7. 6 × 2 = 12
8. 2 × 7 = 14
9. 2 × 2 = 4
10. 2 × 9 = 18
11. 5 × 2 = 10
12. 2 × 6 = 12
13. 2 × 1 = 2
14. 2 × 3 = 6
15. 2 × 8 = 16
16. 7 × 2 = 14
17. 4 × 2 = 8
18. 1 × 2 = 2

Name ______________________

Another Look 5-5

5 as a Factor

You can use a hundred chart to find the product when 5 is a factor.

Skip count by 5s on the chart when 5 is a factor and shade in the numbers you land on.

To find 5 × 4, start at 5 and shade 4 boxes. You will land at 20. You can shade the boxes you land on to see patterns.

The product of 5 and 4 is 20.

5 × 4 = 20

↑ factor ↑ factor ↑ product

1	2	3	4	5	6	7	8	9	10
11	12	13	14	15	16	17	18	19	20
21	22	23	24	25	26	27	28	29	30
31	32	33	34	35	36	37	38	39	40
41	42	43	44	45	46	47	48	49	50
51	52	53	54	55	56	57	58	59	60
61	62	63	64	65	66	67	68	69	70
71	72	73	74	75	76	77	78	79	80
81	82	83	84	85	86	87	88	89	90
91	92	93	94	95	96	97	98	99	100

Use the chart. Find each product.

1. 4 × 5 = 20
2. 2 × 5 = 10
3. 3 × 5 = 15
4. 5 × 7 = 35
5. 5 × 6 = 30
6. 8 × 5 = 40
7. 5 × 5 = 25
8. 9 × 5 = 45

9. 7 × 5 = 35
10. 2 × 5 = 10
11. 4 × 5 = 20
12. 5 × 9 = 45
13. 5 × 1 = 5
14. 6 × 5 = 30
15. 3 × 5 = 15
16. 5 × 8 = 40
17. 9 × 5 = 45
18. 1 × 5 = 5
19. 5 × 4 = 20
20. 5 × 5 = 25

Name ______________________

Another Look 5-6

Exploring Patterns on a Hundred Chart: 2s and 5s

In your book you skip counted to find patterns on a hundred chart. Here's another way to find patterns.

1	2	3	4	5	6	7	8	9	10
11	12	13	14	15	16	17	18	19	20
21	22	23	24	25	26	27	28	29	30
31	32	33	34	35	36	37	38	39	40
41	42	43	44	45	46	47	48	49	50

Even numbers are numbers with 0, 2, 4, 6, or 8 as their last digit. Even numbers are multiples of 2. Shade all the even numbers with dots.

Multiples of 5 always end in 0 or 5. Shade all the multiples of 5 with stripes.

You can use the hundred chart to multiply.

To find the product of 5 and 4, count 4 striped squares starting with 5. Your finger should land on 20.

To find the product of 2 and 9, count 9 dotted squares starting with 2. Your finger should land on 18.

Find each product.

1. 5 × 7
   a. How many striped squares should you count? 7
   b. On which square do you start? 5
   c. 5 × 7 = 35
2. 2 × 6
   a. How many dotted squares should you count? 6
   b. On which square do you start? 2
   c. 2 × 6 = 12
3. Use the partial hundred chart to complete the table.

×	1	2	3	4	5	6	7	8	9
2	2	4	6	8	10	12	14	16	18
5	5	10	15	20	25	30	35	40	45

Name ______________________

Another Look 5-7

Exploring 0 and 1 as Factors

In your book you looked for patterns in a table. Here's another way to find patterns.

Drawing pictures can help you see patterns.

What does 1 group of 5 look like?

This group can be described in three ways.

1 group of 5   1 × 5   5

Draw pictures to show each grouping.

1. 1 group of 6
2. 6 groups of 1

Students should realize they cannot draw anything for 3, 4, 7, and 8.

3. 0 groups of 6
4. 6 groups of 0
5. 1 group of 8
6. 8 groups of 1
7. 0 groups of 8
8. 8 groups of 0

Use the patterns you see to find each product.

9. 5 × 1 = 5
10. 9 × 0 = 0
11. 1 × 8 = 8
12. 0 × 2 = 0
13. 1 × 6 = 6
14. 5 × 0 = 0

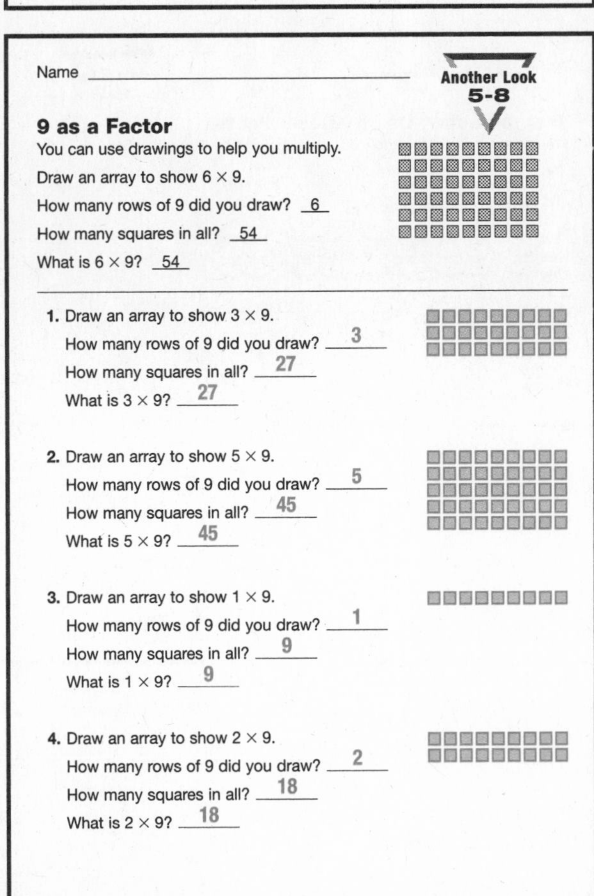

Name ______________________

Another Look 5-8

9 as a Factor

You can use drawings to help you multiply.

Draw an array to show 6 × 9.

How many rows of 9 did you draw? 6

How many squares in all? 54

What is 6 × 9? 54

1. Draw an array to show 3 × 9.
   How many rows of 9 did you draw? 3
   How many squares in all? 27
   What is 3 × 9? 27
2. Draw an array to show 5 × 9.
   How many rows of 9 did you draw? 5
   How many squares in all? 45
   What is 5 × 9? 45
3. Draw an array to show 1 × 9.
   How many rows of 9 did you draw? 1
   How many squares in all? 9
   What is 1 × 9? 9
4. Draw an array to show 2 × 9.
   How many rows of 9 did you draw? 2
   How many squares in all? 18
   What is 2 × 9? 18

Name ______________________

Another Look 5-9

Analyze Word Problems: Too Much or Too Little Information

Asian elephants have 4 nails on each hind foot. African elephants have 3 nails on each hind foot. How many nails does an Asian elephant have on 2 hind feet?

Underline what you need to find.

Circle the information you need to solve the problem.

Asian elephants have 4 nails on each hind foot. African elephants have 3 nails on each hind foot. How many nails does an Asian elephant have on 2 hind feet?

Since there are 4 nails on one hind foot, there must be 4 × 2 or 8 nails on 2 hind feet.

Underline what you need to find. Circle the information you need. Then solve if possible. If not possible, tell what information is needed.

1. Cougars can travel 20 feet in one leap and 25 miles in a day. How many feet could a cougar travel in 2 leaps?
   40 feet
2. Elephants are heavy eaters. They eat 130 pounds of food—hay, fruit, and vegetables—every day. How much hay does an elephant eat in 3 days?
   Need to know how much hay alone it eats in 1 day
3. A newborn giraffe can be up to 6 feet tall. An adult giraffe can grow up to 3 times this height. Giraffes do not weigh as much as African elephants. How tall can an adult giraffe grow?
   18 feet
4. A newborn giraffe is 6 feet tall. How tall is it when it is one year old?
   Need to know how many feet it grows in one year

Name ______________________

Another Look 5-10

Analyze Strategies: Draw a Picture

Draw a picture to solve the problem.

Jason has 15 pepper plants. He wants to plant them in three equal rows. How many plants will each row have? 5

How could you set up your picture? Start by setting up 3 rows.

How did you use the picture to help solve the problem? Keep adding one plant to each of the rows until there are 15 plants in all.

Draw a picture to solve each problem.

1. Emily is making a tile tabletop for art class. The tabletop is 4 tiles wide on each side.
   a. Finish the picture.
   b. How many tiles will she need? 16
2. Robert caught 9 fish today. There were twice as many bass as there were trout. How many trout did Robert catch?
   a. Finish the picture. Check students' drawings.
   b. How many trout did Robert catch? 3

Use with pages 226–227. 69

Name ______________________

Another Look 6-1

3 as a Factor: Using Known Facts

You can draw an array to find 3 × 5.

Shade one group of 3 squares.

This shows 3 × 1.

Draw four more groups of 3. Shade all the squares.
This shows 3 × 5.

How many total squares are shaded? 15

What is 3 × 5? 15

Draw an array on a separate sheet of paper to show the following. Find each product. Check students' drawings.

1. 3 × 6
   How many total squares? 18
   What is 3 × 6? 18
2. 3 × 8
   How many total squares? 24
   What is 3 × 8? 24
3. 3 × 4
   How many total squares? 12
   What is 4 × 3? 12
4. 9 × 3
   How many total squares? 27
   What is 9 × 3? 27
5. How could you add to the array for 3 × 4 to show 3 × 5?
   Add one more group of 3.

70 Use with pages 240–241.

Name ______________________

Another Look 6-2

4 as a Factor: Doubling

To multiply by 4, first multiply by 2. Then double the product.
You can draw an array to find 4 × 6.

Draw 6 on a grid. Shade the squares.

This shows 1 × 6.

Draw the same number of squares again. Shade the squares.
This shows 2 × 6.

How many total squares are shaded? 12

What is 2 × 6? 12

Double this product. What is 4 × 6? 24

1. What is the product of 4 and 3?
   Draw an array to find the product of 2 and 3.
   How many total squares are shaded? 6
   What is 2 × 3? 6
   Double this product.
   What is 4 × 3? 12
2. What is the product of 4 and 9?
   Draw an array to find the product of 2 and 9.
   How many total squares are shaded? 18
   What is 2 × 9? 18
   Double this product.
   What is 4 × 9? 36

Use with pages 242–243. 71

Name ______________________

Another Look 6-3

6 as a Factor: Using Known Facts

You can use what you know about multiplying by 5 to multiply by 6.

Find 6 × 6.

What is 5 × 6? 30

Now add one more group of 6.

How many total counters are there? 36

What is 6 × 6? 36

Use what you know about multiplying by 5 to find each product.

1. 6 × 3
   a. What is 5 × 3? 15
   Add one group of 3.
   b. What is 6 × 3? 18
2. 6 × 8
   a. What is 5 × 8? 40
   Add one group of 8.
   b. What is 6 × 8? 48
3. 6 × 5
   a. What is 5 × 5? 25
   b. Add one group of 5.
   c. What is 6 × 5? 30
4. 7 × 6
   a. What is 7 × 5? 35
   b. Add one group of 7.
   c. What is 7 × 6? 42
5. 9 × 6
   a. What is 9 × 5? 45
   b. Add one group of 9.
   c. What is 9 × 6? 54
6. 6 × 4
   a. What is 5 × 4? 20
   b. Add one group of 4.
   c. What is 6 × 4? 24

72 Use with pages 244–245.

Name ______________________

7 and 8 as Factors

You can use basic facts of 5 and 2 to find 7 × 7.

What is the product of 5 and 7? 35

What is the product of 2 and 7? 14

What is the sum of these products? 49

What is the product of 7 and 7? 49

Draw a picture that shows how you can use basic facts of 5 and 2 to find each product.

1. You can use basic facts of 5 and 2 to find 7 × 9.

What is the product of 5 and 9? 45

What is the product of 2 and 9? 18

What is the sum of these products? 63

What is the product of 7 and 9? 63

2. What is the product of 7 and 8? 56

5 Fact $5 \times 8 = 40$ 2 Fact $2 \times 8 = 16$

3. What is the product of 7 and 6? 42

5 Fact $5 \times 6 = 30$ 2 Fact $2 \times 6 = 12$

Name ______________________

Decision Making

Multiplication can help you solve problems when you have groups of equal numbers.

Seven people are going on a hiking trip. Each person will carry five pounds of food. What is the total weight of the food the group can carry?

7 backpacks each with 5 pounds of food

7 groups of 5 = 7 × 5 = 35 pounds

Use multiplication to help you solve each problem.

A well-balanced diet includes 3 servings of fruit a day. How many servings of fruit should a person eat in a 7-day week?

1. What do you know?
   A person should eat 3 servings of fruit a day.
2. What do you need to know?
   How many servings of fruit should you have in a week?
3. What basic fact can you use to find the answer?
   3 × 7
4. How many servings of fruit should a person eat in a 7-day week?
   21 servings

A well-balanced diet also includes 4 servings of vegetables a day. How many servings of vegetables should a person eat in a 7-day week?

5. What do you know?
   A person should eat 4 servings of vegetables each day.
6. What do you need to know?
   How many servings of vegetables should you eat in a week?
7. Write a number sentence and solve the problem.
   $4 \times 7 = 28$; 28 servings of vegetables

Name ______________________

Another Look
6-6

Exploring Patterns on a Hundred Chart: 3s and 6s

In your book you looked for patterns on a hundred chart to help you multiply with 3 and 6 as factors.

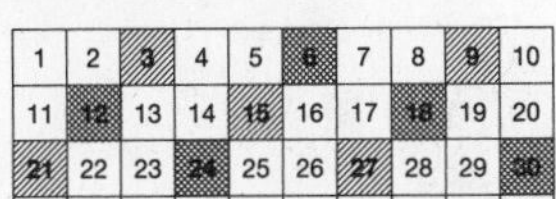

1	2	3	4	5	6	7	8	9	10
11	12	13	14	15	16	17	18	19	20
21	22	23	24	25	26	27	28	29	30

Find the product of 3 and 6 on the hundred chart. 3 groups of 6

Use your finger to skip count 3 sixes. Your finger should land on 6, 12, and 18. The last number you land on is the product.

3 × 6 = 18

Use the hundred chart to find each product. You can point to multiples as you skip count to help you multiply.

1. 5 × 6 = 30
   a. 5 groups of 6
   b. Your finger lands on 6, 12, 18, 24, 30
2. 9 × 3 = 27
   a. 9 groups of 3
   b. Your finger lands on 3, 6, 9, 12, 15, 18, 21, 24, 27
3. 7 × 3 = 21
4. 4 × 6 = 24
5. 5 × 3 = 15
6. 3 × 6 = 18
7. 7 × 6 = 42
8. 3 × 4 = 12
9. 3 × 8 = 24
10. 6 × 6 = 36

Name ______________________

Another Look
6-7

Exploring Patterns on a Fact Table

In your book you found patterns in a fact table to help you remember multiplication facts. Here is another way you can use a fact table.

×	1	2	3	4	5	6	7	8	9	10	11	12
1	1	2	3	4	5	6	7	8	9	10	11	12
2	2	4	6	8	10	2	14	16	18	20	22	24
3	3	6	9	12	15	18	21	24	27	30	33	36
4	4	8	12	16	20	24	28	32	36	40	44	48
5	5	10	15	20	25	30	35	40	45	50	55	60
6	6	12	18	24	30	36	42	48	54	60	66	72
7	7	14	21	28	35	42	49	56	63	70	77	84
8	8	16	24	32	40	48	56	64	72	80	88	96
9	9	18	27	36	45	54	63	72	81	90	99	108
10	10	20	30	40	50	60	70	80	90	100	110	120
11	11	22	33	44	55	66	77	88	99	110	121	132
12	12	24	36	48	60	72	84	96	108	120	132	144

Find the product of 8 and 7 in the fact table. Look for 8 in the first row. Draw a line down from 8. Look for 7 in the first column. Draw a line to the right from 7. Where do the lines cross? This is the product of 8 and 7.

8 × 7 = 56

Use the table to find each product.

1. 2 × 7 = 14
2. 8 × 10 = 80
3. 9 × 4 = 36
4. 11 × 5 = 55
5. 6 × 12 = 72
6. 6 × 8 = 48
7. 11 × 12 = 132
8. 7 × 7 = 49
9. 11 × 4 = 44
10. 6 × 10 = 60
11. 12 × 6 = 72
12. 10 × 10 = 100
13. 6 × 9 = 54
14. 9 × 9 = 81
15. 11 × 11 = 121
16. 12 × 8 = 96

Name ______________________

Another Look 6-8

Multiplying with 3 Factors

Parentheses show you which pair of numbers to multiply first.

$4 \times (2 \times 3) =$

$4 \times$ 6 = 24

If there are no parentheses, you can choose which pair of numbers to multiply first.

$4 \times 2 \times 6 =$

8 $\times 6 =$ 48

1. Find the product of $6 \times (2 \times 3)$.
   $6 \times$ 6 = 36
2. Find the product of $3 \times 5 \times 2$. Multiply the two lesser numbers first.
   $3 \times 2 \times 5 =$
   6 $\times 5 =$ 30

Find each product.

3. $(4 \times 2) \times 6$
   8 $\times 6 =$ 48
4. $5 \times (5 \times 2)$
   $5 \times$ 10 = 50
5. $8 \times 1 \times 9$
   8 $\times 9 =$ 72
6. $(7 \times 0) \times 8$
   0 $\times 8 =$ 0
7. $3 \times (3 \times 1)$
   $3 \times$ 3 = 9
8. $2 \times 6 \times 3$
   6 $\times 6 =$ 36
9. $(1 \times 6) \times 6$
   6 $\times 6 =$ 36
10. $6 \times 2 \times 2$
    $6 \times$ 4 = 24
11. $(3 \times 9) \times 0$
    27 $\times 0 =$ 0
12. $5 \times 4 \times 2$
    $5 \times$ 8 = 40
13. Find the product of 9, 3, and 1. 27
14. Find the product of 2, 5, and 4. 40
15. Find the product of 6, 7, and 1. 42
16. Find the product of 5, 3, and 2. 30

Name ______________________

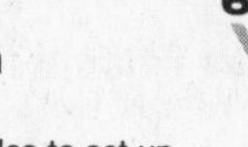

Compare Strategies: Look for a Pattern and Draw a Picture

Plan a party! You must decide how many tables to set up. Each table seats 6 people. If there are 34 people coming, how many tables do you need?

Each table seats 6 people. 34 people are coming.
I need to find out how many tables will seat 34 people.

You can draw a picture to find the answer.

Each **x** is one person. Draw 6 **xs** on each table until you have 34 **xs**. Count to see how many tables are used.

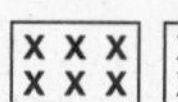

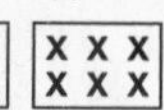

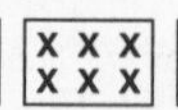

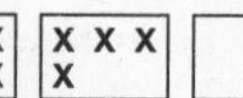

X X X
X

6 tables are needed for 34 people.

You can also look for a pattern to solve the problem.

Tables	1	2	3	4	5	6
People	6	12	18	24	30	36

6 tables for 34 people

Look for a pattern or draw a picture to solve each problem.

1. You are planning a picnic and you must decide how many blankets to bring. Five people can sit on each blanket. How many blankets will you need if 27 people are coming?
   6 blankets
2. One package of muffins contains 4 muffins. If each person gets 1 muffin, how many packages will you need to feed 14 people?
   4 packages

Name ______________________

Exploring Division As Sharing

In your book you used counters to explore division. Here is another way to understand division.

A road construction crew boss has 18 people in his crew. There are 3 jobs that need to be done. He's going to divide up the crew equally. Draw pictures to show how many people will do each job. Draw one picture in each box until all the workers have a job.

Job 1

Job 2

Job 3

1. On the second day of the job, 3 workers are absent. The crew boss still wants to divide the work equally among the 15 workers. Draw stick figures in the boxes below to show how many people will be assigned to each job.

Job 1

Job 2

Job 3

2. By the third day of the job, everyone is back at work. Job 1 is finished. So the crew boss decides to divide the 18 workers into 2 groups in order to finish the 2 remaining jobs. Draw pictures in the boxes below to show how many people will be assigned to each job.

Job 2

Job 3

Name ______________________

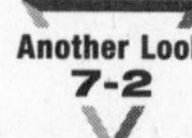

Exploring Division as Repeated Subtraction

In your book you used counters to explore division. Here is another way to understand division.

You can use an array. This array shows 27 stamps.

How many stamps are in 1 row? 9
If you take 1 row away, how many stamps are left? 18
If you take another row away, how many stamps are left? 9
How many rows of stamps can you take away? 3
$27 \div 9 = 3$

1. Sam is packing his toy cars into boxes. Each row has 8 cars.
   How many rows are needed for 24 cars?

   a. Draw a box around each set of 8 cars.
   b. How many boxes did you draw? 3
   c. $24 \div 8 =$ 3
2. Sam is organizing his stuffed animals. Each shelf will hold 5 stuffed animals. How many shelves will he need for 10 stuffed animals?
   2

Name ______________________

Another Look 7-3

Exploring Division Stories

A round pizza has been cut into 6 equal slices.

There are 3 people.

How many slices does each person get?

Take away one for each of the three people.

Take away another for each of the three people.

6 ÷ 3 = 2

1. Look at how the muffins are arranged in the box. There are three rows, each with four muffins.

   a. How would four children share the muffins?
   Four children can each have 3 muffins.

   b. How would three children share the muffins?
   Three children can each have 4 muffins.

Write a division story for each. Use counters or drawings to help.

2. 24 ÷ 8
   Look for 24 divided into 3 groups of 8 or 8 groups of 3.

3. 16 ÷ 4
   Look for 16 divided into 4 groups of 4.

4. 18 ÷ 3
   Look for 18 divided into 6 groups of 3 or 3 groups of 6.

Use with pages 280–281. **81**

Name ______________________

Another Look 7-4

Connecting Multiplication and Division

You have 24 marbles that you want to give away to your friends. You want each friend to get 6 marbles. To how many friends can you give marbles?

24 ÷ 6

Think: What multiplication fact do you know that includes 24 and 6?

6 × 4 = 24

So, 24 ÷ 6 = 4

You can give 6 marbles to 4 friends.

1. 36 ÷ 4
   a. What multiplication fact includes 36 and 4? 4 × 9 = 36
   b. 36 ÷ 4 = 9

2. 28 ÷ 7
   a. What multiplication fact includes 28 and 7? 7 × 4 = 28
   b. 28 ÷ 7 = 4

Complete. You may use counters to help.

3. 14 ÷ 7 = 2
   7 × 2 = 14

4. 32 ÷ 4 = 8
   4 × 8 = 32

5. 30 ÷ 5 = 6
   5 × 6 = 30

6. 18 ÷ 6 = 3
   6 × 3 = 18

7. 27 ÷ 9 = 3
   9 × 3 = 27

8. 24 ÷ 8 = 3
   8 × 3 = 24

9. 15 ÷ 3 = 5
   3 × 5 = 15

10. 16 ÷ 4 = 4
    4 × 4 = 16

11. 28 ÷ 4 = 7
    4 × 7 = 28

12. 18 ÷ 2 = 9
    2 × 9 = 18

82 Use with pages 284–285.

Name ______________________

Another Look 7-5

Dividing by 2

There are 18 students in Mr. Tang's third grade class. The class is evenly divided between girls and boys.

Draw a line to divide the class into 2 groups with the same number of students in each. How many are in each group? 9

18 ÷ 2 = 9

Draw a line to divide each group into 2 groups with the same number of items.

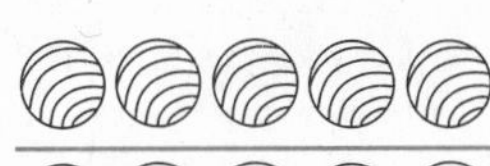

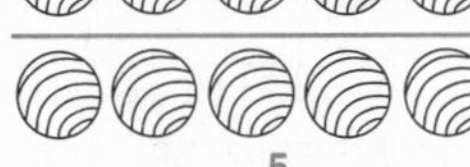

1. 12 ÷ 2 = 6

2. 10 ÷ 2 = 5

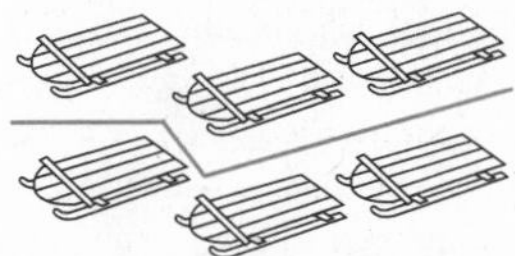

3. 14 ÷ 2 = 7

4. 6 ÷ 2 = 3

5. Draw a picture to show 16 ÷ 2.

Use with pages 286–287. **83**

Name ______________________

Another Look 7-6

Dividing by 5

Find $5\overline{)20}$

Take away groups of 5 from 20 to find the answer. Stop subtracting when you get to 0.

$$\begin{array}{r}20\\-\ 5\\\hline 15\end{array}\quad\begin{array}{r}15\\-\ 5\\\hline 10\end{array}\quad\begin{array}{r}10\\-\ 5\\\hline 5\end{array}\quad\begin{array}{r}5\\-\ 5\\\hline 0\end{array}$$

You had to subtract 5 **four** times to get to 0.

So, 20 ÷ 5 = 4

Take away groups of 5 to find each quotient.

1. $5\overline{)30}$
   a. Begin subtracting. 30 − 5 = 25
   b. Keep subtracting until you get to 0. How many times did you subtract 5? 6 times
   c. 30 ÷ 5 = 6

2. Draw lines to divide the cars into equal groups of 5.

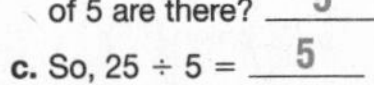

   a. How many cars are there? 25
   b. How many groups of 5 are there? 5
   c. So, 25 ÷ 5 = 5

Find each quotient. Use taking away or equal groups if you need to.

3. 45 ÷ 5 = 9

4. 10 ÷ 5 = 2

5. $5\overline{)35}$ 7

6. $5\overline{)15}$ 3

7. $5\overline{)5}$ 1

8. $5\overline{)40}$ 8

84 Use with pages 288–289.

Name ______________________

Another Look 7-7

Dividing by 3 and 4

Find $3\overline{)12}$.

Take away groups of 3 from 12 to find the answer. Stop subtracting when you get to 0.

$\begin{array}{r} 12 \\ -\ 3 \\ \hline 9 \end{array}$ $\begin{array}{r} 9 \\ -\ 3 \\ \hline 6 \end{array}$ $\begin{array}{r} 6 \\ -\ 3 \\ \hline 3 \end{array}$ $\begin{array}{r} 3 \\ -\ 3 \\ \hline 0 \end{array}$

You had to subtract 3 **four** times to get to 0.

So, 12 ÷ 3 = 4

Take away equal groups to find each quotient.

1. $4\overline{)16}$

a. Begin subtracting. 16 − 4 = 12

b. Keep subtracting until you get to 0. How many times did you subtract 4? 4

c. 16 ÷ 4 = 4

2. Divide the fish into equal groups of 3.

a. How many fish are there? 6

b. How many groups of 3 are there? 2

c. So, 6 ÷ 3 = 2

Find each quotient. Use taking away or equal groups if you need to.

3. 21 ÷ 3 = 7 **4.** 24 ÷ 4 = 6

5. 24 ÷ 3 = 8 **6.** 12 ÷ 4 = 3

7. $3\overline{)27}$ 9 **8.** $4\overline{)32}$ 8

9. $4\overline{)28}$ 7 **10.** $3\overline{)21}$ 7

11. $4\overline{)8}$ 2 **12.** $3\overline{)9}$ 3

13. $4\overline{)20}$ 5 **14.** $4\overline{)36}$ 9

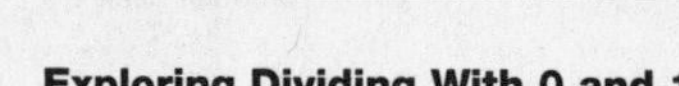

Name ______________________

Another Look 7-8

Exploring Dividing With 0 and 1

In your book you divided using a calculator. Here is another way to divide.

Find 3 ÷ 1.

Think: 1 times what number equals 3?

1 × **3** = 3

So, 3 ÷ 1 = **3**

Find 3 ÷ 3.

Think: 3 times what number equals 3?

3 × **1** = 3

So, 3 ÷ 3 = **1**

Find 0 ÷ 4.

Think: 4 times what number equals 0?

4 × **0** = 0

So, 0 ÷ 4 = **0**

(You cannot divide by 0.)

Find each quotient.

1. 5 ÷ 1

a. 1 times what number equals 5? 5

b. 5 ÷ 1 = 5

2. 0 ÷ 3

a. 3 times what number equals 0? 0

b. 0 ÷ 3 = 0

3. 5 ÷ 5 = 1 **4.** 0 ÷ 5 = 0

5. 6 ÷ 1 = 6 **6.** 4 ÷ 4 = 1

7. $7\overline{)7}$ 1 **8.** $1\overline{)9}$ 9

9. $1\overline{)4}$ 4 **10.** $3\overline{)3}$ 1

11. Divide the cups into groups of 1.

a. How many cups are there? 7

b. How many groups of 1 are there? 7

c. So, 7 ÷ 1 = 7

Name ______________________

Another Look 7-9

Analyze Word Problems: Choose an Operation

Solve the problem.

Ann works at a local grocery store on Saturdays. She is paid $4 for every hour that she works. If she works for 3 hours, how much will she be paid?

What do you know?

Ann is paid $4 for each hour she works. Ann works for 3 hours.

What do you need to find out?

How much money Ann will be paid.

What operation could you choose to solve the problem?

Since you need to put together equal groups of $4, multiply.

Multiply. $4 (amount each hour) × 3 (hours) = $12 (total amount)

So, Ann will be paid $12.

Does your answer make sense?

Yes, because 12 ÷ 4 = 3 and 12 ÷ 3 = 4.

1. Rhonda bought 18 bagels. If there are 6 bagels in each package, how many packages did she buy?

a. How many bagels are in a package? 6 bagels

b. How many bagels does Rhonda have? 18 bagels

c. What operation could you use to solve the problem? Division

d. Write the number sentence. What is the answer? 18 ÷ 6 = 3; Rhonda bought 3 packages of bagels.

Write the operation, then solve each problem.

2. Pete had 8 marbles. Then John gave him 5 marbles. How many marbles does Pete have? Addition; 13 marbles

3. Fiona bought 9 treats for her dog Spot. If Spot ate 2 treats, how many treats are left? Subtraction; 7 treats

Name ______________________

Another Look 7-10

Dividing by 6 and 7

Suppose you are given a page of 30 animal stickers for your collection. Your sticker album holds 6 stickers on each page. How many pages do you need for your animal stickers?

Find 30 ÷ 6.

You can solve this problem using counters.

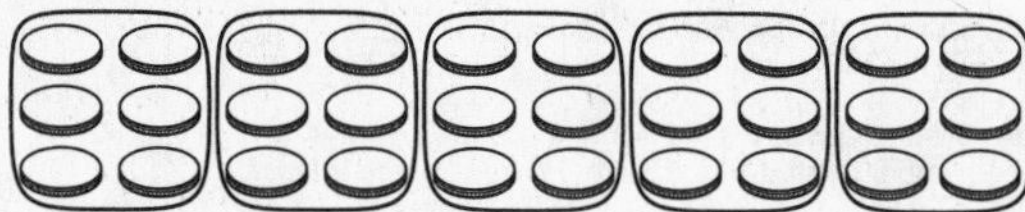

Draw boxes around groups of 6 counters.

How many boxes did you draw? 5

30 ÷ 6 = 5

You need 5 pages for your animal stickers.

Find each quotient. Use counters or draw a picture to help you.

1. Find 35 ÷ 7.

Draw or set out 35 counters. Sort counters into groups of 7.

a. How many groups do you have? 5

b. So, 35 ÷ 7 = 5

2. Find 42 ÷ 6.

Draw or set out 42 counters. Sort counters into groups of 6.

a. How many groups do you have? 7

b. So, 42 ÷ 6 = 7

Find each quotient.

3. $7\overline{)28}$ 4 **4.** $6\overline{)54}$ 9 **5.** $7\overline{)49}$ 7

6. 18 ÷ 6 = 3 **7.** 56 ÷ 7 = 8 **8.** 28 ÷ 7 = 4

9. If you wanted to share 18 crackers between 3 friends, how many crackers would you give to each friend? 6

10. Divide 14 counters into 7 groups. How many are in each group? 2

Name ____________________

Another Look 7-11

Dividing by 8 and 9

Find 40 ÷ 8 by drawing a picture.

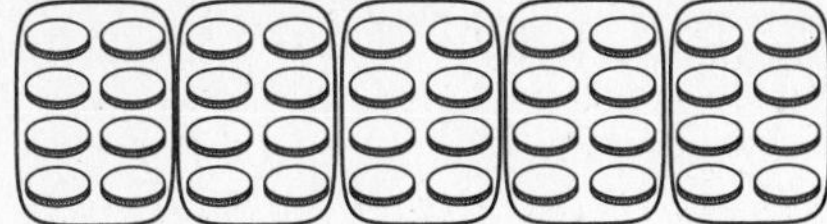

Draw a ring around groups of 8 circles.

How many groups of 8 are there? 5

So, 40 ÷ 8 = 5

Find each quotient. Use counters or draw a picture to help you.

1. Find 24 ÷ 8
   Draw 24 stars.
   Ring groups of 8 stars.
   a. How many groups are there? 3
   b. So, 24 ÷ 8 = 3
2. Find 27 ÷ 9
   Draw 27 squares.
   Ring groups of 9 squares.
   a. How many groups are there? 3
   b. So, 27 ÷ 9 = 3

Find each quotient.

3. $8\overline{)40}$ 5
4. $9\overline{)36}$ 4
5. $8\overline{)56}$ 7
6. 48 ÷ 8 = 6
7. 72 ÷ 9 = 8
8. 45 ÷ 9 = 5
9. Divide the flowers into groups of 8.

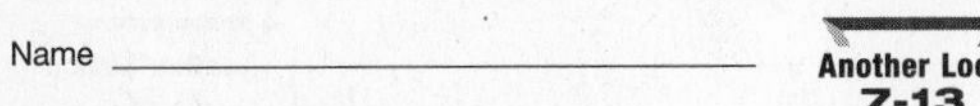

   a. How many flowers are there? 16
   b. How many groups of 8 are there? 2
   c. So 16 ÷ 8 = 2

Name ____________________

Another Look 7-12

Exploring Even and Odd Numbers

In your book you used division to test for even and odd numbers. Here is another way to check for even and odd numbers.

Here is a picture of 10 counters.

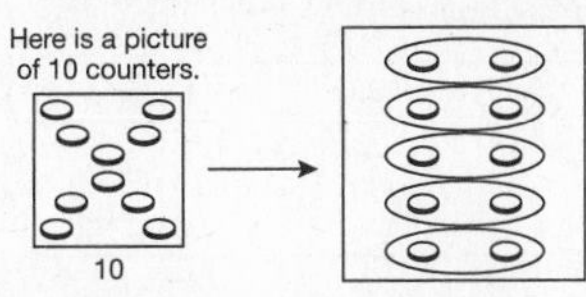

10

An *even* number can be divided by 2.

10 is an *even* number.

Here is a picture of 11 counters.

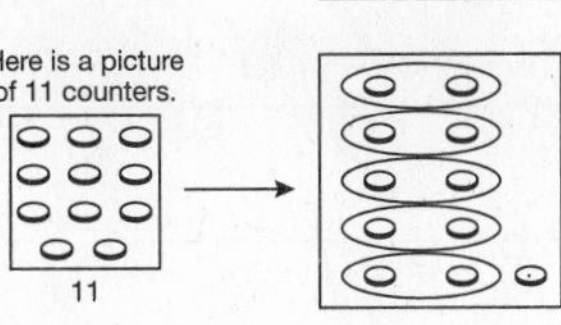

11

An *odd* number has one left over when it is divided by 2.

11 is an *odd* number.

On a separate sheet of paper, draw a picture of counters to determine if each number is even or odd. Then answer each question.

1. 12
   a. Circle groups of 2 counters. How many counters are left over? 0
   b. Is 12 even or odd? Even
2. 27
   a. Circle groups of 2 counters. How many counters are left over? 1
   b. Is 27 even or odd? Odd

Write even or odd for each number.

3. 22 Even
4. 17 Odd
5. 21 Odd
6. 30 Even
7. 4 Even
8. 1 Odd

Name ____________________

Another Look 7-13

Compare Strategies: Use Objects and Make an Organized List

Denise and Robert are making a poster with 6 pictures of endangered animals. They want the pictures in equal rows. What are all the ways to arrange the pictures?

You can make arrays to find all the possible ways.

If you make an array of 1 row how many pictures will be in each row? 6

If you make an array of 2 rows how many pictures will be in each row? 3

If you make an array of 3 rows how many pictures will be in each row? 2

If you make an array of 6 rows how many pictures will be in each row? 1

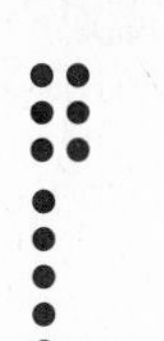

1. Suppose Denise and Robert want to use 18 pictures of animals for their poster. What are all the possible ways to arrange the pictures in rows?

Rows	Pictures in Each Row	Total
1	18	18
2	9	18
3	6	18
6	3	18
9	2	18
18	1	18

2. Denise and Robert decide to use 16 pictures. Take a square piece of paper and arrange 16 counters on it in rows. How many rows fit best on the paper? 4
3. In an album, Ann, Bob, Cal, and Dee's pictures are in a row. From the left, Bob's picture is after Ann's and Dee's but before Cal's. Dee's picture is before Ann's. List the order of the students from left to right.
   Dee, Ann, Bob, Cal

Name ____________________

Another Look 7-14

Exploring Algebra: Balancing Scales

In your book you made tables to balance scales. Here is another way to balance scales. A scale is balanced when the same amount is on both sides. Find all the ways to balance this scale.

A	=	B	+	C
4	=	4	+	0
4	=	3	+	1
4	=	2	+	2
4	=	1	+	3
4	=	0	+	4

Box A has 4 cubes inside. You can find how many cubes can be placed in boxes B and C by finding all the pairs of numbers with a sum of 4.

1. Box A has 3 cubes inside.
   a. The number of cubes in boxes B and C must have a sum of 3.
   b. How many cubes can be in boxes B and C?
   Complete the table to record each way.

A	B	C
3	3	0
3	2	1
3	1	2
3	0	3

2. Each box A has 3 cubes inside.
   a. The number of cubes in boxes B and C must have a sum of 6.
   b. How many cubes can be in boxes B and C?
   Make a table to record each way.

A	A+A	B	C
3	6	0	6
3	6	1	5
3	6	2	4
3	6	3	3
3	6	4	2
3	6	5	1
3	6	6	0

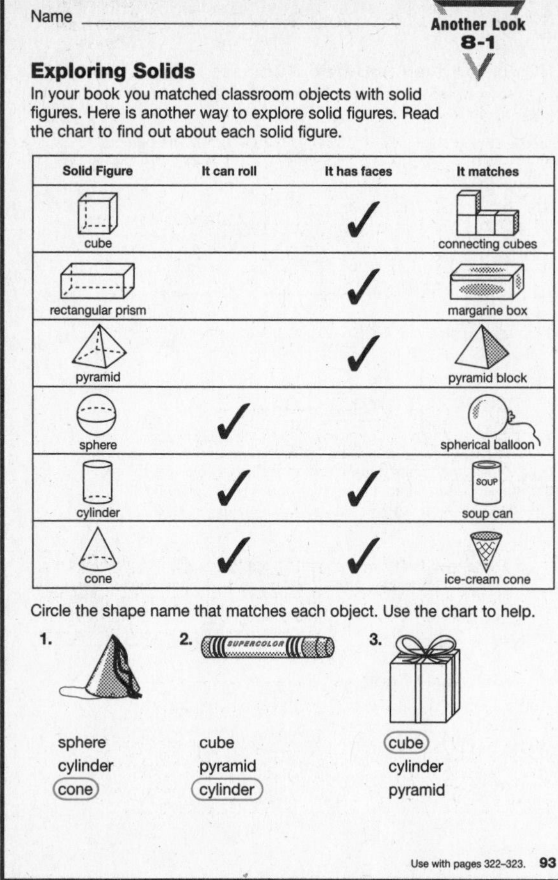

Name ______________________

Another Look 8-1

Exploring Solids

In your book you matched classroom objects with solid figures. Here is another way to explore solid figures. Read the chart to find out about each solid figure.

Solid Figure	It can roll	It has faces	It matches
cube		✓	connecting cubes
rectangular prism		✓	margarine box
pyramid		✓	pyramid block
sphere	✓		spherical balloon
cylinder	✓	✓	soup can
cone	✓	✓	ice-cream cone

Circle the shape name that matches each object. Use the chart to help.

1. sphere, cylinder, (cone)
2. cube, pyramid, (cylinder)
3. (cube), cylinder, pyramid

Use with pages 322–323. 93

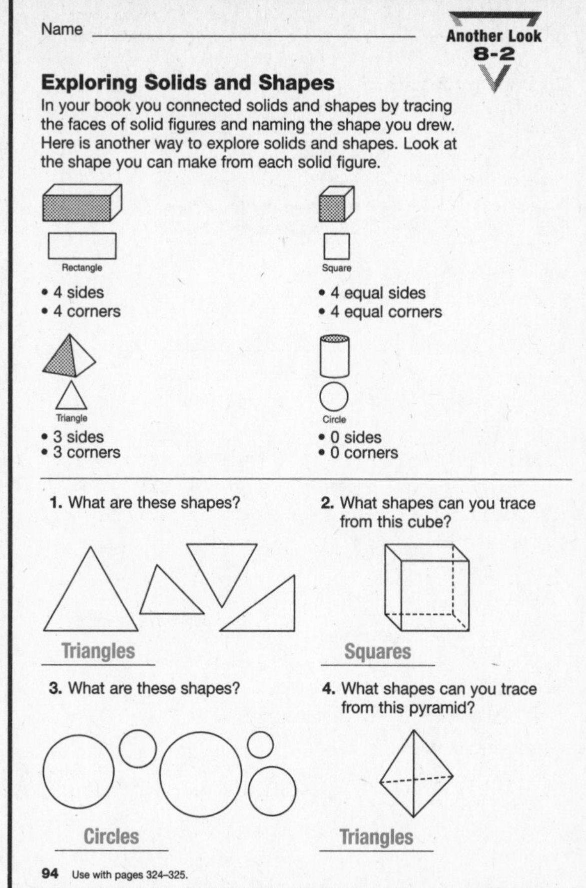

Name ______________________

Another Look 8-2

Exploring Solids and Shapes

In your book you connected solids and shapes by tracing the faces of solid figures and naming the shape you drew. Here is another way to explore solids and shapes. Look at the shape you can make from each solid figure.

Rectangle
- 4 sides
- 4 corners

Square
- 4 equal sides
- 4 equal corners

Triangle
- 3 sides
- 3 corners

Circle
- 0 sides
- 0 corners

1. What are these shapes? **Triangles**
2. What shapes can you trace from this cube? **Squares**
3. What are these shapes? **Circles**
4. What shapes can you trace from this pyramid? **Triangles**

94 Use with pages 324–325.

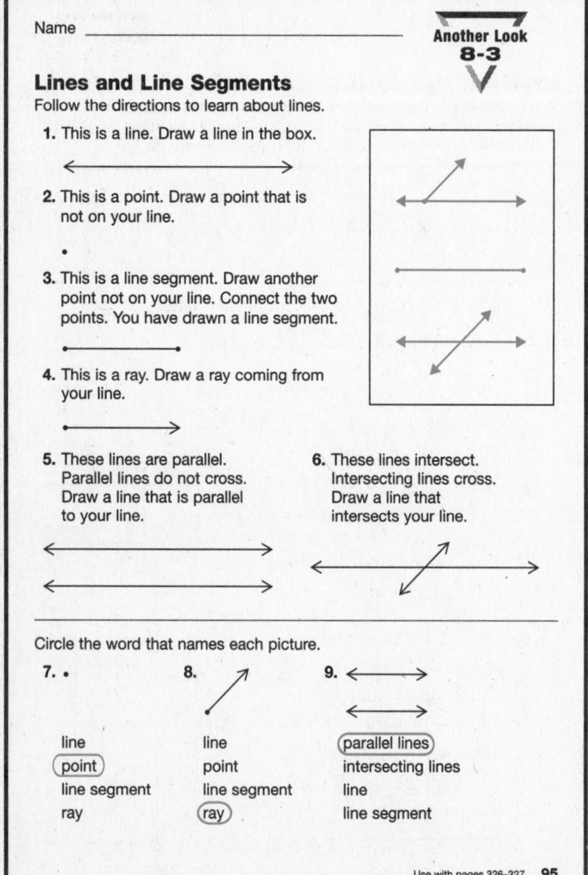

Name ______________________

Another Look 8-3

Lines and Line Segments

Follow the directions to learn about lines.

1. This is a line. Draw a line in the box.
2. This is a point. Draw a point that is not on your line.
3. This is a line segment. Draw another point not on your line. Connect the two points. You have drawn a line segment.
4. This is a ray. Draw a ray coming from your line.
5. These lines are parallel. Parallel lines do not cross. Draw a line that is parallel to your line.
6. These lines intersect. Intersecting lines cross. Draw a line that intersects your line.

Circle the word that names each picture.

7. line, (point), line segment, ray
8. line, point, line segment, (ray)
9. (parallel lines), intersecting lines, line, line segment

Use with pages 326–327. 95

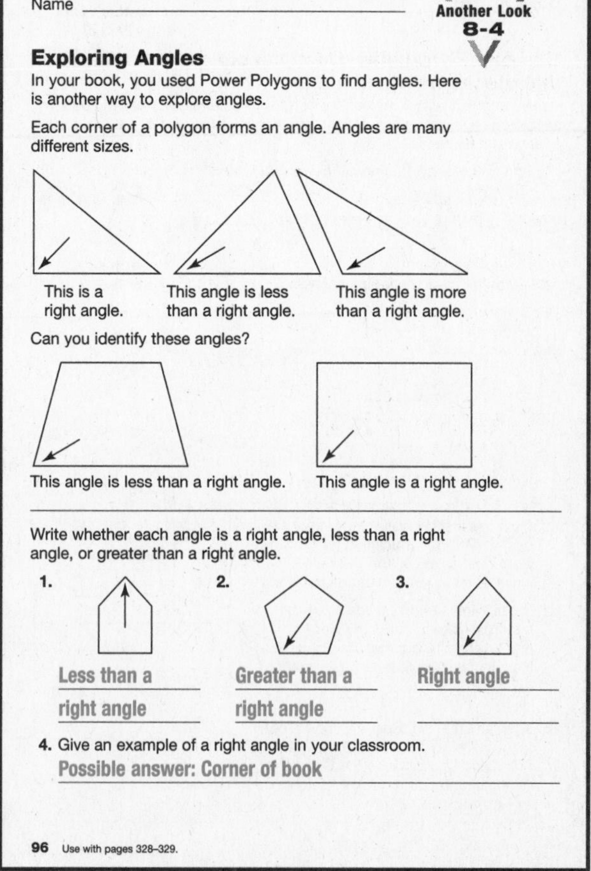

Name ______________________

Another Look 8-4

Exploring Angles

In your book, you used Power Polygons to find angles. Here is another way to explore angles.

Each corner of a polygon forms an angle. Angles are many different sizes.

This is a right angle. This angle is less than a right angle. This angle is more than a right angle.

Can you identify these angles?

This angle is less than a right angle. This angle is a right angle.

Write whether each angle is a right angle, less than a right angle, or greater than a right angle.

1. **Less than a right angle**
2. **Greater than a right angle**
3. **Right angle**
4. Give an example of a right angle in your classroom. **Possible answer: Corner of book**

96 Use with pages 328–329.

Name ____________________

Another Look 8-5

Exploring Slides, Flips, and Turns

In your book, you used power polygons to show slides, flips, and turns. Here is another way to explore slides, flips, and turns.

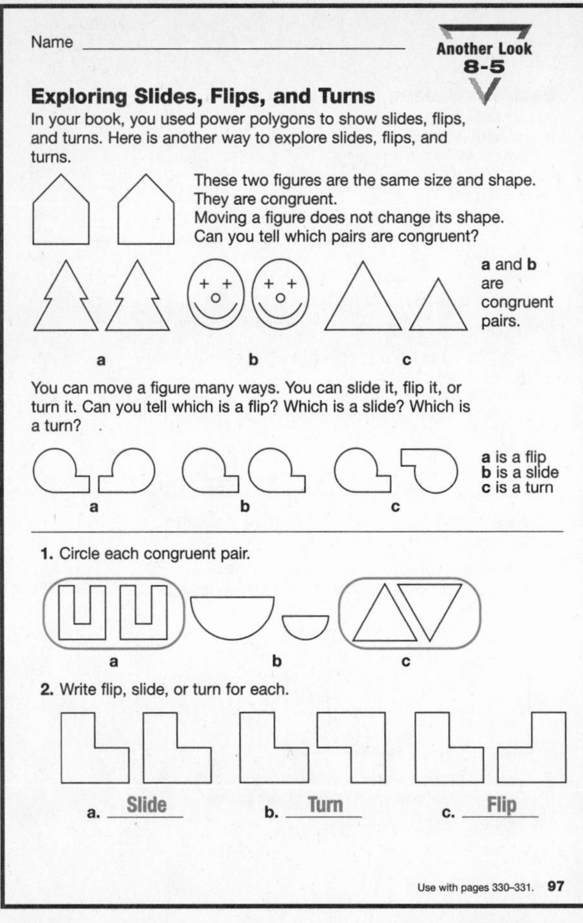

These two figures are the same size and shape.
They are congruent.
Moving a figure does not change its shape.
Can you tell which pairs are congruent?
a and b are congruent pairs.
a
b
c
You can move a figure many ways. You can slide it, flip it, or turn it. Can you tell which is a flip? Which is a slide? Which is a turn?
a is a flip
b is a slide
c is a turn
1. Circle each congruent pair.
2. Write flip, slide, or turn for each.
a. Slide
b. Turn
c. Flip

Name ____________________

Another Look 8-6

Exploring Symmetry

In your book, you folded sheets of paper to find lines of symmetry. Here is another way to explore symmetry.

Each shape below has a line of symmetry. It divides the shape into two equal parts. A grid helps you see that the parts match.

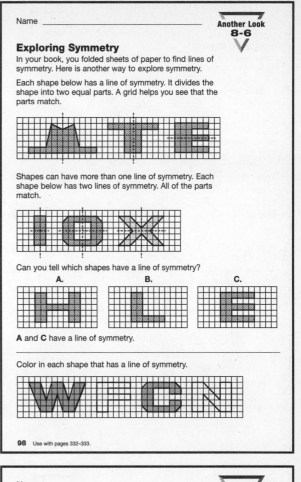

Shapes can have more than one line of symmetry. Each shape below has two lines of symmetry. All of the parts match.

Can you tell which shapes have a line of symmetry?

A. B. C.

A and **C** have a line of symmetry.

Color in each shape that has a line of symmetry.

Name ____________________

Another Look 8-7

Analyze Strategies: Solve a Simpler Problem

Sue Ellen North wants to use her initials in her Internet address. How many different combinations are possible if each letter is used only once?

If S is the first letter, how many ways can the other two letters be written?

SEN SNE Two ways

If E is the first letter, how many ways can the other two be written?

ESN ENS Two ways

What are the combinations using N as the first letter? NES NSE

How many different combinations are there? 6

1. Mark is arranging his model cars on a shelf. He has 1 blue, 2 red, and 1 black car. He wants to put the 2 red cars as the first and last cars on the shelf. How many ways can he arrange the cars?
   a. Which cars can be put second? Blue or black
   b. Which cars can be put third? Black or blue
   c. How many arrangements are there all together? 2
2. Kira has 3 different plants.
   a. If she wants to put the pink tulips first, how many ways can she arrange the plants on a window sill? 2
   b. Kira buys another plant, but she still wants to keep the pink tulips first. How many ways can she arrange her plants now? 6
3. Kevin has flower pots that hold 1 or 3 bulbs. He has 18 bulbs. How many ways can he plant the bulbs? 7

Name ____________________

Another Look 8-8

Exploring Perimeter

In your book you used grid paper to measure perimeter. Here is another way to find perimeter. Count the edges of the tiles around the outside of the rectangle. The distance around is 14 units, since $5 + 2 + 5 + 2 =$ 14.

5 units
2 units 2 units

1. Find the distance around the rectangle made of tiles.

B
A C
D

   a. What is the length of side A? 2 units
   b. What is the length of side B? 6 units
   c. What is the length of side C? 2 units
   d. What is the length of side D? 6 units
   e. What is the distance around the shape? 16 units

2. Find the distance around the shape.

B
C
A D
E
F

   a. What is the length of each side?
      A 5 units B 4 units C 3 units
      D 3 units E 2 units F 7 units
   b. What is the distance around the shape? 24 units

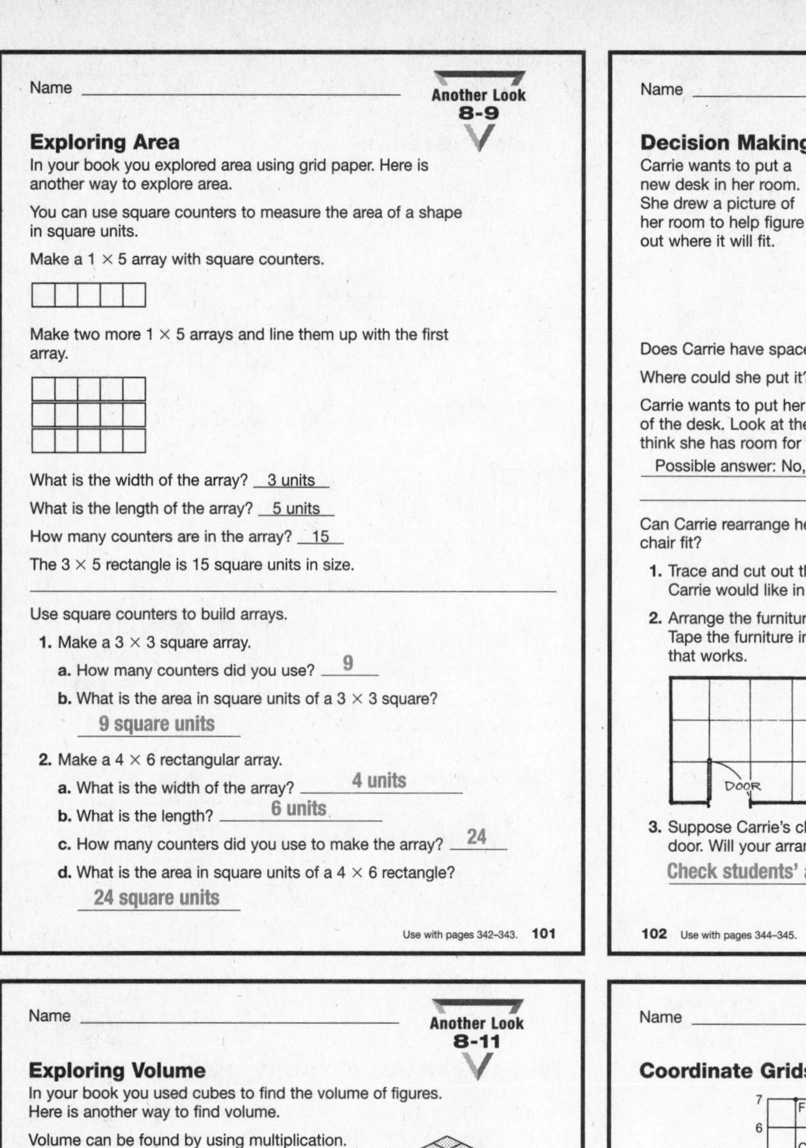

Name ______________________

Another Look 8-9

Exploring Area

In your book you explored area using grid paper. Here is another way to explore area.

You can use square counters to measure the area of a shape in square units.

Make a 1×5 array with square counters.

Make two more 1×5 arrays and line them up with the first array.

What is the width of the array? 3 units

What is the length of the array? 5 units

How many counters are in the array? 15

The 3×5 rectangle is 15 square units in size.

Use square counters to build arrays.

1. Make a 3×3 square array.
   a. How many counters did you use? 9
   b. What is the area in square units of a 3×3 square? 9 square units
2. Make a 4×6 rectangular array.
   a. What is the width of the array? 4 units
   b. What is the length? 6 units
   c. How many counters did you use to make the array? 24
   d. What is the area in square units of a 4×6 rectangle? 24 square units

Use with pages 342–343. **101**

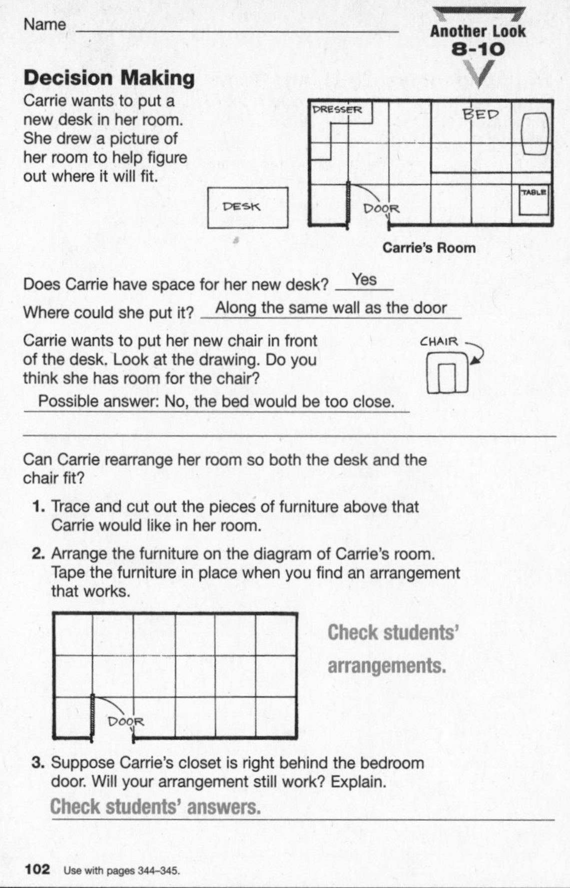

Name ______________________

Another Look 8-10

Decision Making

Carrie wants to put a new desk in her room. She drew a picture of her room to help figure out where it will fit.

Carrie's Room

Does Carrie have space for her new desk? Yes

Where could she put it? Along the same wall as the door

Carrie wants to put her new chair in front of the desk. Look at the drawing. Do you think she has room for the chair?

Possible answer: No, the bed would be too close.

Can Carrie rearrange her room so both the desk and the chair fit?

1. Trace and cut out the pieces of furniture above that Carrie would like in her room.
2. Arrange the furniture on the diagram of Carrie's room. Tape the furniture in place when you find an arrangement that works.

Check students' arrangements.

3. Suppose Carrie's closet is right behind the bedroom door. Will your arrangement still work? Explain.
   Check students' answers.

102 Use with pages 344–345.

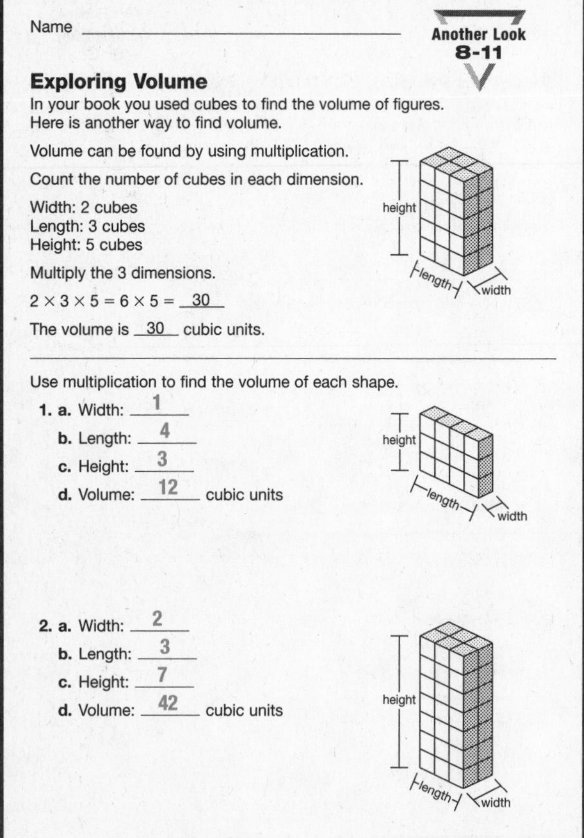

Name ______________________

Another Look 8-11

Exploring Volume

In your book you used cubes to find the volume of figures. Here is another way to find volume.

Volume can be found by using multiplication.

Count the number of cubes in each dimension.

Width: 2 cubes
Length: 3 cubes
Height: 5 cubes

Multiply the 3 dimensions.

$2 \times 3 \times 5 = 6 \times 5 =$ 30

The volume is 30 cubic units.

Use multiplication to find the volume of each shape.

1. a. Width: 1
   b. Length: 4
   c. Height: 3
   d. Volume: 12 cubic units

2. a. Width: 2
   b. Length: 3
   c. Height: 7
   d. Volume: 42 cubic units

Use with pages 346–347. **103**

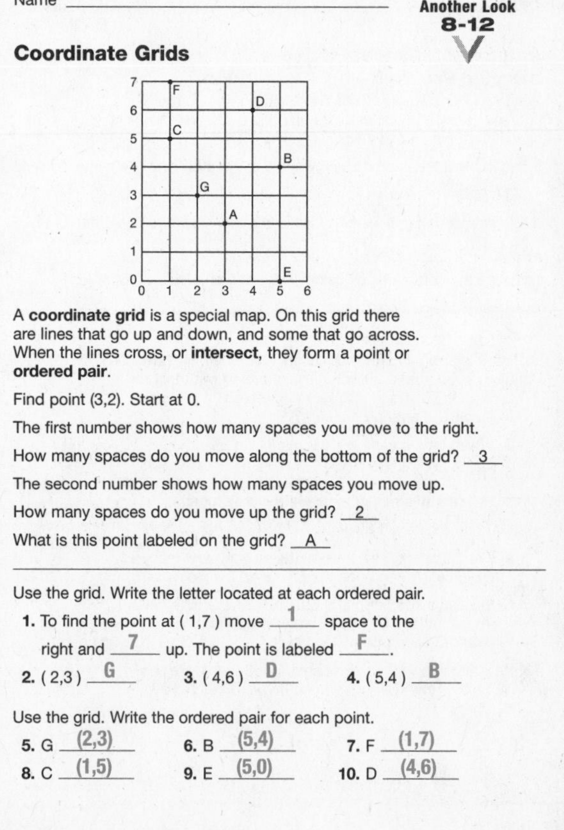

Name ______________________

Another Look 8-12

Coordinate Grids

A **coordinate grid** is a special map. On this grid there are lines that go up and down, and some that go across. When the lines cross, or **intersect**, they form a point or **ordered pair**.

Find point (3,2). Start at 0.

The first number shows how many spaces you move to the right.

How many spaces do you move along the bottom of the grid? 3

The second number shows how many spaces you move up.

How many spaces do you move up the grid? 2

What is this point labeled on the grid? A

Use the grid. Write the letter located at each ordered pair.

1. To find the point at (1,7) move 1 space to the right and 7 up. The point is labeled F.
2. (2,3) G
3. (4,6) D
4. (5,4) B

Use the grid. Write the ordered pair for each point.

5. G (2,3)
6. B (5,4)
7. F (1,7)
8. C (1,5)
9. E (5,0)
10. D (4,6)

104 Use with pages 348–349.

Name ______________________

Another Look 9-1

Exploring Multiplying Tens

In your book you multiplied tens using place-value blocks. Here is another way. You can think of a symbol to represent 10, like you did with a pictograph.

To multiply by 10, you can think of basic facts.

To find 4 × 80, think about 4 × 8

4 × 8 = 32
4 × 8 tens = 32 tens
32 tens = 320
So, 4 × 80 = 320.

❀ = 10

1. 3 × 50
   a. 3 groups of 5 tens
   b. 3 × 5 tens = 15 tens
   c. 3 × 50 = 150

❀ = 10

2. 6 × 30
   a. 6 groups of 3 tens
   b. 6 × 3 tens = 18 tens
   c. 6 × 30 = 180

❀ = 10

3. 4 × 7 tens = 28 tens
   a. 4 × 70 = 280

4. 5 × 4 tens = 20 tens
   a. 5 × 40 = 200

5. 6 × 8 tens = 48 tens
   a. 6 × 80 = 480

6. 7 × 2 tens = 14 tens
   a. 7 × 20 = 140

7. 8 × 9 tens = 72 tens
   a. 8 × 90 = 720

8. 5 × 6 tens = 30 tens
   a. 5 × 60 = 300

Name ______________________

Another Look 9-2

Exploring Multiplication Patterns

In your book you used a calculator to help you multiply by tens and hundreds. Here are two rules you can follow to multiply by tens and hundreds.

To multiply by tens, write a zero in the ones place. Then multiply the non-zero digits

4 × 5 = 20
4 × 50 = 200

To multiply by hundreds, write *two* zeros, one in the ones place, and one in the tens place. Then multiply the non-zero digits.

4 × 5 = 20
4 × 500 = 2,000

Complete.

1. 3 × 6 = 18
   3 × 60 = 180
   3 × 600 = 1,800

2. 2 × 3 = 6
   2 × 30 = 60
   2 × 300 = 600

3. 5 × 3 = 15
   5 × 30 = 150
   5 × 300 = 1,500

4. 3 × 8 = 24
   3 × 80 = 240
   3 × 800 = 2,400

5. 4 × 8 = 32
   4 × 80 = 320
   4 × 800 = 3,200

6. 2 × 6 = 12
   2 × 60 = 120
   2 × 600 = 1,200

7. 1 × 7 = 7
   1 × 70 = 70
   1 × 700 = 700

8. 3 × 7 = 21
   3 × 70 = 210
   3 × 700 = 2,100

9. 5 × 4 = 20
   5 × 40 = 200
   5 × 400 = 2,000

10. 4 × 7 = 28
    4 × 70 = 280
    4 × 700 = 2,800

Name ______________________

Another Look 9-3

Estimating Products

An estimate tells *about* how many. To estimate a product, round the greater factor to the nearest ten or hundred. Then multiply.

You can use a number line to help you round.

Example 1 Estimate 3 × 22.

Step 1 Round 22 to the nearest ten.

22 is closer to 20 than 30, so 22 rounds to 20.

Step 2 Multiply the factors.

3 × 20 = 60

3 × 22 is about 60.

Example 2 Estimate 8 × 389.

Step 1 Round 389 to the nearest hundred.

389 is closer to 400 than 300, so 389 rounds to 400.

Step 2 Multiply the factors.

8 × 400 = 3,200

8 × 389 is about 3,200.

Circle the better estimate.

1. 5 × 34 — a. (5 × 30 = 150) — b. 5 × 40 = 200
2. 6 × 57 — a. 6 × 50 = 300 — b. (6 × 60 = 360)
3. 4 × 416 — a. (4 × 400 = 1,600) — b. 4 × 500 = 2,000
4. 3 × 345 — a. (3 × 300 = 900) — b. 3 × 200 = 600
5. 8 × 678 — a. 8 × 600 = 4,800 — b. (8 × 700 = 5,600)
6. 2 × 729 — a. (2 × 700 = 1,400) — b. 2 × 600 = 1,200

Name ______________________

Another Look 9-4

Exploring Multiplication with Arrays

In your book you used place-value blocks to show an array. Here is another way to show an array.

When multiplying 2-digit numbers, break apart the number into tens and ones. You can use grid paper to help.

Multiply 2 and 28. 28 = 20 + 8

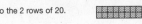

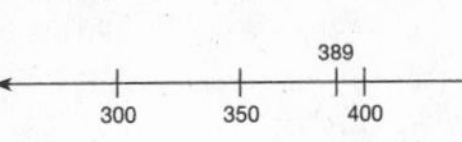

Step 1 Shade 2 rows of 20.

2 × 20 = 40

Step 2 Shade 2 rows of 8 next to the 2 rows of 20.

2 × 8 = 16

Step 3 Add the number of squares in the 2 pieces you shaded. This is the product.

(2 × 20) + (2 × 8) = 40 + 16 = 56

Step 4 2 × 28 = 56

Find each product. You may use place-value blocks or grid paper to help.

5. Find 3 × 29.
   a. 3 × 20 = 60
   b. 3 × 9 = 27
   c. 60 + 27 = 87

6. Find 2 × 43.
   a. 2 × 40 = 80
   b. 2 × 3 = 6
   c. 80 + 6 = 86

7. Find 4 × 17.
   a. 4 × 10 = 40
   b. 4 × 7 = 28
   c. 40 + 28 = 68

8. Find 2 × 37.
   a. 2 × 30 = 60
   b. 2 × 7 = 14
   c. 60 + 14 = 74

Name ______________________

Another Look 9-5

Multiplying: Partial Products

You can draw rectangles to help you multiply.

Find 4 × 27.

Draw a rectangle 27 squares long by 4 squares wide. Divide the rectangle into smaller rectangles by 10s. Find the sum of the number of squares in each section.

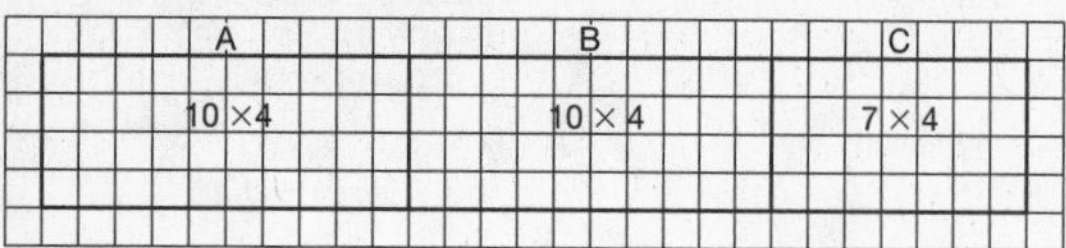

Section A 10 × 4 = 40 Section B 10 × 4 = 40 Section C 7 × 4 = 28

40 + 40 + 28 = 108

4 × 27 = 108

Find each product. Use grid paper to help you.

1. 6 × 23

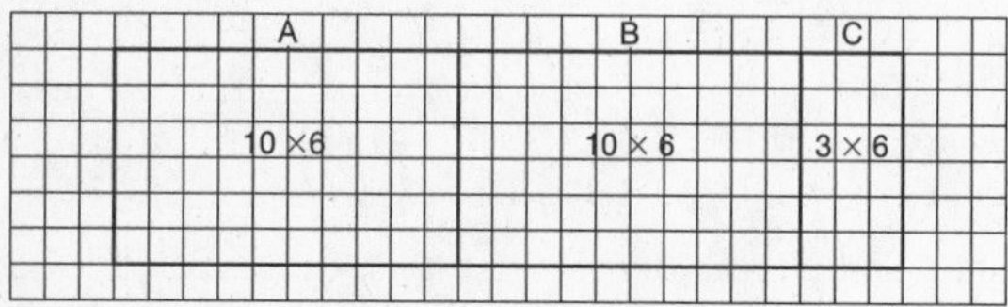

How many squares are in

a. Section A? 60 b. Section B? 60 c. Section C? 18

d. How many squares are there in all? 138

e. 6 × 23 = 138

2. 15 × 3 45 3. 72 × 2 144 4. 23 × 7 161

Name ______________________

Another Look 9-6

Multiplying 2-Digit Numbers

You can break up a 2-digit number to make it easier to multiply. You can multiply the tens, multiply the ones, and add these products together.

Find 4 × 18.

a. Break up the 2-digit number into tens and ones. 1 ten and 8 ones

b. Multiply the tens. 1 ten × 4 = 4 tens (40)

Multiply the ones. 8 ones × 4 = 32 ones (32)

c. Add the products. 40 + 32 = 72

Find each product. Use place-value blocks to help.

1. Find 12 × 5.

a. Break up the 2-digit number into tens and ones. 1 ten and 2 ones

b. Multiply the tens. 1 ten × 5 = 5 tens (50)

Multiply the ones. 2 ones × 5 = 10 ones (10)

c. Add the products. 50 + 10 = 60

2. Find 28 × 5.

a. Break up the 2-digit number into tens and ones. 2 tens and 8 ones

b. Multiply the tens. 2 tens × 5 = 10 tens (100)

Multiply the ones. 8 ones × 5 = 40 ones (40)

c. Add the products. 100 + 40 = 140

3. Find 43 × 7.

a. Break up the 2-digit number into tens and ones. 4 tens and 3 ones

b. Multiply the tens. 4 tens × 7 = 28 tens (280)

Multiply the ones. 3 ones × 7 = 21 ones (21)

c. Add the products. 280 + 21 = 301

Name ______________________

Another Look 9-7

Multiplying 3-Digit Numbers

Find 138 × 5.

Step 1 Multiply the ones. 8 × 5 = 40 ones

Write tens digit above the 3 in the tens place.

Write the ones digit in the ones place.

```
  4
 138
×  5
   0
```

Step 2 Multiply the tens. 3 × 5 = 15

Add the tens from Step 1. 15 + 4 = 19

Write the 1 above the 1 in the hundreds place.

Write the 9 in the tens place.

```
 [1]4
 138
×  5
  [9]0
```

Step 3 Multiply the hundreds. 1 × 5 = 5

Add the hundreds from Step 2. 5 + 1 = 6

Write the sum in the hundreds place.

```
 14
 138
×  5
 [6]90
```

138 × 5 = 690

Complete. Find each product.

```
1.   1[1]      2.  [1]4      3.  [2]
     236           418           571
   ×   3         ×   6         ×   4
    [7][0]8      [2],[5]0[8]   2,[2][8]4

4.  [2][7]     5.  [6]       6.  [1][1]
     329           607           387
   ×   8         ×   9         ×   2
  [2],[6][3][2]  [5],[4][6][3]  [7][7][4]
```


Name ______________________

Another Look 9-8

Multiplying Money

When you multiply dollars by a whole number, your answer will be in dollars. Is there a dollar sign and decimal point in the number you're multiplying? If there is, remember to put one in your answer!

Example 1 $3.75 × 2

Does the answer to this problem need a dollar sign or a decimal point? It needs both.

$3.75 × 2 = $7.50

Example 2 $375 × 2

Does the answer to this problem need a dollar sign or a decimal point? It needs a dollar sign.

$375 × 2 = $750

Multiply the same way you would with whole numbers. Use a dollar sign or a decimal point if needed.

1. $1.15 × 2 = $2.30

Does the answer to this problem need a dollar sign or a decimal point? It needs both.

2. $2.56 × 3 = $7.68

Does the answer to this problem need a dollar sign or a decimal point? It needs both.

3. $491 × 5 = $2,455

Does the answer to this problem need a dollar sign or a decimal point? It needs a dollar sign.

4. $3.75 × 4 = $15.00

Does the answer to this problem need a dollar sign or a decimal point? It needs both.

Name ______________________

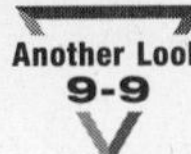

Mental Math

When you multiply a 2-digit number, try this method for multiplying mentally:

Find the nearest multiple of 10 for the 2-digit number. Multiply the multiple by the other number and adjust.

Example Find 6 × 32.

a. What is the nearest multiple of 10 to 32? 30

b. Multiply with that number: 6 × 30 = 180

c. Is 32 greater than or less than 30? By how much? Greater; 2

d. Add 2 groups of 6 to your answer for **b.** 180 + 12 = 192

Example Find 6 × 38.

a. What is the nearest multiple of 10 to 38? 40

b. Multiply with that number: 6 × 40 = 240

c. Is 38 greater or less than 40? By how much? Less; 2

d. Subtract 2 groups of 6 from your answer in **b.** 240 − 12 = 228

1. Find 5 × 17.

a. What is the nearest multiple of 10 to 17? 20

b. Multiply with that number: 5 × 20 = 100

c. Is 17 less than or greater than 20? By how much? Less; 3

d. Subtract 3 groups of 5 from your answer for **b.** 100 − 15 = 85

Solve each problem mentally.

2. 3 × 21 = 63 **3.** 42 × 5 = 210

4. 2 × 58 = 116 **5.** 26 × 4 = 104

Name ______________________

Analyze Strategies: Make a Table

Your family gets 3 magazines in January and your father puts them on the shelf. In February, there are 6 magazines on the shelf. In March, there are 9.

How many magazines will there be in June? One way to figure this out is to make a table. Fill in what you know.

Month	Jan.	Feb.	Mar.	Apr.	May	June
Magazines	3	6	9	12	15	18

Look for patterns in your table. The number of magazines is always 3 more than the previous month.

Continue the pattern. How many magazines will there be in June? 18

Complete the tables to solve each problem.

1. Marty washes the dishes 3 nights each week. How many times does he wash the dishes in one month (4 weeks)? 12 times

Week	1	2	3	4
Dishes	3	6	9	12

2. Carolyn mows the lawn twice a week. How many weeks will it take for Carolyn to mow the lawn 12 times? 6 weeks

Week	1	2	3	4	5	6
Mowing the Lawn	2	4	6	8	10	12

Name ______________________

Exploring Division Patterns

In your book, you used place-value patterns to divide numbers. Here is another way to explore division patterns.

Example 1

80 ÷ 2 =

8 tens ÷ 2 = 4 tens

4 tens is the same as 40.

Example 2

800 ÷ 2 =

8 hundreds ÷ 2 = 4 hundreds

4 hundreds is the same as 400.

1. 40 ÷ 4

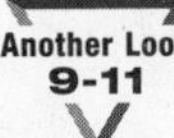

a. 4 ÷ 4 = 1

b. 4 tens ÷ 4 = 1 ten

c. 40 ÷ 4 = 10

2. 400 ÷ 4

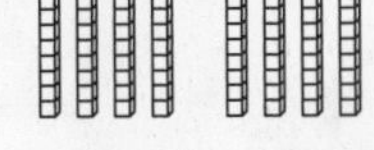

a. 4 ÷ 4 = 1

b. 4 hundreds ÷ 4 = 1 hundred

c. 400 ÷ 4 = 100

3. 240 ÷ 8

a. 24 tens ÷ 8 = 3 tens

b. 240 ÷ 8 = 30

4. 70 ÷ 1

a. 7 tens ÷ 1 = 7 tens

b. 70 ÷ 1 = 70

5. 600 ÷ 3

a. 6 hundreds ÷ 3 = 2 hundreds

b. 600 ÷ 3 = 200

Name ______________________

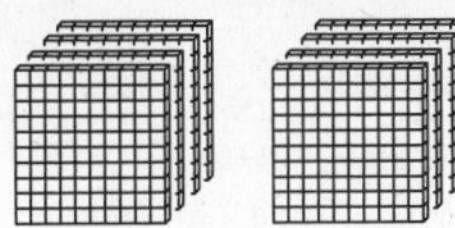

Estimating Quotients

Estimate 79 ÷ 9.

Step 1 Write the closest number to 79 that 9 divides evenly: 81

Step 2 81 ÷ 9 = 9

79 ÷ 9 is about 9.

1. Write the closest number to 38 that can be evenly divided by:

a. 4 36 or 40 **b.** 5 40

c. 6 36 **d.** 7 35

e. 8 40 **f.** 9 36

2. Write the closest number to 58 that can be evenly divided by:

a. 7 56 **b.** 8 56

c. 9 54 **d.** 6 60

e. 5 60 **f.** 4 56 or 60

Estimate each quotient.

3. 16 ÷ 5

a. Write the closest number to 16 that 5 divides evenly. 15

b. Write a new number sentence. 15 ÷ 5 = 3

c. 16 ÷ 5 is about 3.

4. 64 ÷ 7

a. Write the closest number to 64 that 7 divides evenly: 63

b. Write a new number sentence. 63 ÷ 7 = 9

c. 64 ÷ 7 is about 9.

5. 58 ÷ 8 56 ÷ 8 = 7 **6.** 31 ÷ 4 32 ÷ 4 = 8

7. 37 ÷ 5 35 ÷ 5 = 7 **8.** 70 ÷ 9 72 ÷ 9 = 8

9. 26 ÷ 7 28 ÷ 7 = 4 **10.** 41 ÷ 6 42 ÷ 6 = 7

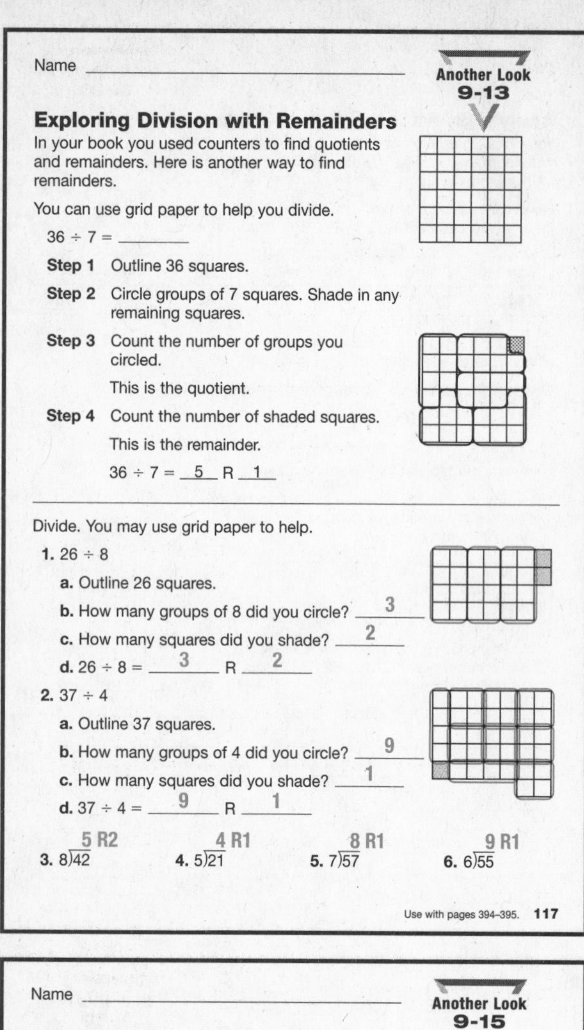

Name ______________

Another Look 9-13

Exploring Division with Remainders

In your book you used counters to find quotients and remainders. Here is another way to find remainders.

You can use grid paper to help you divide.

36 ÷ 7 = ______

Step 1 Outline 36 squares.

Step 2 Circle groups of 7 squares. Shade in any remaining squares.

Step 3 Count the number of groups you circled.

This is the quotient.

Step 4 Count the number of shaded squares.

This is the remainder.

36 ÷ 7 = 5 R 1

Divide. You may use grid paper to help.

1. 26 ÷ 8
   a. Outline 26 squares.
   b. How many groups of 8 did you circle? 3
   c. How many squares did you shade? 2
   d. 26 ÷ 8 = 3 R 2
2. 37 ÷ 4
   a. Outline 37 squares.
   b. How many groups of 4 did you circle? 9
   c. How many squares did you shade? 1
   d. 37 ÷ 4 = 9 R 1

3. 8)42 5 R2 4. 5)21 4 R1 5. 7)57 8 R1 6. 6)55 9 R1

Use with pages 394–395. 117

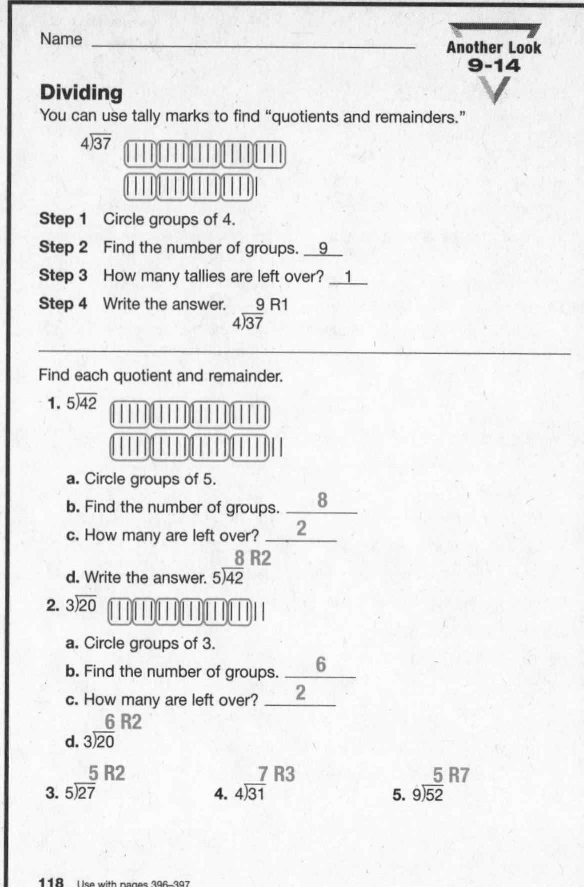

Name ______________

Another Look 9-14

Dividing

You can use tally marks to find "quotients and remainders."

4)37

Step 1 Circle groups of 4.

Step 2 Find the number of groups. 9

Step 3 How many tallies are left over? 1

Step 4 Write the answer. 4)37 9 R1

Find each quotient and remainder.

1. 5)42
   a. Circle groups of 5.
   b. Find the number of groups. 8
   c. How many are left over? 2
   d. Write the answer. 5)42 8 R2
2. 3)20
   a. Circle groups of 3.
   b. Find the number of groups. 6
   c. How many are left over? 2
   d. 3)20 6 R2

3. 5)27 5 R2 4. 4)31 7 R3 5. 9)52 5 R7

118 Use with pages 396–397.

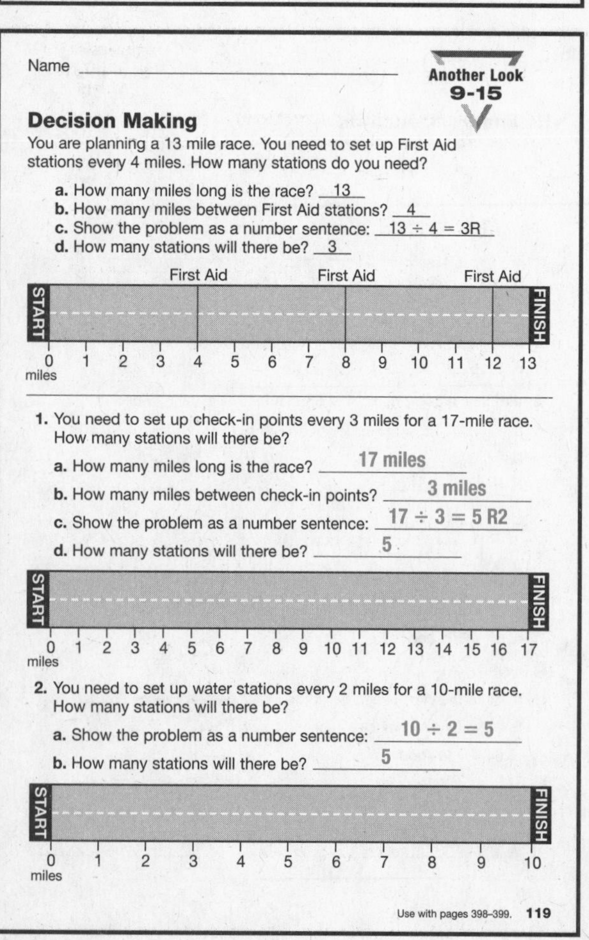

Name ______________

Another Look 9-15

Decision Making

You are planning a 13 mile race. You need to set up First Aid stations every 4 miles. How many stations do you need?

a. How many miles long is the race? 13
b. How many miles between First Aid stations? 4
c. Show the problem as a number sentence: 13 ÷ 4 = 3R
d. How many stations will there be? 3

1. You need to set up check-in points every 3 miles for a 17-mile race. How many stations will there be?
   a. How many miles long is the race? 17 miles
   b. How many miles between check-in points? 3 miles
   c. Show the problem as a number sentence: 17 ÷ 3 = 5 R2
   d. How many stations will there be? 5

2. You need to set up water stations every 2 miles for a 10-mile race. How many stations will there be?
   a. Show the problem as a number sentence: 10 ÷ 2 = 5
   b. How many stations will there be? 5

Use with pages 398–399. 119

Name ______________

Another Look 10-1

Exploring Equal Parts

In your book you found equal parts using geoboards. Here is another way to find equal parts.

Use fraction strips. Match or cover a whole with $\frac{1}{2}$ strips. How many strips do you need?

$\frac{1}{2}$	$\frac{1}{2}$
1	

You need 2 strips.

Use fraction strips. Tell how many equal strips cover a whole.

1. $\frac{1}{3}$ strips 3 2. $\frac{1}{4}$ strips 4 3. $\frac{1}{5}$ strips 5

4. $\frac{1}{6}$ strips 6 5. $\frac{1}{8}$ strips 8 6. $\frac{1}{10}$ strips 10

7. What pattern do you see in the number of strips needed to cover a whole?

Possible answer: The number of strips needed is the same as the bottom number of the fraction.

Name the equal parts of each whole.

8. Fourths 9. Sixths

10. Thirds 11. Fourths

12. Sixths 12. Eighths

120 Use with pages 412–413.

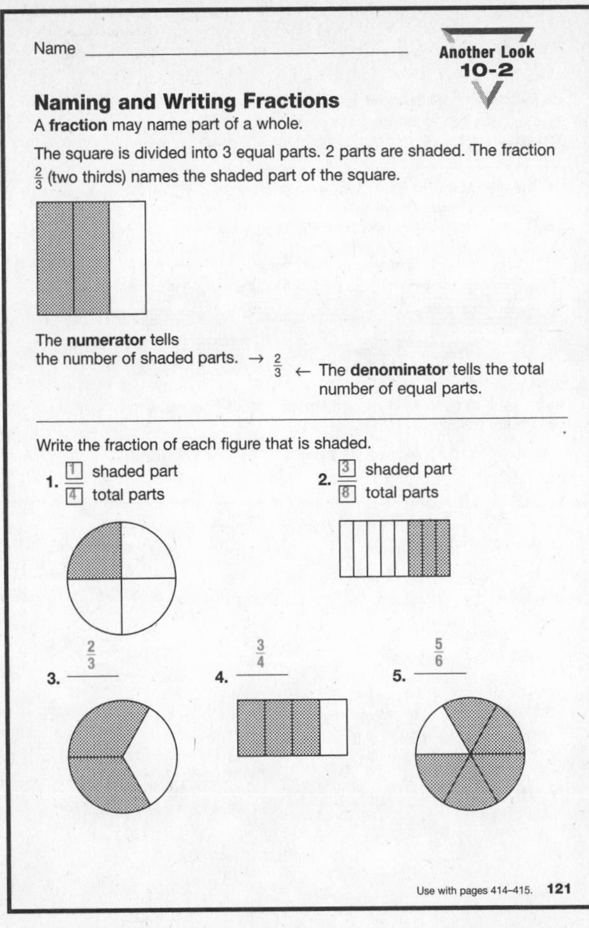

Name ______________________

Another Look 10-2

Naming and Writing Fractions

A **fraction** may name part of a whole.

The square is divided into 3 equal parts. 2 parts are shaded. The fraction $\frac{2}{3}$ (two thirds) names the shaded part of the square.

The **numerator** tells the number of shaded parts. → $\frac{2}{3}$ ← The **denominator** tells the total number of equal parts.

Write the fraction of each figure that is shaded.

1. [1] shaded part / [4] total parts
2. [3] shaded part / [8] total parts
3. $\frac{2}{3}$
4. $\frac{3}{4}$
5. $\frac{5}{6}$

Use with pages 414–415. 121

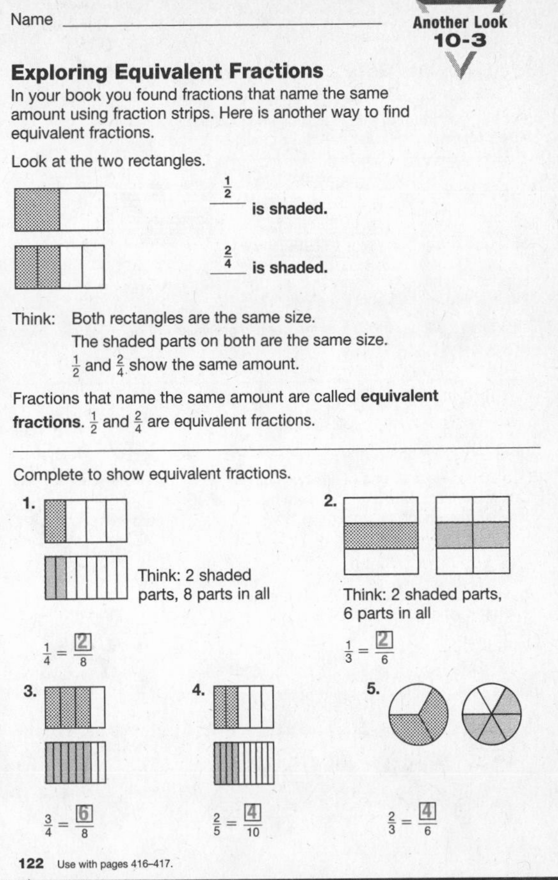

Name ______________________

Another Look 10-3

Exploring Equivalent Fractions

In your book you found fractions that name the same amount using fraction strips. Here is another way to find equivalent fractions.

Look at the two rectangles.

$\frac{1}{2}$ is shaded.

$\frac{2}{4}$ is shaded.

Think: Both rectangles are the same size.
The shaded parts on both are the same size.
$\frac{1}{2}$ and $\frac{2}{4}$ show the same amount.

Fractions that name the same amount are called **equivalent fractions.** $\frac{1}{2}$ and $\frac{2}{4}$ are equivalent fractions.

Complete to show equivalent fractions.

1. Think: 2 shaded parts, 8 parts in all
$\frac{1}{4} = \frac{[2]}{8}$
2. Think: 2 shaded parts, 6 parts in all
$\frac{1}{3} = \frac{[2]}{6}$
3. $\frac{3}{4} = \frac{[6]}{8}$
4. $\frac{2}{5} = \frac{[4]}{10}$
5. $\frac{2}{3} = \frac{[4]}{6}$

122 Use with pages 416–417.

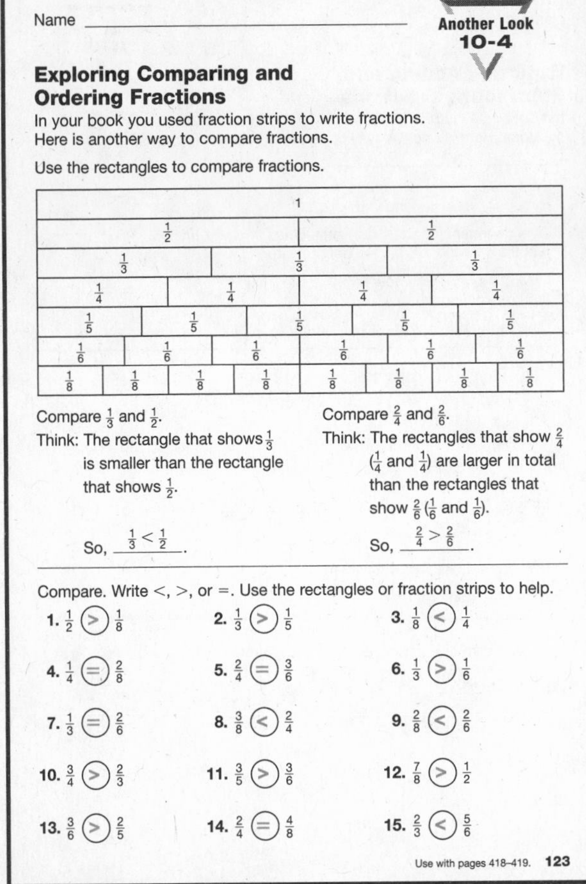

Name ______________________

Another Look 10-4

Exploring Comparing and Ordering Fractions

In your book you used fraction strips to write fractions. Here is another way to compare fractions.

Use the rectangles to compare fractions.

1
$\frac{1}{2}$ | $\frac{1}{2}$
$\frac{1}{3}$ | $\frac{1}{3}$ | $\frac{1}{3}$
$\frac{1}{4}$ | $\frac{1}{4}$ | $\frac{1}{4}$ | $\frac{1}{4}$
$\frac{1}{5}$ | $\frac{1}{5}$ | $\frac{1}{5}$ | $\frac{1}{5}$ | $\frac{1}{5}$
$\frac{1}{6}$ | $\frac{1}{6}$ | $\frac{1}{6}$ | $\frac{1}{6}$ | $\frac{1}{6}$ | $\frac{1}{6}$
$\frac{1}{8}$ | $\frac{1}{8}$ | $\frac{1}{8}$ | $\frac{1}{8}$ | $\frac{1}{8}$ | $\frac{1}{8}$ | $\frac{1}{8}$ | $\frac{1}{8}$

Compare $\frac{1}{3}$ and $\frac{1}{2}$.
Think: The rectangle that shows $\frac{1}{3}$ is smaller than the rectangle that shows $\frac{1}{2}$.
So, $\frac{1}{3} < \frac{1}{2}$.

Compare $\frac{2}{4}$ and $\frac{2}{6}$.
Think: The rectangles that show $\frac{2}{4}$ ($\frac{1}{4}$ and $\frac{1}{4}$) are larger in total than the rectangles that show $\frac{2}{6}$ ($\frac{1}{6}$ and $\frac{1}{6}$).
So, $\frac{2}{4} > \frac{2}{6}$.

Compare. Write <, >, or =. Use the rectangles or fraction strips to help.

1. $\frac{1}{2} > \frac{1}{8}$
2. $\frac{1}{3} > \frac{1}{5}$
3. $\frac{1}{8} < \frac{1}{4}$
4. $\frac{1}{4} = \frac{2}{8}$
5. $\frac{2}{4} = \frac{3}{6}$
6. $\frac{1}{3} > \frac{1}{6}$
7. $\frac{1}{3} = \frac{2}{6}$
8. $\frac{3}{8} < \frac{2}{4}$
9. $\frac{2}{8} < \frac{2}{6}$
10. $\frac{3}{4} > \frac{2}{3}$
11. $\frac{3}{5} > \frac{3}{6}$
12. $\frac{7}{8} > \frac{1}{2}$
13. $\frac{3}{6} > \frac{2}{5}$
14. $\frac{2}{4} = \frac{4}{8}$
15. $\frac{2}{3} < \frac{5}{6}$

Use with pages 418–419. 123

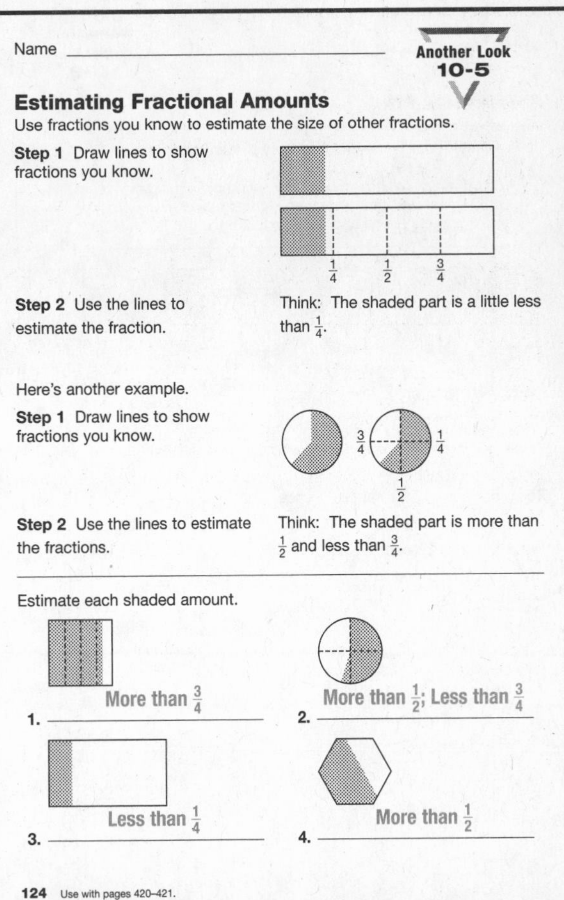

Name ______________________

Another Look 10-5

Estimating Fractional Amounts

Use fractions you know to estimate the size of other fractions.

Step 1 Draw lines to show fractions you know.

$\frac{1}{4}$ $\frac{1}{2}$ $\frac{3}{4}$

Step 2 Use the lines to estimate the fraction.

Think: The shaded part is a little less than $\frac{1}{4}$.

Here's another example.

Step 1 Draw lines to show fractions you know.

$\frac{3}{4}$ $\frac{1}{4}$ $\frac{1}{2}$

Step 2 Use the lines to estimate the fractions.

Think: The shaded part is more than $\frac{1}{2}$ and less than $\frac{3}{4}$.

Estimate each shaded amount.

1. More than $\frac{3}{4}$
2. More than $\frac{1}{2}$; Less than $\frac{3}{4}$
3. Less than $\frac{1}{4}$
4. More than $\frac{1}{2}$

124 Use with pages 420–421.

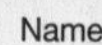

Name ______________________

Another Look 10-6

Fractions and Sets

- A **set** is a group of things that can be counted.
- A **fraction** is a number that describes part of the set.

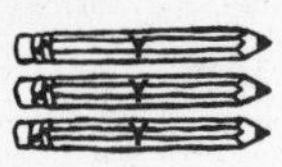

Suppose you have 10 pencils and 3 of them are yellow. What fraction of the pencils are yellow?

There are 10 pencils in all. 3 of the pencils are yellow. 3 out of 10 is written as $\frac{3}{10}$.

1. If you have 2 apples and 1 of them is green, what fraction of the apples are green? $\frac{1}{2}$

2. If you have 3 hats and 2 of them have feathers, what fraction of the hats have feathers? $\frac{2}{3}$

3. If you have 4 pets and 3 of them are dogs, what fraction of the pets are dogs? $\frac{3}{4}$

Write a fraction to tell what part of the set is circled.

4. $\frac{2}{8}$ 5. $\frac{4}{5}$ 6. $\frac{2}{6}$

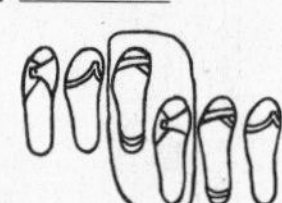

Name ______________________

Another Look 10-7

Exploring Finding a Fraction of a Number

In your book you found fractions of numbers using counters. You can think about sets to find fractional parts of numbers.

- The **denominator** tells how many equal groups to make. Divide the set by this number.
- The **numerator** tells how many of the groups to count.

$\frac{1}{5}$ ← numerator / ← denominator

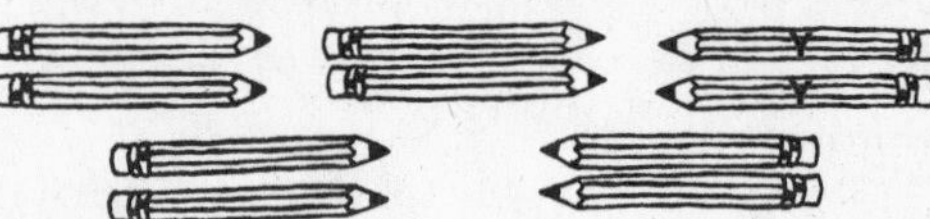

If you have 10 pencils and $\frac{1}{5}$ of them are yellow, how many pencils are yellow?

The denominator, 5, tells you to make 5 groups. The numerator 1 tells you to count 1 of the groups.

2 of the pencils are yellow.

1. $\frac{1}{2}$ of the apples are green. How many apples are green? 3

2. $\frac{2}{3}$ of the hats are blue. How many hats are blue? 4

3. $\frac{3}{4}$ of the cats like to play with yarn. How many like to play with yarn? 9

4. $\frac{1}{4}$ of 12 = 3 5. $\frac{1}{6}$ of 24 = 4

Name ______________________

Another Look 10-8

Mixed Numbers

- A **whole number** can tell how many complete (or whole) things are in a set.
- A **fraction** can tell how much of an incomplete thing is in a set.
- A **mixed number** can describe a set that has one or more complete things and an incomplete thing in it.

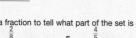

Count the number of whole items. 5 full glasses

Write a fraction for the partial item. $\frac{3}{4}$ full glass

Combine the whole number and fraction to write a mixed number.

The picture shows $5\frac{3}{4}$ glasses of juice.

Write a mixed number for each.

1.  $3\frac{1}{2}$

2.  $2\frac{1}{6} - 2\frac{1}{4}$

3.  $4\frac{1}{2}$

4.  $2\frac{1}{6}$

Name ______________________

Another Look 10-9

Exploring Adding and Subtracting Fractions

In your book you used fraction strips to add and subtract fractions. Here is another way to add and subtract fractions.

The denominator describes *the kind* of groups you're working with.

The denominator stays the same when you add or subtract fractions with like denominators.

The numerator tells *how many* of the groups you're working with.

This is the number to add or subtract.

$\frac{1}{3}$ ← numerator / ← denominator

$\frac{1}{3} + \frac{1}{3} = \frac{2}{3}$

The denominator stays the same.

Add the numerators.

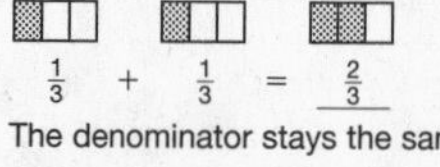

$\frac{4}{5} - \frac{1}{5} = \frac{3}{5}$

The denominator stays the same.

Subtract the numerators.

Find each sum or difference.

1. $\frac{1}{4} + \frac{1}{4} =$ $\frac{2}{4}$ or $\frac{1}{2}$
2. $\frac{5}{8} + \frac{3}{8} =$ $\frac{8}{8}$ or 1
3. $\frac{3}{10} + \frac{4}{10} =$ $\frac{7}{10}$
4. $\frac{6}{9} + \frac{2}{9} =$ $\frac{8}{9}$
5. $\frac{1}{5} + \frac{3}{5} =$ $\frac{4}{5}$
6. $\frac{2}{3} - \frac{1}{3} =$ $\frac{1}{3}$
7. $\frac{2}{6} + \frac{3}{6} =$ $\frac{5}{6}$
8. $\frac{8}{12} - \frac{4}{12} =$ $\frac{4}{12}$ or $\frac{1}{3}$

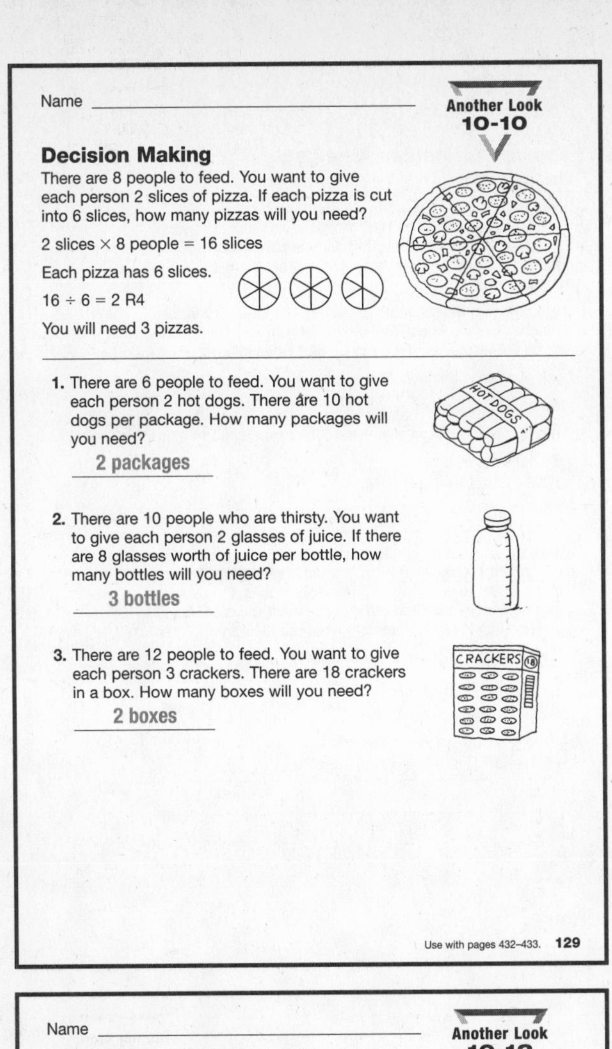

Name ______________________

Another Look 10-10

Decision Making

There are 8 people to feed. You want to give each person 2 slices of pizza. If each pizza is cut into 6 slices, how many pizzas will you need?

2 slices × 8 people = 16 slices

Each pizza has 6 slices.

16 ÷ 6 = 2 R4

You will need 3 pizzas.

1. There are 6 people to feed. You want to give each person 2 hot dogs. There are 10 hot dogs per package. How many packages will you need? 2 packages

2. There are 10 people who are thirsty. You want to give each person 2 glasses of juice. If there are 8 glasses worth of juice per bottle, how many bottles will you need? 3 bottles

3. There are 12 people to feed. You want to give each person 3 crackers. There are 18 crackers in a box. How many boxes will you need? 2 boxes

Use with pages 432–433. 129

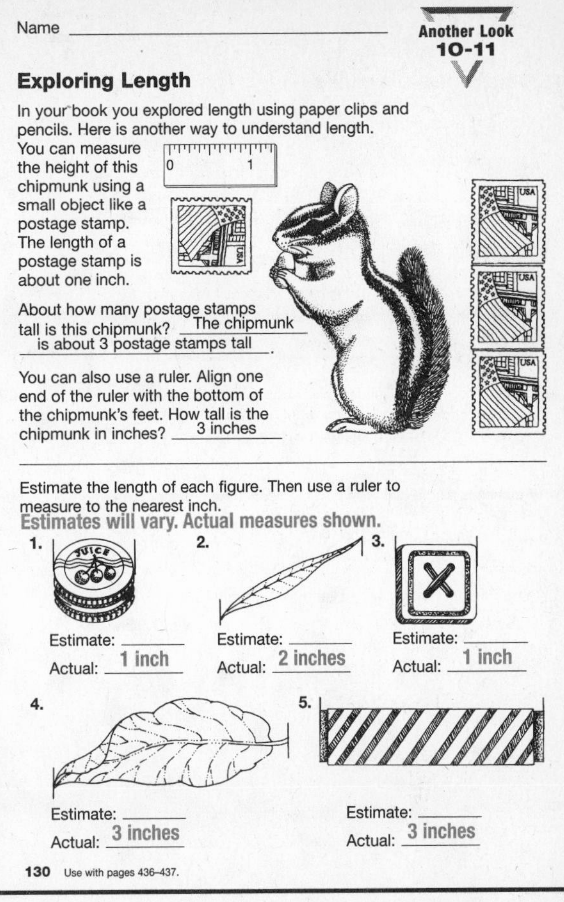

Name ______________________

Another Look 10-11

Exploring Length

In your book you explored length using paper clips and pencils. Here is another way to understand length.

You can measure the height of this chipmunk using a small object like a postage stamp. The length of a postage stamp is about one inch.

About how many postage stamps tall is this chipmunk? The chipmunk is about 3 postage stamps tall.

You can also use a ruler. Align one end of the ruler with the bottom of the chipmunk's feet. How tall is the chipmunk in inches? 3 inches

Estimate the length of each figure. Then use a ruler to measure to the nearest inch.

Estimates will vary. Actual measures shown.

1. Estimate: ______ Actual: 1 inch
2. Estimate: ______ Actual: 2 inches
3. Estimate: ______ Actual: 1 inch
4. Estimate: ______ Actual: 3 inches
5. Estimate: ______ Actual: 3 inches

130 Use with pages 436–437.

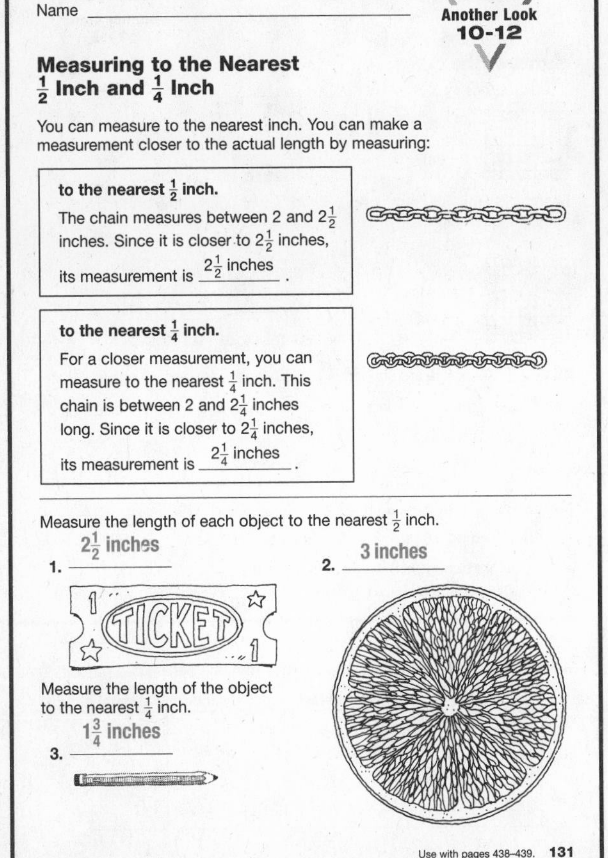

Name ______________________

Another Look 10-12

Measuring to the Nearest $\frac{1}{2}$ Inch and $\frac{1}{4}$ Inch

You can measure to the nearest inch. You can make a measurement closer to the actual length by measuring:

to the nearest $\frac{1}{2}$ inch.
The chain measures between 2 and $2\frac{1}{2}$ inches. Since it is closer to $2\frac{1}{2}$ inches, its measurement is $2\frac{1}{2}$ inches.

to the nearest $\frac{1}{4}$ inch.
For a closer measurement, you can measure to the nearest $\frac{1}{4}$ inch. This chain is between 2 and $2\frac{1}{4}$ inches long. Since it is closer to $2\frac{1}{4}$ inches, its measurement is $2\frac{1}{4}$ inches.

Measure the length of each object to the nearest $\frac{1}{2}$ inch.

1. $2\frac{1}{2}$ inches
2. 3 inches

Measure the length of the object to the nearest $\frac{1}{4}$ inch.

3. $1\frac{3}{4}$ inches

Use with pages 438–439. 131

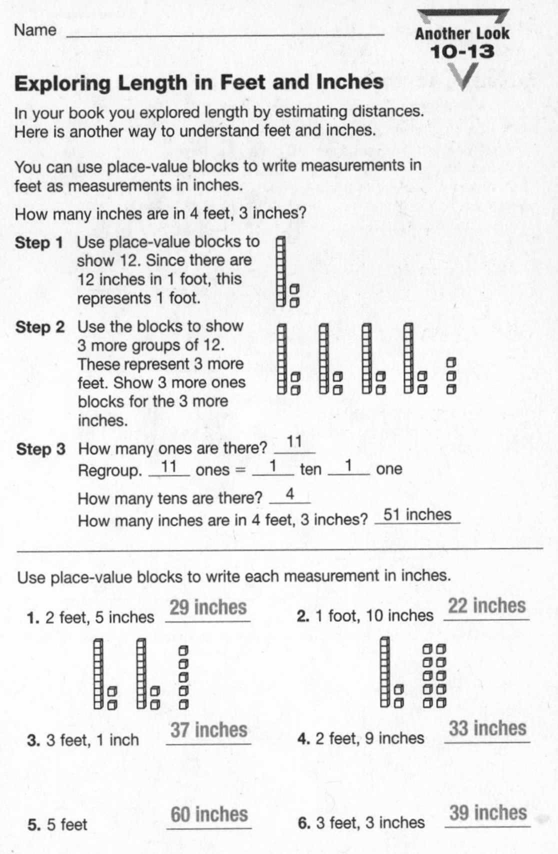

Name ______________________

Another Look 10-13

Exploring Length in Feet and Inches

In your book you explored length by estimating distances. Here is another way to understand feet and inches.

You can use place-value blocks to write measurements in feet as measurements in inches.

How many inches are in 4 feet, 3 inches?

Step 1 Use place-value blocks to show 12. Since there are 12 inches in 1 foot, this represents 1 foot.

Step 2 Use the blocks to show 3 more groups of 12. These represent 3 more feet. Show 3 more ones blocks for the 3 more inches.

Step 3 How many ones are there? 11
Regroup. 11 ones = 1 ten 1 one
How many tens are there? 4
How many inches are in 4 feet, 3 inches? 51 inches

Use place-value blocks to write each measurement in inches.

1. 2 feet, 5 inches 29 inches
2. 1 foot, 10 inches 22 inches
3. 3 feet, 1 inch 37 inches
4. 2 feet, 9 inches 33 inches
5. 5 feet 60 inches
6. 3 feet, 3 inches 39 inches

132 Use with pages 440–441.

Name ______________________

Another Look 10-14

Feet, Yards, and Miles

The standard units of measure for distance are inches, feet, yards, and miles. Inches are used to measure the length of very small objects such as bugs and leaves. Miles are used to measure distances you would travel in a car or plane.

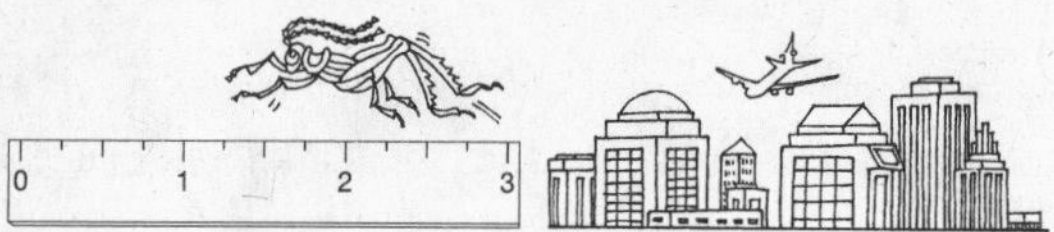

Which is the greater distance? 2 feet or 17 inches?

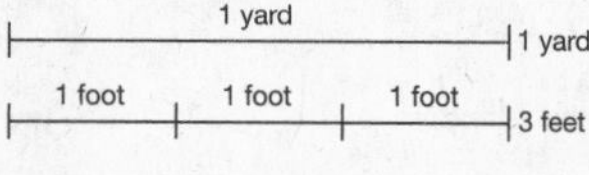

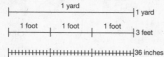

Look at the diagram. There are 12 inches in every foot. 17 inches is a little over 1 foot. So, 2 feet is the greater distance.

2 feet > 17 inches

Compare. Write <, >, or =. Use the diagram to help.

1. 1 yard (>) 2 feet
2. 5 feet (>) 27 inches
3. 21 feet (<) 16 yards
4. 1 yard (=) 3 feet
5. 36 inches (<) 3 yards
6. 6 feet (>) 60 inches

Choose an estimate for each.

b 7. an adult's height — a. 2 inches

c 8. the height of a skyscraper — b. 5 feet

a 9. the length of a butterfly — c. 250 yards

Name ______________________

Another Look 10-15

Analyze Strategies: Use Logical Reasoning

Josh, Seth, Amy, and Kim measured their heights. Their measurements are 47 inches, 49 inches, 51 inches, and 52 inches. Kim is 49 inches tall. Seth is taller than Kim. Josh is shorter than Kim. Amy is the tallest. How tall is each person?

You know that the students are either 47 inches, 49 inches, 51 inches or 52 inches. You know that Kim is 49 inches tall. Amy is the tallest, so she must be 52 inches tall.

Look at what you know. Who is taller, Kim or Josh? Kim

What is Josh's height? 47 inches

What is the only height that has not been matched to a student? 51 inches

How tall is Seth? 51 inches

Liang, Steve, Marcie, and Bob are trying to figure out the order in which they were born. Marcie is older than Bob. Liang and Steve are younger than Bob. Bob is 11 years old. Liang is younger than the other students. If the students are either 9, 10, 11, or 12 years old, what are their ages?

1. Whose age is given in the problem? Bob
2. Who is older than Bob? Marcie
3. Who is the youngest? Liang
4. Write each person's name and age. Marcie is 12 years old, Bob is 11, Steve is 10, and Liang is 9.

Name ______________________

Another Look 11-1

Exploring Tenths

In your book you explored tenths with grids. Here is another way to understand tenths.

1 dime is one-tenth of a dollar. 0.10 is one tenth.

10 dimes are the same as 1 whole dollar. 10 tenths are the same as 1 whole.

7 dimes are seven-tenths of a dollar.

$0.70 = $\frac{7}{10}$ = 0.7

2 dimes are two-tenths of a dollar. 1 dollar 2 dimes can be shown as $1.20.

$1.20 = $1\frac{2}{10}$ = 1.2

1.2 is read "one and two tenths."

Use what you know about decimals and fractions to complete the table.

	Money	Money Amount	Fraction	Decimal	Word Name
1.		$0.40	$\frac{4}{10}$	0.4	four tenths
2.		$0.90	$\frac{9}{10}$	0.9	nine tenths
3.		$1.60	$1\frac{6}{10}$	1.6	one and six tenths
4.		$3.10	$3\frac{1}{10}$	3.1	three and one tenth

Name ______________________

Another Look 11-2

Hundredths

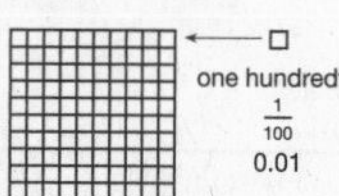

Each block in a hundredth grid equals one hundredth.

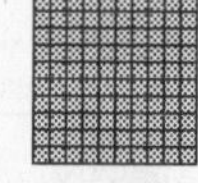

An entire hundredths grid equals one whole.

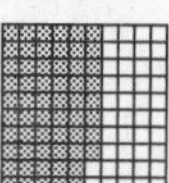

58 out of 100 boxes are shaded.

So, $\frac{58}{100}$ of the grid is shaded.

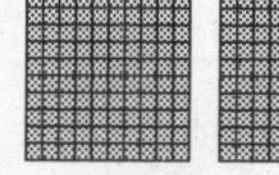

1 whole square and 40 out of 100 boxes of the second square are shaded. $1\frac{40}{100}$ of the grids are shaded.

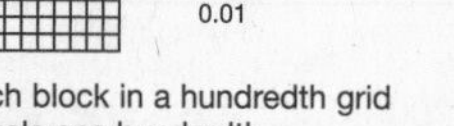

You can name the same number in different ways.

word name	fraction	decimal
fifty-eight hundredths	$\frac{58}{100}$	0.58
one and forty hundredths	$1\frac{40}{100}$	1.40

Write the word name, fraction, and decimal to name the shaded part.

	Grids	Word Name	Fraction	Decimal
1.		seventy-five hundredths	$\frac{75}{100}$	0.75
2.		one and seventeen hundredths	$1\frac{17}{100}$	1.17

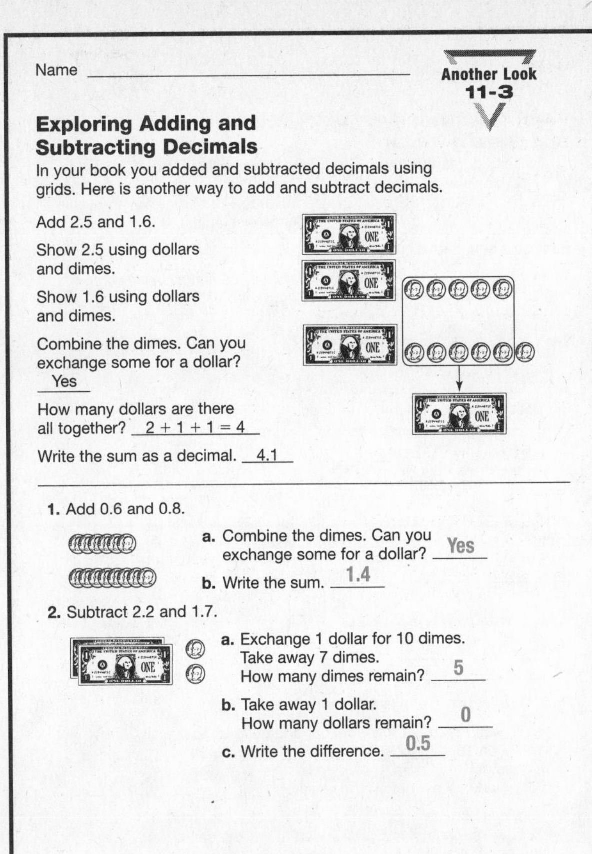

Name ______________________

Another Look 11-3

Exploring Adding and Subtracting Decimals

In your book you added and subtracted decimals using grids. Here is another way to add and subtract decimals.

Add 2.5 and 1.6.

Show 2.5 using dollars and dimes.

Show 1.6 using dollars and dimes.

Combine the dimes. Can you exchange some for a dollar? Yes

How many dollars are there all together? 2 + 1 + 1 = 4

Write the sum as a decimal. 4.1

1. Add 0.6 and 0.8.
   a. Combine the dimes. Can you exchange some for a dollar? Yes
   b. Write the sum. 1.4
2. Subtract 2.2 and 1.7.
   a. Exchange 1 dollar for 10 dimes. Take away 7 dimes. How many dimes remain? 5
   b. Take away 1 dollar. How many dollars remain? 0
   c. Write the difference. 0.5

Use with pages 460–461. 137

Name ______________________

Another Look 11-4

Connecting Decimals and Money

Money amounts are written as decimals. You can think of cents as fractional parts of whole dollars.

This square shows 100 pennies. Each column in the square shows 10 pennies.

10 Pennies = 1 Dime

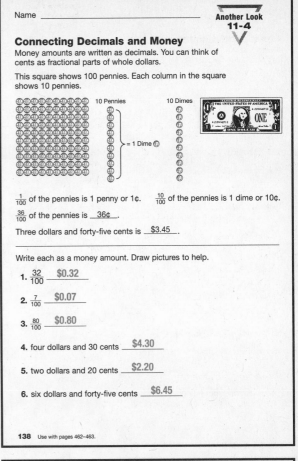

10 Dimes

$\frac{1}{100}$ of the pennies is 1 penny or 1¢. $\frac{10}{100}$ of the pennies is 1 dime or 10¢.

$\frac{36}{100}$ of the pennies is 36¢.

Three dollars and forty-five cents is $3.45.

Write each as a money amount. Draw pictures to help.

1. $\frac{32}{100}$ $0.32
2. $\frac{7}{100}$ $0.07
3. $\frac{80}{100}$ $0.80
4. four dollars and 30 cents $4.30
5. two dollars and 20 cents $2.20
6. six dollars and forty-five cents $6.45

138 Use with pages 462–463.

Name ______________________

Another Look 11-5

Decision Making

It's June 24, and you and your family are visiting Mt. Washington in New Hampshire. It is 1:30 P.M. Do you have enough time to visit the top?

The mountain road closes at 6:00 P.M.

The one-way driving time is about 1 hour.

The guidebooks suggest a one-hour stay at the top in order to have enough time to visit the Summit Museum, which remains open until 8:00 P.M.

Drive Time: 1 Hour — Spend an Hour Sightseeing Museum — 1 Hour Return Trip

1:30 bottom of mountain — 2:30 top — 3:30 top — 4:30 bottom of mountain

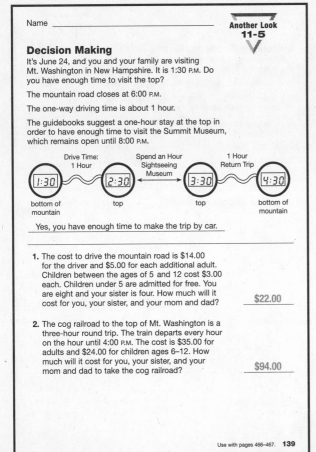

Yes, you have enough time to make the trip by car.

1. The cost to drive the mountain road is $14.00 for the driver and $5.00 for each additional adult. Children between the ages of 5 and 12 cost $3.00 each. Children under 5 are admitted for free. You are eight and your sister is four. How much will it cost for you, your sister, and your mom and dad? $22.00
2. The cog railroad to the top of Mt. Washington is a three-hour round trip. The train departs every hour on the hour until 4:00 P.M. The cost is $35.00 for adults and $24.00 for children ages 6–12. How much will it cost for you, your sister, and your mom and dad to take the cog railroad? $94.00

Use with pages 466–467. 139

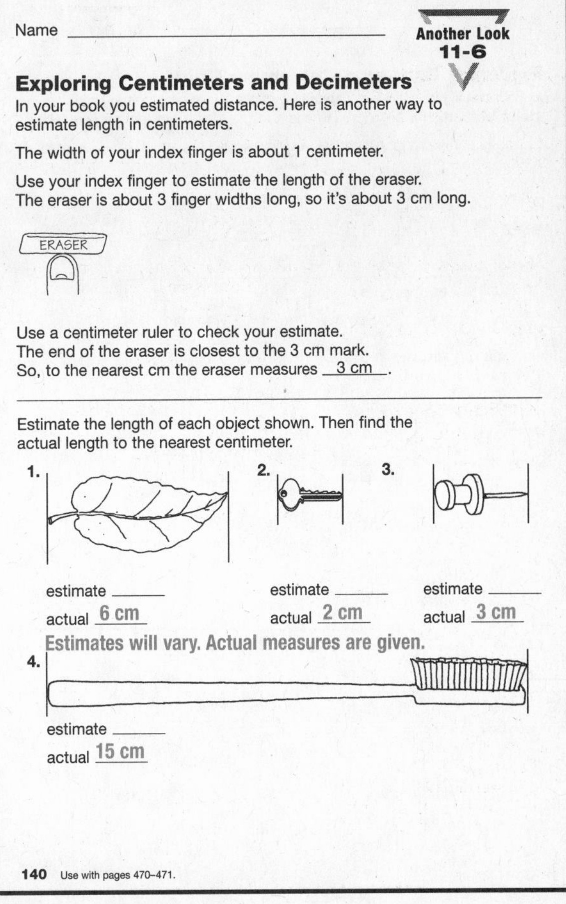

Name ______________________

Another Look 11-6

Exploring Centimeters and Decimeters

In your book you estimated distance. Here is another way to estimate length in centimeters.

The width of your index finger is about 1 centimeter.

Use your index finger to estimate the length of the eraser. The eraser is about 3 finger widths long, so it's about 3 cm long.

Use a centimeter ruler to check your estimate. The end of the eraser is closest to the 3 cm mark. So, to the nearest cm the eraser measures 3 cm.

Estimate the length of each object shown. Then find the actual length to the nearest centimeter.

1. estimate ______ actual 6 cm
2. estimate ______ actual 2 cm
3. estimate ______ actual 3 cm

Estimates will vary. Actual measures are given.

4. estimate ______ actual 15 cm

140 Use with pages 470–471.

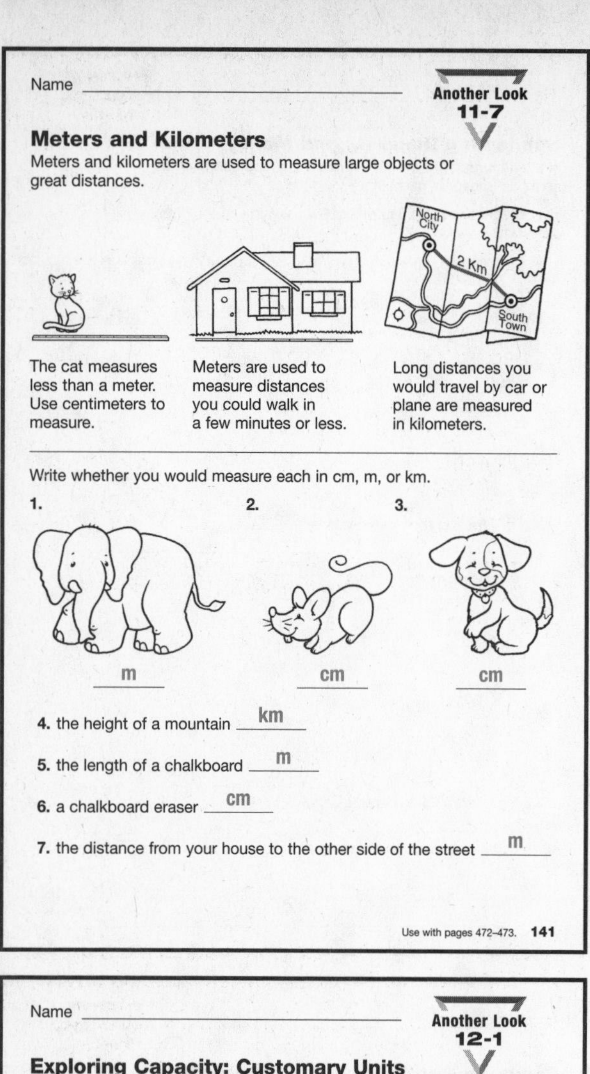

Name

Another Look 11-7

Meters and Kilometers

Meters and kilometers are used to measure large objects or great distances.

The cat measures less than a meter. Use centimeters to measure.

Meters are used to measure distances you could walk in a few minutes or less.

Long distances you would travel by car or plane are measured in kilometers.

Write whether you would measure each in cm, m, or km.

1. m
2. cm
3. cm
4. the height of a mountain km
5. the length of a chalkboard m
6. a chalkboard eraser cm
7. the distance from your house to the other side of the street m

Use with pages 472–473. 141

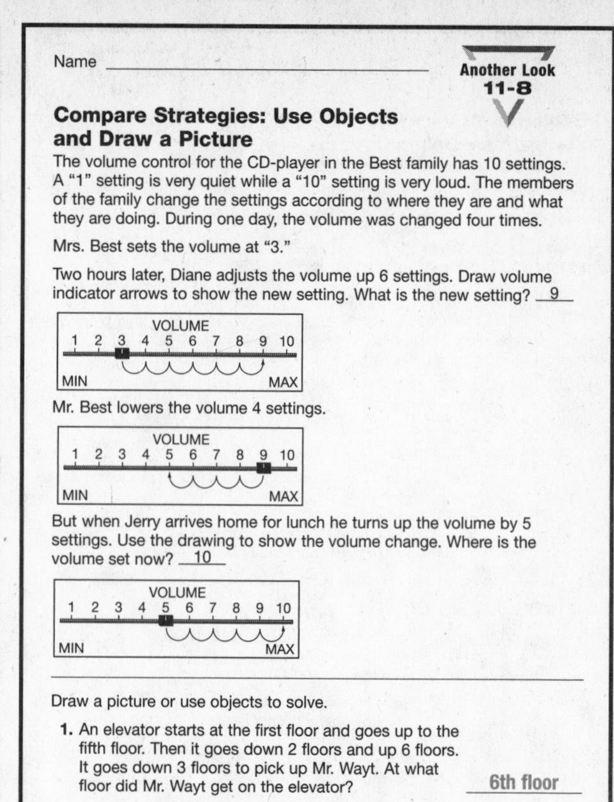

Name

Another Look 11-8

Compare Strategies: Use Objects and Draw a Picture

The volume control for the CD-player in the Best family has 10 settings. A "1" setting is very quiet while a "10" setting is very loud. The members of the family change the settings according to where they are and what they are doing. During one day, the volume was changed four times.

Mrs. Best sets the volume at "3."

Two hours later, Diane adjusts the volume up 6 settings. Draw volume indicator arrows to show the new setting. What is the new setting? 9

Mr. Best lowers the volume 4 settings.

But when Jerry arrives home for lunch he turns up the volume by 5 settings. Use the drawing to show the volume change. Where is the volume set now? 10

Draw a picture or use objects to solve.

1. An elevator starts at the first floor and goes up to the fifth floor. Then it goes down 2 floors and up 6 floors. It goes down 3 floors to pick up Mr. Wayt. At what floor did Mr. Wayt get on the elevator? 6th floor
2. Suppose you are decorating a square cake. You have 12 flowers made of icing. You want to put the same number of flowers on each of the cake's 4 sides. How many flowers can you put on each side? 3 flowers

142 Use with pages 474–475.

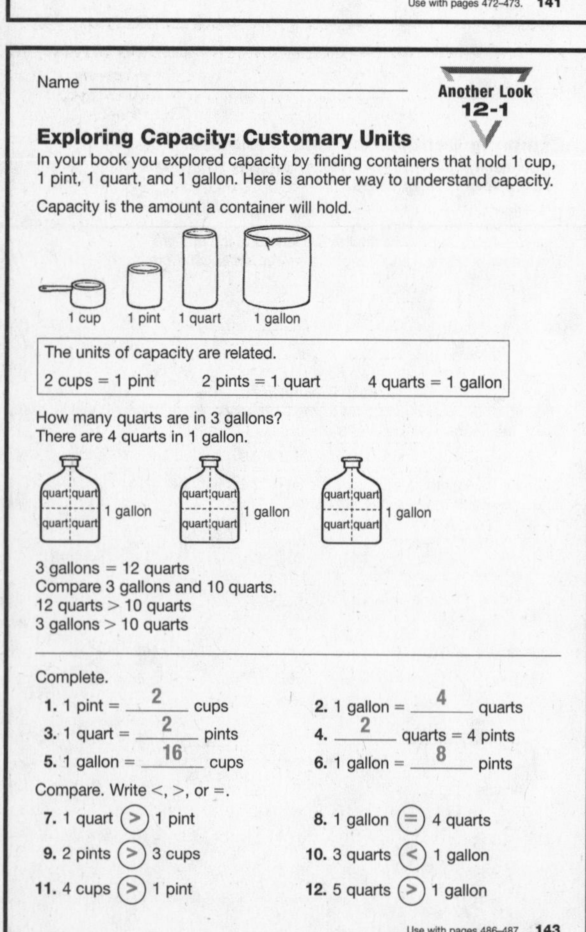

Name

Another Look 12-1

Exploring Capacity: Customary Units

In your book you explored capacity by finding containers that hold 1 cup, 1 pint, 1 quart, and 1 gallon. Here is another way to understand capacity.

Capacity is the amount a container will hold.

The units of capacity are related.

2 cups = 1 pint   2 pints = 1 quart   4 quarts = 1 gallon

How many quarts are in 3 gallons?
There are 4 quarts in 1 gallon.

3 gallons = 12 quarts
Compare 3 gallons and 10 quarts.
12 quarts > 10 quarts
3 gallons > 10 quarts

Complete.

1. 1 pint = 2 cups
2. 1 gallon = 4 quarts
3. 1 quart = 2 pints
4. 2 quarts = 4 pints
5. 1 gallon = 16 cups
6. 1 gallon = 8 pints

Compare. Write <, >, or =.

7. 1 quart (>) 1 pint
8. 1 gallon (=) 4 quarts
9. 2 pints (>) 3 cups
10. 3 quarts (<) 1 gallon
11. 4 cups (>) 1 pint
12. 5 quarts (>) 1 gallon

Use with pages 486–487. 143

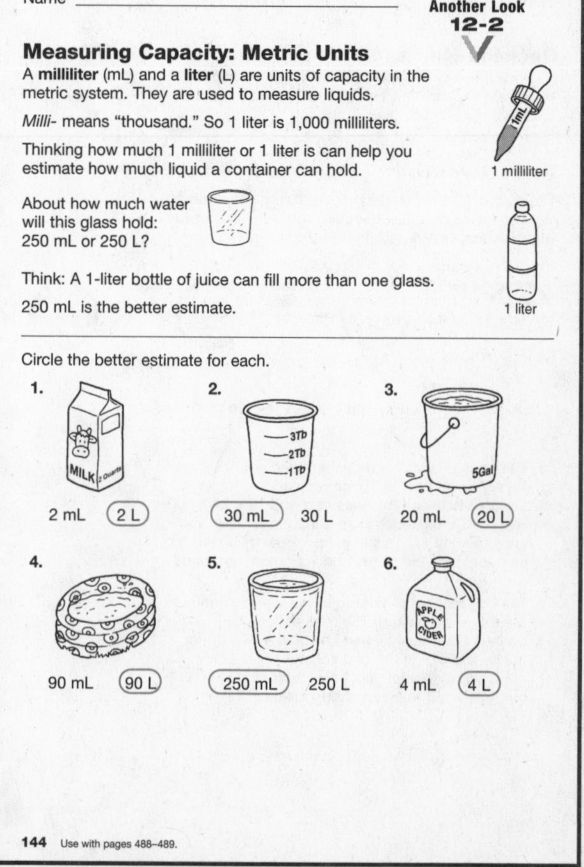

Name

Another Look 12-2

Measuring Capacity: Metric Units

A **milliliter** (mL) and a **liter** (L) are units of capacity in the metric system. They are used to measure liquids.

Milli- means "thousand." So 1 liter is 1,000 milliliters.

Thinking how much 1 milliliter or 1 liter is can help you estimate how much liquid a container can hold.

About how much water will this glass hold: 250 mL or 250 L?

Think: A 1-liter bottle of juice can fill more than one glass.

250 mL is the better estimate.

Circle the better estimate for each.

1. 2 mL (2 L)
2. (30 mL) 30 L
3. 20 mL (20 L)
4. 90 mL (90 L)
5. (250 mL) 250 L
6. 4 mL (4 L)

144 Use with pages 488–489.

Name ______________________

Exploring Weight: Customary Units

In your book you explored weight by using a balance scale. Here is another way to understand weight.

Think about how much 1 ounce or 1 pound weighs to estimate other weights.

Example

About how much does a child's T-shirt weigh: 6 oz or 6 lb?

Think: A child's T-shirt weighs more than a key but less than a loaf of bread. So 6 pounds is much greater than the weight of a child's T-shirt.

6 oz is the better estimate.

Circle the better estimate for each.

1. 1 oz 1 lb
2. 1 oz 1 lb
3. 5 oz 5 lb

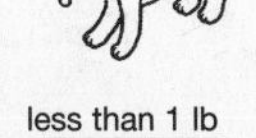

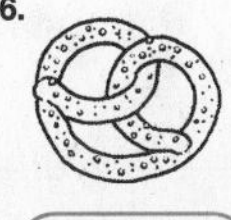

4. less than 1 lb / more than 1 lb
5. less than 1 lb / more than 1 lb
6. less than 1 lb / more than 1 lb

Name ______________________

Another Look
12-4

Grams and Kilograms

How much is a gram? How much is a kilogram? Find out.

Take a sheet of paper. Fold it in half. Then fold it in half again. Unfold the page and cut out one of the 4 sections. Hold this one section in your hand. This is about 1 gram.

Now hold your math book in your other hand. This is about 1 kilogram (kg).

Use the $\frac{1}{4}$ sheet of paper and your math book to estimate how heavy other items are.

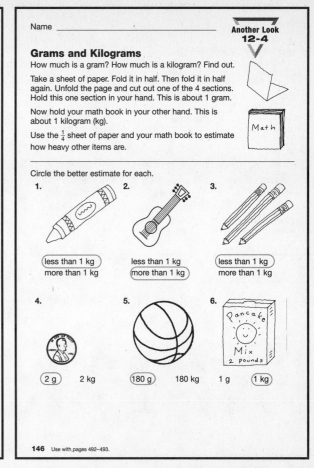

Circle the better estimate for each.

1. less than 1 kg / more than 1 kg
2. less than 1 kg / more than 1 kg
3. less than 1 kg / more than 1 kg
4. 2 g 2 kg
5. 180 g 180 kg
6. 1 g 1 kg

Name ______________________

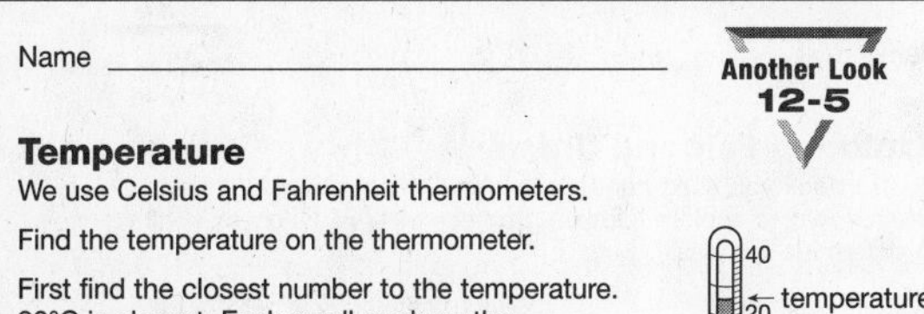

Temperature

We use Celsius and Fahrenheit thermometers.

Find the temperature on the thermometer.

First find the closest number to the temperature. 20°C is closest. Each small mark on the thermometer shows 2°, so count up by 2s from 20° to the temperature.

The temperature shown on this thermometer is 26°C.

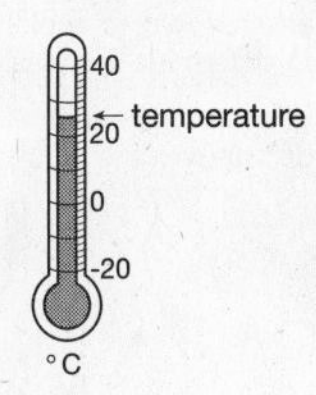

Write each temperature using °C or °F.

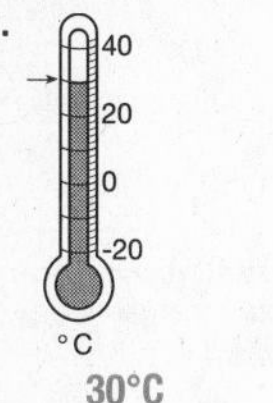

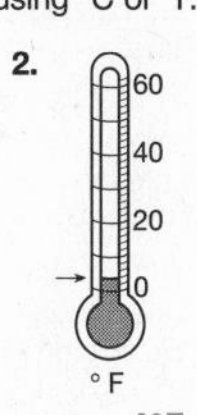

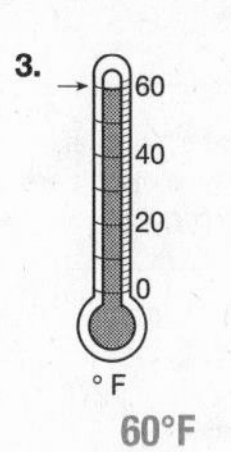

1. 30°C
2. 4°F
3. 60°F

Count backward to find negative temperatures. Write each temperature, using – and °C. The first one has been done for you.

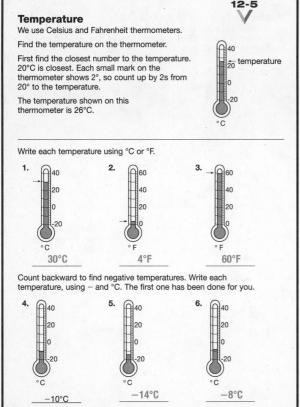

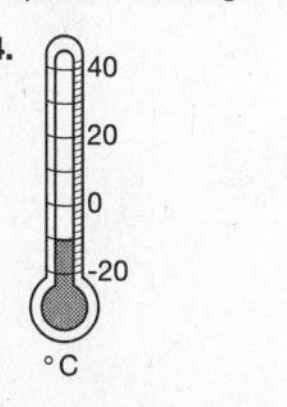

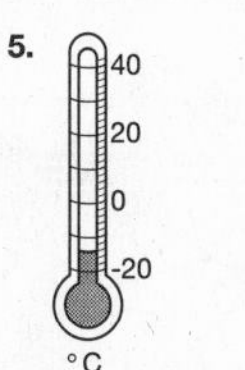

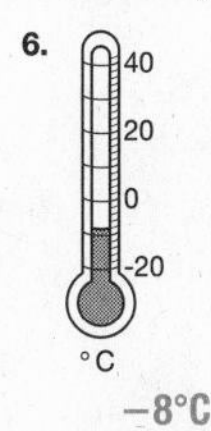

4. –10°C
5. –14°C
6. –8°C

Name ______________________

Another Look
12-6

Decision Making

Suppose you're packing for a visit to a friend's house. You will be staying 7 days. You are going to carry your things in a backpack. You don't want to carry more than 15 pounds. Here's what you're taking so far.

Item	Weight
backpack	3 lb
2 pairs of pants	1 lb
3 shirts	1 lb
4 books	3 lb
1 tape player	1 lb
8 cassette tapes	1 lb
extra shoes	2 lb
socks, t-shirts, and so on	2 lb

How much do the items on your list weigh in all? Add all the weights to find out.

3 + 1 + 1 + 3 + 1 + 1 + 2 + 2 = 14 lb

Do they weigh under or over 15 lb? Under 15 lb

What if you decide to take 2 more pairs of pants (4 pairs in all) and 3 more shirts (6 shirts in all)?

1. How much extra weight is 2 pairs of pants? 1 lb
   3 shirts? 1 lb
2. How much weight would you carry in all? 16 lb
3. Is the weight under or over 15 lb? Over 15 lb
4. What could you do to make the weight exactly 15 lb?
   Possible answers: Take 3 shirts, not 6 shirts. Leave the cassettes at home.

Name ______________________

Another Look 12-7

Exploring Likely and Unlikely

In your book you made a table to decide whether statements were impossible, possible, or certain. Here is another way to explore likely and unlikely.

The pictures show things that are impossible, possible, and certain.

Impossible	**Possible**	**Certain**
something that would never happen	something that could happen	something that will definitely happen

Look at each picture. Decide whether it is impossible, possible, or certain. Write the answer on the line.

This rock will float.

1. Impossible

You may already have won a prize.

2. Possible

The 3 P.M. train will be late.

3. Possible

The sun's heat will melt the snow.

4. Certain

Name ______________________

Another Look 12-8

Exploring Predictions

In your book you tested predictions by recording data in a table. Here is another way to explore predictions.

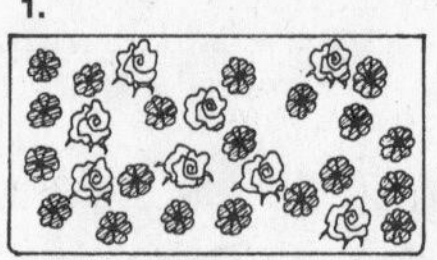

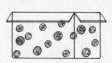

	More Likely to Pull out of Box	Less Likely to Pull out of Box
(dime)	✔	
(nickel)		✔

Think: There are more dimes in the box than nickels. Since there are more dimes to choose from, you are more likely to pull a dime out of the box.

Look at each box. Predict what you are more likely and less likely to pull out of it. Complete each table.

1.

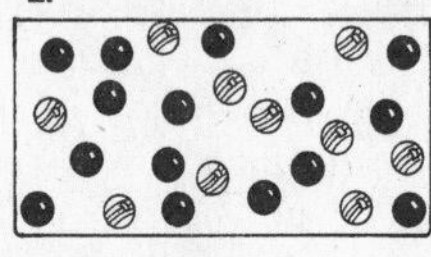

	More Likely to Pull out of Box	Less Likely to Pull out of Box
(rose)		✔
(flower)	✔	

2.

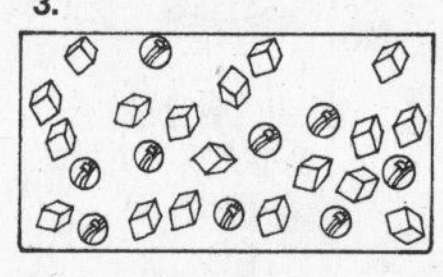

	More Likely to Pull out of Box	Less Likely to Pull out of Box
(striped marble)		✔
(black marble)	✔	

3.

	More Likely to Pull out of Box	Less Likely to Pull out of Box
(cube)	✔	
(striped marble)		✔

Name ______________________

Another Look 12-9

Exploring Probability

In your book you explored probability with spinners to predict outcomes in the form of fractions. Here is another way to understand probability.

Count the flowers.

There are 8 flowers all together.

2 out of 8 flowers are roses. The probability of picking a rose is $\frac{2}{8}$.

3 out of 8 flowers are daisies. The probability of picking a daisy is $\frac{3}{8}$.

1 out of 8 flowers is a tulip. The probability of picking a tulip is $\frac{1}{8}$.

2 out of 8 flowers are daffodils. The probability of picking a daffodil is $\frac{2}{8}$.

Look at each picture. Imagine picking one item with your eyes closed. Complete a fraction to show the probability of getting each thing listed.

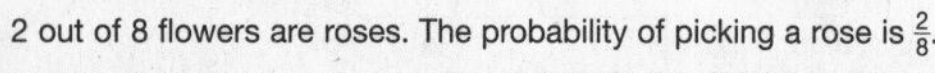

1. A striped card $\frac{5}{20}$
2. A spotted card $\frac{10}{20}$
3. A plain card $\frac{4}{20}$
4. A black card $\frac{1}{20}$

5. A spotted fish $\frac{4}{13}$
6. A white fish $\frac{4}{13}$
7. A striped fish $\frac{2}{13}$
8. A black fish $\frac{3}{13}$

Name ______________________

Another Look 12-10

Exploring Fair and Unfair

In your book you used fractions to determine if spinners were fair. Here is another way to explore fairness. Sometimes a visual check is all you need to determine fairness.

Look at these spinners. Without counting sections or writing fractions, decide which one is fair.

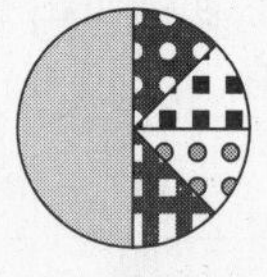

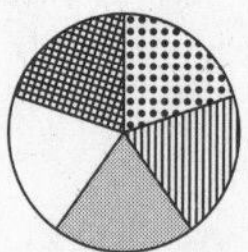

The spinner on the right is fair if you are playing a game, and each of 5 players is assigned a section. There are 5 equal sections, so there are 5 equally likely outcomes.

The spinner on the left has 5 sections of unequal size. So, if you are playing a game where each person is assigned a section for the same number of points, the 5 outcomes are not equally likely. The game is unfair.

Look at these spinners. Are the outcomes equally likely? If game players were each assigned a different possible outcome, would the game be fair? Write *fair* or *unfair* on the line.

1. Fair
2. Unfair

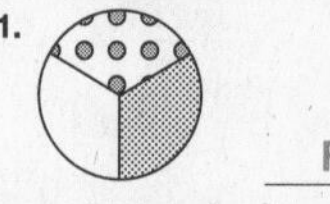

3. Unfair
4. Fair

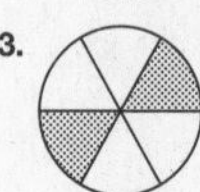

5. Fair

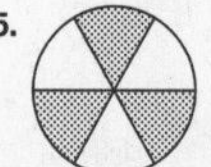

6. Unfair

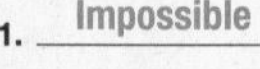

Name ______________________

Another Look
12-11

Analyze Strategies: Work Backward

Alison puts half of her book collection on 4 shelves. She puts 12 books on 1 short shelf. Then she puts 18 books on each of 3 long shelves. How many books does Alison have?

Figure out how many books in all went on the long shelves. 18 × 3 = 54

Add that number to the number of books that went on the short shelf. 54 + 12 = 66

Since this is only half of Alison's collection, double the result.

66 × 2 = 132

Work backward to solve these problems.

1. Carly read her book in 4 days. She read 36 pages on Monday, 24 pages on Tuesday, and 48 pages on Wednesday. On Thursday, she read twice as many pages as on Wednesday. How many pages did the book have?
   a. How many pages in all did Carly read on Monday, Tuesday, and Wednesday? 108
   b. How many pages did Carly read on Thursday? 96
   c. How many pages are there in Carly's book? 204
2. Linda picked a number. She added 43, subtracted 9, and multiplied the result by 4. If Linda ended up with 164, what number did she start with?
   a. Fill in the diagram to show what Linda did.

   7 → +43 → 50 → −9 → 41 → ×4 → 164

   Work backwards to complete the diagram.

   b. What number did Linda start with? 7